W9-ANK-223

Some Properties of Polyhedra in Euclidean Space

by

V. J. D. BASTON

PERGAMON PRESS

OXFORD · LONDON · EDINBURGH · NEW YORK
PARIS · FRANKFURT

Pergamon Press Ltd., Headington Hill Hall, Oxford
4 & 5 Fitzroy Square, London W. 1
Pergamon Press (Scotland) Ltd., 2 & 3 Teviot Place, Edinburgh 1
Pergamon Press Inc., 122 East 55th St., New York 22, N. Y.
Gauthier-Villars, 55 Quai des Grands-Augustins, Paris 6
Pergamon Press GmbH, Kaiserstraße 75, Frankfurt-am-Main

Copyright © 1965
PERGAMON PRESS LTD.

First edition 1965

Library of Congress Catalog Card No 64-15319

INTERNATIONAL SERIES OF MONOGRAPHS IN
PURE AND APPLIED MATHEMATICS
GENERAL EDITORS: I. N. SNEDDON, M. STARK AND S. ULAM

VOLUME 71

SOME PROPERTIES OF
POLYHEDRA IN EUCLIDEAN SPACE

917676

PHYSICS-MATH.
LIBRARY

QA
491
B32s

Physics-Math.
Cat. as sep.

CONTENTS

	Acknowledgements	vi
	Introduction	vii
One	Some Preliminary Results	1
Two	On the Non-existence of an n-con for n greater than 13	11
Three	On a Property of the Columns of a Matrix Representation of a 9-con	57
Four	On the Existence of a 9-con containing one Tetre	86
Five	On the Non-existence of a 9-con containing nine D_m-planes, one of which is a Tetre	99
Six	On the Non-existence of a 9-con containing eleven D_m-planes, one of which is a Tetre	130
Seven	On the Non-existence of a 9-con containing a Tetre	157
Eight	On the Existence of a 9-con	179
Nine	On the Non-existence of a 10-con	197
Ten	On the Existence of an 8-con	205
Eleven	Conclusions	206
	Index	209
	Other Titles in the Series in Pure and Applied Mathematics	210

ACKNOWLEDGEMENTS

It is undoubtedly most fitting to begin by expressing my gratitude and indebtedness to Professor Eggleston, who suggested the main problem of the book to me and whose critical remarks and suggestions have been invaluable. As the main body of the book was approved by the University of London for the award of their Ph.D. degree, I would also like to thank the D.S.I.R. for a Research Studentship whilst carrying out this work.

INTRODUCTION

THE PROBLEM considered in this book can be said to have evolved from the well-known Four Colour Problem. Whilst considering this problem, Wernicke raised the question "What is the chromatic number of three-dimensional space?", or in other words, "What is the least number of colours we must have in order that, given any division of space or part of space into closed domains, two domains which have an area in common should have different colours?" Stäckel showed that the answer to this question is "infinity", by giving a method of constructing any given number of "touching bodies" in space, where n "touching bodies" are defined as n non-overlapping closed domains such that each closed domain has a positive area in common with every other. In his paper Stäckel remarked that, in his construction, the "touching bodies" were not all convex and asked the question whether the number of convex "touching bodies" in three-dimensional space was bounded. In 1905 Tietze proved[3] that this was not true by producing a method of constructing any given number of "touching bodies", all of which were convex polyhedra. In 1947, unaware of Tietze's work, Besicovitch published[1] a solution of Crum's Problem which asks. "What is the maximum number of non-overlapping convex polyhedra such that any pair of them have a common boundary of positive area?"; in fact it was from Besicovitch's acknowledgement that I traced Tietze's paper which also gives the references for the work done by Wernicke and Stäckel.

Of course, several questions arise quite naturally from Crum's Problem. Rado[4] has considered a more general problem arising from Crum's Problem and showed that there exists an infinite sequence of n-dimensional polyhedra $S_1, S_2, \ldots$ which lie in n-dimensional space, and have the property that if k is any integer satisfying $1 \leqslant k \leqslant \frac{1}{2}(n+1)$ then any k of the $S_1, S_2, \ldots$ have a $(n-k+1)$-dimensional intersection. In the same paper he also gave an example of $(n+2)$ polyhedra in n-dimensional space every k of which have an $(n - k + 1)$-dimensional inter-section, for $1 \leqslant k \leqslant n$. Eggleston [5] proved that Rado's results were best possible in the sense that the range of k in the first of Rado's results cannot be increased to $1 \leqslant k \leqslant \frac{1}{2}(n + 1) + 1$ and that the number of polyhedra, $n + 2$, in the second result cannot be increased to $n + 3$, the latter limitation having been conjectured by Rado in his paper.

Another set of problems arise from Crum's Problem when we ask what are the answers when the convex polyhedra of the problem are restricted to be polyhedra of a special type, say tetrahedra or cuboids. In the following chapters we shall concern ourselves with the particular problem concerning tetrahedra but, before we consider the results obtained on it, it is perhaps in-structive to look at the corresponding problems in two dimen-sions. Firstly, as was pointed out by Besicovitch [1], the maxi-mum number of convex non-overlapping polygons such that any pair of them have a common boundary of positive length is four. From this, it follows immediately that when we restrict the polygons to be triangles the answer cannot be greater than four, and the fact that it is four is clearly shown by the following diagram:

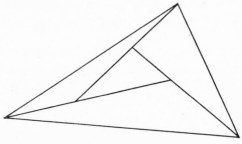

Fig. 1

However, if we instead restrict the polygons to be rectangles (or squares) the answer is quite easily seen to be three.

In general therefore the problems in two dimensions tend to be of a rather easy nature, but on moving into three dimensions the situation changes drastically. Judging from the answer to Crum's Problem in two dimensions, it might easily have been expected that for the corresponding problem in three dimen-sions, the answer would be a finite rather small number whereas we have seen that it is in fact "infinity". Certainly, if one restricts the polyhedra in the question to either tetrahedra or cuboids, one will obtain, as expected, a finite small number but the proofs are by no means as simple as in the two-dimensional cases. For instance, the solution for the problem concerning tetrahedra does not follow directly from the solution of Crum's Problem and a given configuration of tetrahedra, as happened in the corresponding two-dimensional situation.

For convenience we shall now introduce the following definition:

DEFINITION. In three-dimensional space a set of n bodies is said to possess Crum's Property if each pair of them have a common boundary of positive area but no pair of them overlap.

Let us now consider the question "What is the maximum number of cuboids possessing Crum's Property?" By using methods similar to those developed in this book it is easy to show that the answer cannot be greater than six, and the fact that the answer is six may be shown as follows:

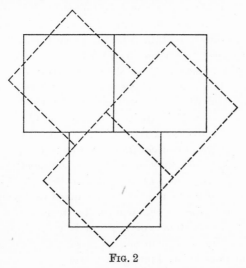

Fig. 2

Consider the above diagram, supposing the plane of the paper to have equation $x = 0$. We may clearly regard this as the section by the plane $x = 0$ of a configuration of six cubes with faces in $x = 0$, where three, say those defined by dotted lines in the diagram, lie in the half-space $x \geqslant 0$ and the other three lie in $x \leqslant 0$. This configuration clearly gives an example of six cubes possessing Crum's Property so the answer remains the same even if we restrict the cuboids to be cubes.

Finally let us examine more closely the question "What is the maximum number of tetrahedra possessing Crum's Property?" and survey the results that have been obtained in the following chapters. One of the main difficulties was that no theory had been developed to cope with this type of problem and consequently there was no structure on which to build. Of course the method of solution of Crum's Problem was no help since, by the nature of its answer, it could be, and in fact was, solved by giving a complicated geometrical configuration.

In this book we show that the problem concerning tetrahedra may be dealt with by means of simple techniques applied in an appropriate manner to a number of particular cases. For convenience in stating our results a configuration of n tetrahedra possessing Crum's Property will be called an n-con. In Chapter One we show that an n-con can be represented by an n-rowed matrix whose elements consist only of $(+1)$s, (-1)s and zeros and whose minors satisfy certain conditions; we then develop arguments from which we deduce that, for an n-con to exist, n must be less than 18. Chapter Two shows that this bound may be reduced to n less than 14. The subsequent five chapters are mainly concerned with the conditions under which a 9-con can exist and we eventually show that if an n-con for $n \geqslant 9$ exists, then no plane contains six faces of the tetrahedra of the n-con. Our analysis of the 9-con continues in Chapter Eight where we show that what one may describe as the most symmetrical case for a 9-con cannot exist, and also that the faces of the tetrahedra of the 9-con must be so arranged that they are contained in either nine or ten planes. To demonstrate that the existence or non-existence of a 9-con is critical, we show in Chapter Nine that a 10-con cannot exist and in Chapter Ten that a 8-con does exist. Finally in Chapter Eleven we discuss the results that have been obtained and from these we are led to conjecture that a 9-con does not exist. In other words, we conjecture that the maximum number of non-overlapping tetrahedra such that any pair of them have a common boundary of positive area is eight.

When the results in three dimensions are known it is of course natural to ask what happens in the corresponding problems in higher dimensions. In the case of Crum's Problem, it follows immediately from the three-dimensional case that the answer in n-dimensional space is "infinity" for $n \geqslant 3$. For the problems corresponding to those of the cuboids and tetrahedra it seems likely that the answers in n-dimensional space are $3 \times 2^{n-2}$ and 2^n respectively for $n \geqslant 2$, although the latter, in particular, cannot be put forward too confidently when the case $n = 3$ has not even been completely verified.

NOTE ADDED IN PROOF

In Ref. (6) Bagemihl showed by a similar construction to that in Chapter 10 that an 8-con exists and conjectured that a 9-con does not. He also pointed out that it was easy to verify that an n-con can exist only if $n \leqslant 17$, which is our Theorem 1.

REFERENCES

1. A. S. BESICOVITCH, On Crum's Problem. *J. London Math. Soc.* **22**, 285–287 (1947).
2. H. G. EGGLESTON, *Convexity*. Cambridge Math. Tracts (47).
3. H. TIETZE, Über das Problem der Nachbargebiete im Raum. *Monatshefte für Mathematik und Physik*, **16**, 211–216 (1905).
4. R. RADO, A Sequence of Polyhedra having Intersections of Specified Dimensions. *J. London Math. Soc.* **22**, 287–289 (1947).
5. H. G. EGGLESTON, On Rado's Extension of Crum's Problem. *J. London Math. Soc.* **28**, 467–471 (1953).
6. F. BAGEMIHL, A Conjecture Concerning Neighboring Tetrahedra. *American Math. Monthly*, **63**, 328–329 (1956).

CHAPTER ONE

SOME PRELIMINARY RESULTS

WE BEGIN the chapter by introducing a number of definitions including the following one: a set of n non-overlapping tetrahedra such that each pair of them have a common boundary of positive area is called an n-con. We then show how an n-con may be represented by a matrix whose elements consist only of $(+1)$s, (-1)s and zeros. Using this fact and a Proposition concerning certain classes of matrices, we develop the outline of an argument which will be used extensively in later chapters. We then prove seven lemmas which give some necessary conditions for a matrix to be a representation of an n-con. These simple lemmas provide the main tools of the thesis and continual reference will be made to them. Finally from Lemma 7 we deduce our first important result, namely, Theorem 1. An n-con can exist only if $n \leqslant 17$.

We need the following definitions.

DEFINITION. In three-dimensional Euclidean space a set of n bodies is said to possess Crum's Property if each pair of them have a common boundary of positive area but no pair of them overlap.

DEFINITION. A set of n tetrahedra possessing Crum's Property is called an n-con.

DEFINITION. The faces of an n-con are defined to be the $4n$ faces of the tetrahedra which are contained in the n-con.

DEFINITION. For $m \geqslant 1$ a plane that contains m faces of an n-con is called a D_m-plane.

We now define three elementary transformations on a matrix.

P.1. Interchange of two rows.

P.2. Interchange of two columns.

P.3. Multiplication of a column by (-1).

DEFINITION. We say that the matrix B is equivalent to the matrix A if B can be obtained from A by the elementary transformations defined above.

Clearly equivalence is an equals relation so given a set M of matrices we may divide M into mutually disjoint equivalence classes, two matrices being in the same equivalence class if and only if they are equivalent.

Suppose an n-con exists and that it contains a total of l D_m-planes (m not necessarily being a fixed integer). Denote the tetrahedra by $\mathbf{T}.1, \ldots, \mathbf{T}.n$ and the D_m-planes by $D^{(1)} = 0, \ldots, D^{(l)} = 0$. We construct an $(n \times l)$ matrix $A = \{a_{ij}\}$ to represent the n-con as follows:

(i) If $\mathbf{T}.p$ does not have a face contained in $D^{(q)} = 0$ put $a_{pq} = 0$.

(ii) If $\mathbf{T}.p$ lies in $D^{(q)} \geqslant 0$ and has a face contained in $D^{(q)} = 0$ put $a_{pq} = 1$.

(iii) If $\mathbf{T}.p$ lies in $D^{(q)} \leqslant 0$ and has a face contained in $D^{(q)} = 0$ put $a_{pq} = -1$.

Clearly one and only one of (i), (ii) and (iii) arises, so each element is uniquely defined and the elements of A consist only of $(+1)$s, (-1)s and zeros.

DEFINITION. The matrix A is called a matrix representation of the n-con.

It should perhaps be noted that an n-con does not in general have a unique matrix representation since, for example, a renumbering of the tetrahedra will in general lead to a different matrix, but it is true that if A and B are matrix representations of the same n-con then A and B are equivalent. However, this result is of little use to us because instead of starting with an n-con we generally start from a given set of conditions and want to know whether or not an n-con exists under them. The following Proposition is therefore more useful.

PROPOSITION. Given an equivalence class E of matrices, then either every member of E is a matrix representation of an n-con or no member of E is.

Proof. Suppose the latter does not hold then there exists a matrix M contained in E such that M is a matrix representation of an n-con. Consider the effect of the elementary transformations on M; $P.1$ is merely equivalent to a renumbering of the tetrahedra of the n-con, $P.2$ to a renumbering of the D_m-planes and $P.3$ to replacing $D^{(q)} = 0$ by $(-D^{(q)}) = 0$. Hence every matrix equivalent to M is a matrix representation of an n-con and the Proposition is proved.

Thus on being confronted with the question, "Does an n-con exist under a set of conditions, C say ?", we argue as follows:

Argument. From the above if an n-con does exist under C it must have a matrix representation, so it is sufficient to consider the set M of all those matrices which satisfy C and may be representations of an n-con. However, the Proposition now tells us that if we divide M into equivalence classes we need only consider one member from each equivalence class so that, when building up a matrix from the prescribed conditions we may use elementary transformations to bring units into convenient positions in the matrix. If the set M is void then clearly an n-con cannot exist under C and the question has been answered, but it does not necessarily follow that an n-con can exist under C if M is non-void. Consider a matrix of M; if it is a matrix representation of an n-con we may suppose that the equations of the D_m-planes, $D^{(1)} = 0, \ldots D^{(l)} = 0$, are respectively $A = a_1 x + a_2 y + a_3 z - a_4 = 0, B = b_1 x + b_2 y + b_3 z - b_4 = 0$, and so on. For convenience if the D_m-plane represented by the column q has equation $(-1)^k B = 0$ we show this by putting $(-1)^k B$ at the head of column q. Since a tetrahedron is a bounded set we may obtain certain restrictions on the $a_i, b_i, \ldots$ $(i = 1, 2, 3)$ as follows.

Let the tetrahedron **T** be defined by $A \geqslant 0, B \geqslant 0, C \geqslant 0, D \geqslant 0$, and let (p_1, p_2, p_3) be a point of **T**. Consider a point P of the form $P = (p_1 + \lambda, p_2, p_3)$. If a_1, b_1, c_1, and d_1 are all non-negative then for all positive values of λ, P will also lie in **T** so that, on letting $\lambda \to +\infty$, **T** is seen to be unbounded in the x-direction. Since this is not so, a_1, b_1, c_1, d_1, cannot all be non-negative. Similarly, by considering negative values of λ it is easily seen that a_1, b_1, c_1, d_1, cannot all be non-positive either. If in the definition of **T**, $A \geqslant 0$ is replaced by $A \leqslant 0$ then $(-A) \geqslant 0$ so that we then have $(-a_1), b_1, c_1, d_1$, cannot all be non-negative nor can they all be non-positive. Clearly similar results follow if $B \leqslant 0$ replaces $B \geqslant 0$, etc. The above has all been obtained using the x-coordinates of the planes, but it is clear that exactly

1*

similar results hold for the y-coordinates and the z-coordinates of the planes.

By applying the above to each of the tetrahedra represented by the rows of the matrix, we obtain various relations between the coordinates of the planes. If the matrix is a representation of an n-con these relations will clearly not be self-contradictory nor will they lead to a situation where two tetrahedra of the n-con do not have a common boundary of positive area.

The above argument will always be used to prove that for the appropriate n an n-con does not exist under the prescribed conditions.

To simplify the above relations between the coordinates of the D_m-planes, we use the following well-known result—see, for example, Ref. (2), p.6. If A is a non-degenerate tetrahedron, there exists an affine transformation which transforms A into the tetrahedron $x \geqslant 0$, $y \geqslant 0$, $z \geqslant 0$, $1 - x - y - z \geqslant 0$.

Before we can use this result however, we need to show that Crum's Property is unaffected by an affine transformation. Thus, consider a pair of tetrahedra T_1 and T_2 having a common boundary of positive area, say on the face F of T_1; then the ratio of the common area to the area of F is fixed and positive. As T_1 will be transformed into a non-degenerate tetrahedron, the transformed area of F will be positive. Since the ratio of areas lying in parallel planes is unaltered by an affine transformation the transforms of T_1 and T_2 must therefore have a common boundary of positive area also. Hence Crum's Property is preserved under an affine transformation. Thus, given an n-con, by the above result we may choose our coordinate system in such a manner that the tetrahedron of our choice is defined by $x \geqslant 0$, $y \geqslant 0$, $z \geqslant 0$, $w = 1 - x - y - z \geqslant 0$. By choosing the coordinate system in this way it is clear that the equations of four of the D_m-planes are automatically determined so that twelve of the coordinates of the D_m-planes are known immediately.

Notation. By $w \geqslant 0$ we will always mean $1 - x - y - z \geqslant 0$.

We now prove a number of important lemmas which give necessary conditions for a matrix to be a representation of an n-con; in the course of some of the proofs we will use the argument outlined above.

LEMMA 1. *If A is a matrix representation of an n-con, then each row of A contains four and only four non-zero elements.*

Proof. Since a tetrahedron has exactly four faces, no two of which lie in the same plane, the Lemma follows directly from the way in which A is constructed.

LEMMA 2. *If A is a matrix representation of an n-con, then given any two rows of A, say p and q, there is a column, l say, of A such that $a_{pl} = -a_{ql} \neq 0$.*

Proof. The rows p and q represent two tetrahedra **T**.p and **T**.q of an n-con; these tetrahedra possess Crum's Property so they must have an area in common. Since they do not overlap, this area must clearly lie in a plane, L say, and **T**.p must lie in one of the closed half-spaces defined by L and **T**.q in the other. Hence L is one of the D_m-planes of **T**.p and also one of the D_m-planes of **T**.q. As **T**.p and **T**.q lie in opposite closed half-spaces defined by L the result follows.

LEMMA 3. *If A is a matrix representation of an n-con it contains no minor equivalent to $\begin{pmatrix} 1 & 1 \\ -1 & -1 \end{pmatrix}$.*

Proof. Suppose A does contain a minor equivalent to $\begin{pmatrix} 1 & 1 \\ -1 & -1 \end{pmatrix}$ then by elementary transformations and the Proposition, we may suppose $a_{11} = 1 = a_{12}$, $a_{21} = -1 = a_{22}$. Let the D_m-planes represented by the first and second columns have equations $A = 0$ and $B = 0$ respectively.

Now **T**.1 lies in $A \geqslant 0$ whilst **T**.2 lies in $A \leqslant 0$, so any area they have in common must lie in $A = 0$.

Similarly the common area of **T**.1 and **T**.2 must lie in $B = 0$.

Hence their common area lies in the intersection of $A = 0$ and $B = 0$ which is a line. Thus the common area is zero and **T**.1 and **T**.2 do not possess Crum's Property. This proves the Lemma.

LEMMA 4. *If A is a matrix representation of an n-con, it does not contain a minor equivalent to $\begin{pmatrix} 1 & 1 & 1 \\ 1 & 1 & 1 \end{pmatrix}$.*

Proof. Suppose A does contain a minor equivalent to $\begin{pmatrix} 1 & 1 & 1 \\ 1 & 1 & 1 \end{pmatrix}$ then, by elementary transformations and the Proposition, we may suppose $a_{1j} = a_{2j} = 1$ ($j = 1, 2, 3$). Further, we may suppose $a_{14} = 1$ then since row 1 contains no more non-zero elements by Lemma 1, we must have $a_{24} = -1$ by Lemma 2. We choose the coordinate system so that the D_m-planes represented by $C.1$, $C.2$, $C.3$ and $C.4$ have equations $x = 0$, $y = 0$, $z = 0$ and $w = 0$ respectively. Thus $T.2$ is defined by $x \geqslant 0$, $y \geqslant 0$, $z \geqslant 0$ and $w \leqslant 0$, which is impossible since it is then unbounded. This proves the Lemma.

LEMMA 5. *If A is a matrix representation of an n-con, it does not contain a minor equivalent* $\begin{pmatrix} 1 & 1 \\ 1 & 1 \\ 1 & 1 \end{pmatrix}$.

Proof. Suppose A does contain a minor equivalent to $\begin{pmatrix} 1 & 1 \\ 1 & 1 \\ 1 & 1 \end{pmatrix}$ then by elementary transformations and the Proposition, we may suppose $a_{i1} = a_{i2}$ ($i = 1, 2, 3$). By Lemma 2 we may further suppose $a_{13} = 1$, $a_{23} = -1$. By Lemma 4 we cannot have either $a_{33} = 1$ or $a_{33} = -1$ so $a_{33} = 0$. Hence by Lemma 2 we may suppose $a_{14} = 1$, $a_{34} = -1$ so that by Lemma 4 $a_{24} = 0$. Thus by Lemma 2 we may suppose $a_{25} = 1$, $a_{35} = -1$ and we have

x	y	z	w	A
1	1	1	1	0
1	1	-1	0	1
1	1	0	-1	-1

If the matrix is a representation of a 3-con choose the coordinate system as shown where $A = a_1 x + a_2 y + a_3 z - a_4$.

From the boundedness of $T.2$, $a_1 < 0$ whereas the boundedness of $T.3$ gives $a_1 > 0$. This contradiction proves the Lemma.

LEMMA 6. Suppose a minor of the form $\begin{pmatrix} a_{il} & a_{im} \\ a_{jl} & a_{jm} \end{pmatrix}$ with $a_{il} = a_{jl} \neq 0$ and $a_{im} = a_{jm} \neq 0$ occurs in a matrix representation of an n-con, then if, for $r \neq i$ and j, $a_{rl} \neq -a_{il}$ and $a_{rm} \neq -a_{im}$ holds for $r = r_0$ there must exist p and q with $p \neq q$ such that $a_{ip} = -a_{r_0 p} \neq 0$ and $a_{jq} = -a_{r_0 q} \neq 0$.

Proof. Consider the row r_0; by Lemma 2 there certainly exists p such that $a_{ip} = -a_{r_0p} \neq 0$. Clearly $p \neq l$ and m, so by Lemma 4 $a_{jp} \neq a_{ip} = -a_{r_0p}$. Hence by Lemma 2 there exists a q with $q \neq p$ such that $a_{jq} = -a_{r_0q} \neq 0$.

Notation. We denote row p by $R.p$, column q by $C.q$ and Lemma n by $L.n$.

Notation. A non-zero element of a matrix will be called a unit.

LEMMA 7. If A is a matrix representation of an n-con, then no column of A can contain five units of the same sign.

Proof. Suppose A has a column that contains five units of the same sign; by elementary transformations we may suppose $a_{i1} = 1 (i = 1 \ldots 5)$ and $a_{12} = a_{13} = a_{14} = 1$. By $L.1$ these are the only units in $R.1$ so, by $L.2$, $R.2$, $R.3$, $R.4$ and $R.5$ each contain a (-1) in the first four columns. Hence one of the columns 2, 3 and 4 must contain two (-1)s; we may clearly suppose that it is $C.2$ and that $a_{22} = -1 = a_{32}$. By $L.5$, $a_{42} \neq -1, a_{52} \neq -1$ so by $L.2$ we may suppose $a_{43} = -1$. By $L.3$ $a_{23} \neq -1, a_{24} \neq -1$, $a_{33} \neq -1$ and $a_{34} \neq -1$ so by $L.2$ we may suppose $a_{25} = 1$, $a_{35} = -1$.

(i) Suppose $a_{53} = -1$. Two cases arise either, (a) at least one of a_{23}, a_{33}, a_{42} and a_{52} is a unit or (b) $a_{23} = 0 = a_{33} = a_{42} = a_{52}$.

(a) We may suppose $a_{23} = 1$ or -1 for the other possibilities are equivalent to this one. However, $a_{23} = -1$ is impossible by $L.3$ so $a_{23} = 1$. Thus by $L.3$ $a_{42} = 0 = a_{52}$ and by $L.5$ $a_{33} = 0$. By $L.6$ we see that one of a_{45} and a_{55} is a $(+1)$ so we may suppose $a_{45} = 1$. By $L.3$ $a_{55} \neq -1$ and by $L.4$ $a_{55} \neq 1$ so $a_{55} = 0$. By $L.3$ $a_{44} \neq -1, a_{54} \neq -1$ so by $L.2$ we may suppose $a_{46} = -a_{56} = 1$. Thus we have

$$
\begin{array}{ccccccc}
x & -w & y & A & z & B & C \\
1 & 1 & 1 & 1 & 0 & 0 & 0 \\
1 & -1 & 1 & 0 & 1 & 0 & 0 \\
1 & -1 & 0 & & -1 & & \\
1 & 0 & -1 & 0 & 1 & 1 & 0 \\
1 & 0 & -1 & & 0 & -1 &
\end{array}
$$

where the extra zeros occur by $L.1$. Choose the coordinate system shown.

From boundedness we have: from **T.**1 $a_2 < 0$, $a_3 < 0$, from T.4 $b_2 > 0$, $b_3 < 0$.

If $a_{54} = 1$, **T**.5 would be unbounded in the y-direction, so $a_{54} \neq 1$. By L.3 $a_{54} \neq -1$ so $a_{54} = 0$. Thus we may suppose $a_{57} = 1$. By L.2 therefore we must have either $a_{36} = 1$ or $a_{37} = -1$.

From the boundedness of **T**.5 $c_2 > 0$, $c_3 < 0$, so if $a_{37} = -1$ **T**.3 is unbounded in the y-direction. Thus $a_{36} = 1$ and **T**.3 is unbounded in the z-direction. Hence (a) cannot arise.

(b) We have $a_{23} = 0 = a_{33} = a_{42} = a_{52}$. From L.6 with $r_0 = 2$ one of a_{45} and a_{55} is a (-1) and from L.6 with $r_0 = 3$ one of a_{45} and a_{55} is a $(+1)$. Thus we may suppose $a_{45} = -a_{55} = 1$. By L.3 $a_{i4} \neq -1$ ($i = 2, \ldots 5$) so by L.2 we may suppose $a_{26} = -a_{46} = 1$. By L.3 $a_{36} \neq -1$ and by L.4 $a_{36} \neq 1$ so $a_{36} = 0$. Thus by L.2 we may suppose $a_{37} = -a_{57} = 1$. Hence, on multiplying C.2 by (-1), we have the following by L.1.

x	y	A	B	w	z	C
1	-1	1	1	0	0	0
1	1	0	0	1	1	0
1	1	0	0	-1	0	1
1	0	-1	0	1	-1	0
1	0	-1	0	-1	0	-1

Choose the coordinate system shown. From boundedness we have: from **T**.4 $a_2 < 0$; from **T**.5 $c_2 > 0$.

However **T**.3 is now unbounded so (b) cannot occur, and so neither can (i).

Hence (ii) $a_{53} \neq -1$ so by L.2 $a_{54} = -1$. Two cases now arise: either (a) at least one of a_{42} and a_{52} is a unit or (b) $a_{42} = 0 = a_{52}$.

(a) By L.5 $a_{42} \neq -1$, $a_{52} \neq -1$ and also $a_{42} = a_{52} = 1$ is impossible. Thus we may suppose by symmetry that $a_{42} = 1$, $a_{52} = 0$. By L.3 $a_{23} = 0 = a_{33} = a_{45}$. Now if $a_{53} = 1$ by elementary transformations we have a case of type (i) above, so we may assume $a_{53} = 0$. Similarly if $a_{55} = \pm 1$ the case is equivalent to (i) so we may further suppose $a_{55} = 0$. By L.3 and L.4 $a_{44} = 0$ so by L.2 we may suppose $-a_{46} = a_{56} = 1$. Hence we may assume $a_{57} = 1$. Now at least one of a_{27} and a_{37} is a (-1) otherwise we again have case (i) so by symmetry we may suppose $a_{27} = -1$.

By $L.3$ $a_{37} \neq 1$ and by $L.4$ $a_{37} \neq -1$ so $a_{37} = 0$. Thus, on multiplying $C.4$ by -1 and using $L.1$ we have

x	A	B	y	C	z	w
1	1	1	-1	0	0	0
1	-1	0	0	1	0	-1
1	-1			-1		0
1	1	-1	0	0	-1	0
1	0	0	1	0	1	1

Choose the coordinate system shown. From boundedness we have: from **T**.1 at least one of $a_1 < 0$ and $b_1 < 0$; from **T**.4 at least one of $a_1 < 0$ and $b_1 > 0$, so we must have $a_1 < 0$. Thus, from **T**.2 $c_1 < 0$. Now if $a_{34} = -1$ or $a_{36} = -1$, **T**.3 is unbounded in the x-direction so $a_{34} \neq -1$ and $a_{36} \neq -1$. Hence $R.3$ and $R.5$ contradict $L.2$, so that (a) cannot occur.

(b) We have $a_{42} = 0 = a_{52}$. Now a_{45} and a_{55} are not both zeros for if they were, let a_{2l} and a_{3m} be the remaining units of $R.2$ and $R.3$ respectively; then by $L.2$ $a_{4l} = a_{5l} = -a_{2l} \neq 0$ and $a_{4m} = a_{5m} = -a_{3m} \neq 0$ so, since $l \neq m$ by $L.4$, $R.4$ and $R.5$ contradict $L.4$. Hence, we may suppose by symmetry that $a_{45} = 1$. By $L.5$ $a_{55} \neq 1$, whilst if $a_{55} = -1$ we have a case of type (a) above. Hence $a_{55} = 0$. Let a_{2l} be the remaining unit of $R.2$ then by $L.2$ $a_{4l} = a_{5l} = -a_{2l}$ so, since $a_{44} \neq -1$, $a_{53} \neq -1$ by $L.3$, we may suppose $l = 6$ and that $a_{26} = 1$. By $L.3$ $a_{36} = 0$ and by $L.2$ on $L.4$ $a_{53} = 1$ since $a_{44} = 0$ by $L.1$. By $L.3$ $a_{33} \neq -1$ so by $L.2$ we must have $a_{34} = 1$. Thus on using $L.1$ we have the following:

x	y	z	w	A	B
1	1	1	1	0	0
1	-1	0	0	1	1
1	-1	0	1	-1	0
1	0	-1	0	1	-1
1	0	1	-1	0	-1

Choose the coordinate system shown. From boundedness we have from **T**.5 $b_2 > 0$; from **T**.4 $a_2 > 0$. However, **T**.3 is now unbounded so (b) does not occur.

Thus, (ii) does not arise and the Lemma is proved.

For a positive integer n, suppose an n-con exists and let A be one of its matrix representations. By elementary transformations we can arrange that $a_{11} = 1 = a_{12} = a_{13} = a_{14}$ and $a_{1j} = 0$ for $j > 4$. Therefore by Lemma 2 every row r with $r \geqslant 2$ must contain a (-1) in the first four columns. Since by Lemma 7 $C.1$, $C.2$, $C.3$ and $C.4$ can each contain at most four (-1)s it follows that there can be at most seventeen rows in the matrix and *a fortiori* at most seventeen tetrahedra in the n-con. We therefore have the following theorem.

THEOREM 1. An n-con can exist only if $n \leqslant 17$.

CHAPTER TWO

ON THE NON-EXISTENCE OF AN N-CON
FOR N GREATER THAN 13

We begin the chapter by proving two lemmas which will be
required later on, and then proceed to enumerate all possible
submatrices B of a matrix representation, where B is a matrix
representation of a 4-con which contains a column with four
units of the same sign. We find that there are five such possibilities which are not equivalent and then show that one of
them cannot occur in a matrix representation of a 9-con. Lemma
11 follows to tell us that if a 9-con exists then none of its D_m-
planes can contain eight faces. Finally the four remaining possibilities are analysed individually to prove that none of them
can occur in a matrix representation of a 9-con. It follows that
if A is a matrix representation of an n-con for $n \geqslant 9$ then no
column of A can contain more than three units of the same sign
and so we have the following theorem:

THEOREM 2. An n-con can exist only if $n \leqslant 13$.
We firstly require the following definitions.

DEFINITION. A column of a matrix representation that contains at least one $(+1)$ and at least one (-1) is called a tem-
column.

DEFINITION. A D_m-plane of an n-con which is represented by
a tem-column is called a tem-plane.

LEMMA 8. Let $P = 0$ be a tem-plane of an n-con. Then each
tetrahedron of the n-con has an intersection of positive area
with $P = 0$.
Proof. Let P be a tem-plane. Then by definition of P there
exist tetrahedra, **T**.1 and **T**.2 say, with faces in P such that **T**.1
lies in $P \geqslant 0$ and **T**.2 in $P \leqslant 0$. The lemma is trivial for the
tetrahedra with faces in P so consider a tetrahedron **T** which
does not have a face in P. Since **T** and **T**.1 possess Crum's Pro-

11

perty $\mathbf{T}$ must therefore have a positive area in $P > 0$. Similarly, since $\mathbf{T}$ and $\mathbf{T}.2$ possess Crum's Property $\mathbf{T}$ must have a positive area in $P < 0$. Hence $P = 0$ has an intersection of positive area with $\mathbf{T}$ (see for example (2), p. 17, Theorem 5 in Eggleston's *Convexity*).

It is convenient to introduce the following notation.

Notation. If we are considering the sections of the tetrahedra of an n-con with a plane, $P = 0$ say, we shall denote by $A^1 \leqslant 0$ the half-plane defined by $A \leqslant 0$, $P = 0$, where $A = 0$ is a D_m-plane of the n-con. Further the line $A = 0$, $P = 0$ will be denoted by $A^1 = 0$ and the intersection of $\mathbf{T}.l$ with $P = 0$ by $\mathbf{T}^1.l$.

DEFINITION. A line is said to "occur" in $\mathbf{T}^1.l$ if it contains a face of $\mathbf{T}^1.l$.

LEMMA 9 A. If A is a matrix representation of a 9-con then it does not contain a minor equivalent to

$$
\begin{array}{ccccc}
1 & 1 & 1 & 0 & 0 \\
1 & 1 & 0 & 1 & 0 \\
1 & 0 & -1 & -1 & 1 \\
-1 & & & & -1
\end{array}
$$

Proof. Suppose A does contain such a minor, then by $L.2$ on the first two rows of the minor we may clearly assume that we have

$$
\begin{array}{cccccc}
x & y & A & B & C & z \\
1 & 1 & 1 & 0 & 0 & 1 \\
1 & 1 & 0 & 1 & 0 & -1 \\
1 & 0 & -1 & -1 & 1 & \\
-1 & & & & -1 &
\end{array}
$$

Choose the coordinate system shown. $y = 0$ is a tem-plane so by $L.8$ every tetrahedron of the 9-con must have an intersection of positive area with $y = 0$. Thus consider the configuration on $y = 0$ (FIG. 3, p. 13).

Some of the lines may be in different positions relative to each other, but these changes do not affect the arguments used below.

From the diagram it is clear that $x^1 = 0$ does not occur in $\mathbf{T}^1.3$ so $C^1 = 0$ must join $A^1 = 0$ to $B^1 = 0$ in such a way that $C^1 \geqslant 0$, $A^1 \leqslant 0$, $B^1 \leqslant 0$ is a triangle. Hence the sector $A^1 \geqslant 0$, $B^1 \geqslant 0$ must lie in $C^1 > 0$. Now at least one of $\mathbf{T}^1.1$ and $\mathbf{T}^1.2$

lies completely in $A^1 \geqslant 0$, $B^1 \geqslant 0$ so at least one of them lies in $C^1 > 0$, say it is $\mathbf{T}^1.l$. As $\mathbf{T}^1.4$ lies in $C^1 \leqslant 0$, $\mathbf{T}^1.4$ and $\mathbf{T}^1.l$ do not have an area in common and so the corresponding tetrahedra do not possess Crum's Property. The lemma now follows.

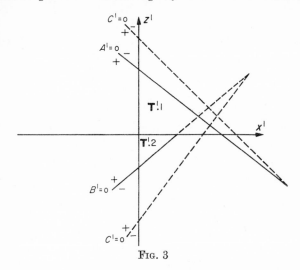

FIG. 3

For reasons which become apparent in Chapter 4, after this chapter we shall only use the following weaker form of the lemma.

LEMMA 9. If A is a matrix representation of a 9-con, then it does not contain a minor equivalent to

$$
\begin{array}{ccccc}
1 & 1 & 1 & 0 & 0 \\
1 & 1 & 0 & 1 & 0 \\
1 & 0 & -1 & -1 & 1 \\
 & -1 & & & -1 \\
-1 & & & &
\end{array}
$$

Let A be a matrix representation of an n-con for $n \geqslant 9$. Then by $L.7$ there are at most four units of the same sign in a column. If A has a column which contains four units of the same sign let $B = (b_{ij})$ be the matrix consisting of the four rows which contain those units. We now consider the possible structures of B. Clearly B is a matrix representation of a 4-con, so by the

Proposition in Chapter 1 we need only enumerate the equivalence classes. By elementary transformations we may arrange that $a_{ij} = b_{ij}$ $(i = 1, \ldots 4)$, $a_{i1} = 1$ $(i = 1, \ldots 4)$, $a_{1j} = 1$ $(j = 1, \ldots 4)$ and $a_{1j} = 0$ $(j > 4)$. By $L.2$ we may further suppose $a_{22} = -1$.

(i) Suppose $a_{32} = -1$, then by $L.3$ $a_{2j} \neq -1, a_{3j} \neq -1$ $(j = 3, 4)$, so by $L.2$ we may suppose $a_{25} = -a_{35} = 1$. By $L.5$ $a_{42} \neq -1$, so by $L.2$ we may suppose $a_{43} = -1$. Two cases now arise (A) $a_{42} = 1$, and (B) $a_{42} = 0$.

(A) Suppose $a_{42} = 1$, then by $L.3$ $a_{23} = 0 = a_{33} = a_{45}$ and $a_{44} \neq -1$. By $L.4$ $a_{44} \neq 1$ so $a_{44} = 0$, and we may put $a_{46} = 1$.

(A$_1$) Suppose $a_{j4} = 0 = a_{j6}$ $(j = 2,3)$ then we may put $a_{27} = 1$. By $L.3$ and $L.4$ $a_{37} = 0$, so we may also put $a_{38} = 1$. Hence on using $L.1$ we have the following possibility for B and we denote it by F_1:

$$
\begin{array}{cccccccc}
1 & 1 & 1 & 1 & 0 & 0 & 0 & 0 \\
1 & -1 & 0 & 0 & 1 & 0 & 1 & 0 \\
1 & -1 & 0 & 0 & -1 & 0 & 0 & 1 \\
1 & 1 & -1 & 0 & 0 & 1 & 0 & 0
\end{array}
$$

(A$_2$) Suppose one of a_{24} and a_{34} is a unit and also that one of a_{26} and a_{36} is a unit. By $L.3$ the units cannot be (-1)s so by the symmetry of $R.2$ and $R.3$ we may suppose $a_{24} = 1 = a_{36}$ so on using $L.1$ we have

$$
\begin{array}{ccccc}
x & y & w\ z & A\ B \\
1 & 1 & 1\ 1 & 0\ 0 \\
1 & -1 & 0\ 1 & 1\ 0 \\
1 & -1 & 0\ 0 & -1\ 1 \\
1 & 1 & -1\ 0 & 0\ 1
\end{array}
$$

Choose the coordinate system shown. From boundedness we have: from **T**.4 $b_2 < 0$; from **T**.3 $a_2 < 0$. However, **T**.2 is now unbounded so the matrix is not a possible structure for B.

Since $a_{24} = a_{34} \neq 0$ and $a_{26} = a_{36} \neq 0$ are both impossible by $L.4$ only two cases are left for consideration under (A). What is more, since the case when $a_{26} = 0 = a_{36}$ and one of a_{24} and a_{34} is a unit is clearly equivalent to the case when $a_{24} = 0 = a_{34}$ and one of a_{26} and a_{36} is a unit, it is only necessary to consider the former. By symmetry we may suppose a_{24} is the unit so that

$a_{34} = 0 = a_{26} = a_{36}$. By $L.3$ $a_{24} \neq -1$ so $a_{24} = 1$. Hence on putting $a_{37} = 1$ and using $L.1$ we have a second possible structure for B and we denote it by F_2:

$$
\begin{array}{rrrrrrr}
1 & 1 & 1 & 1 & 0 & 0 & 0 \\
1 & -1 & 0 & 1 & 1 & 0 & 0 \\
1 & -1 & 0 & 0 & -1 & 0 & 1 \\
1 & 1 & -1 & 0 & 0 & 1 & 0 \\
\end{array}
$$

Hence we have (B) $a_{42} = 0$. By $L.3$ and $L.5$ a_{23} and a_{33} cannot both be units. Thus, either (B_1) one of a_{23} and a_{33} is a unit or (B_2) $a_{23} = 0 = a_{33}$.

(B_1) By symmetry we may suppose a_{23} is the unit and since $a_{23} \neq -1$ by $L.3$ we have $a_{23} = 1$, $a_{33} = 0$. By $L.1$ we have

$$
\begin{array}{rrrrrr}
x & w & y & z & A & B \\
1 & 1 & 1 & 1 & 0 & 0 \\
1 & -1 & 1 & 0 & 1 & 0 \\
1 & -1 & 0 & & -1 & \\
1 & 0 & -1 & & & \\
\end{array}
$$

Choose the coordinate system shown. From boundedness we have: from $T.2$ $a_1 < 0$, $a_2 < 0$. Thus if $a_{34} = 1$, $T.3$ is unbounded in the x-direction so $a_{34} = 0$ since $a_{34} \neq -1$ by $L.3$. Hence we may suppose $a_{36} = 1$. From the boundedness of $T.3$ we have $b_1 < 0$, $b_2 < 0$. By $L.2$ we must have either (B_1^1) $a_{45} = 1$ or (B_1^{11}) $a_{46} = -1$.

(B_1^1) Suppose $a_{45} = 1$, then neither a_{44} nor a_{46} is $(+1)$ for, if either was, $T.4$ would be unbounded in the y-direction. Thus, by $L.3$ $a_{44} = 0 = a_{46}$. Hence on putting $a_{47} = 1$ and using $L.1$ we have another possible structure for B and we denote it by F_3:

$$
\begin{array}{rrrrrrr}
1 & 1 & 1 & 1 & 0 & 0 & 0 \\
1 & -1 & 1 & 0 & 1 & 0 & 0 \\
1 & -1 & 0 & 0 & -1 & 1 & 0 \\
1 & 0 & -1 & 0 & 1 & 0 & 1 \\
\end{array}
$$

(B_1^{11}) Suppose $a_{46} = -1$ then by $L.3$ $a_{45} = 0$. Now if $a_{44} = 1$ $T.4$ is unbounded in the x-direction, so $a_{44} = 0$ by $L.3$. Hence on putting $a_{47} = 1$ and using $L.1$ we have a further possible structure for B and we denote it by F_4:

$$
\begin{array}{ccccccc}
1 & 1 & 1 & 1 & 0 & 0 & 0 \\
1 & -1 & 1 & 0 & 1 & 0 & 0 \\
1 & -1 & 0 & 0 & -1 & 1 & 0 \\
1 & 0 & -1 & 0 & 0 & -1 & 1
\end{array}
$$

Hence we must now have (B_2) $a_{23} = 0 = a_{33}$. Further if a_{45} is a unit we have a case that is equivalent to (B_1) so we may suppose $a_{45} = 0$. By $L.3$ $a_{j4} \neq -1$ $(j = 2, 3, 4)$, so by $L.2$ we may suppose $a_{26} = -a_{46} = 1$. By $L.3$ and $L.4$ $a_{36} = 0$, so by $L.2$ we may further suppose $a_{37} = -a_{47} = 1$. However, on using $L.1$ we see by $L.9$A that this is not a possibility for B.

This completes the analysis of (i).

We need now only consider those matrices B that have at most two units in each column $C.l$ for $l \geqslant 2$ for if three or four units occur in a column $C.l$ for $l \geqslant 2$ we have a case that is equivalent to (i). Hence by $L.2$ we may suppose $a_{33} = -1 = a_{44}$ so that $a_{32} = a_{42} = 0 = a_{23} = a_{43} = a_{24} = a_{34}$. Thus, by $L.2$ we may put $a_{25} = -a_{35} = 1$ so that $a_{15} = 0 = a_{45}$ and $a_{26} = -a_{46} = 1$ so that $a_{16} = 0 = a_{36}$. Finally by $L.2$ we may assume $a_{37} = -a_{47} = 1$ so that $a_{17} = 0 = a_{27}$. Thus the final possible structure F_5 for B is

$$
\begin{array}{ccccccc}
1 & 1 & 1 & 1 & 0 & 0 & 0 \\
1 & -1 & 0 & 0 & 1 & 1 & 0 \\
1 & 0 & -1 & 0 & -1 & 0 & 1 \\
1 & 0 & 0 & -1 & 0 & -1 & -1
\end{array}
$$

LEMMA 10. If A is a matrix representation of a 9-con then A does not contain a minor equivalent to F_5.

Proof. Suppose A does contain a minor equivalent to $F_5 = (f_{ij})$ say. By elementary transformations we may suppose that $a_{ij} = f_{ij}$ $(i = 1, \ldots 4)$ $(j = 1, \ldots 7)$. Since A has nine rows $C.1$ must contain at least one zero by $L.7$ so we may suppose $a_{91} = 0$. It follows from the structure of F_5 that the four units of $R.9$ must lie in columns 2 to 7 if $R.9$ is not to contradict $L.2$.

Now if $a_{51} = -1$ by $L.3$ $a_{5j} = 0$ $(j = 2, \ldots 7)$ so that $R.5$ and $R.9$ contradict $L.2$. Thus, $a_{51} \neq -1$. By $L.7$ $a_{51} \neq 1$ so $a_{51} = 0$. Similarly, $a_{j1} = 0$ $(j = 6, 7, 8)$. Hence the twenty units of $R.5$, $R.6$, $R.7$, $R.8$ and $R.9$ must all be contained in columns 2 to 7. Thus, at least one of the columns must contain units from at least four of $R.l$ $(l = 5, \ldots 9)$ and by the symmetry of F_5 we may assume that $C.2$ is such a column. By elementary transformations we may therefore suppose that $C.2$ has units in $R.l$ $(l = 5, \ldots 8)$.

Two possibilities arise for these units, either (A) Two of them are of one sign and two of the other, or (B) Three of them are of one sign and only one of the other. The four units cannot all be of the same sign for together with a_{12} or a_{22} $L.7$ would then be contradicted.

(A) We may clearly suppose that $a_{52} = 1 = a_{62}$, $a_{72} = -1 = a_{82}$ so that

$$
\begin{array}{ccccccc}
1 & 1 & 1 & 1 & 0 & 0 & 0 \\
1 & -1 & 0 & 0 & 1 & 1 & 0 \\
1 & 0 & -1 & 0 & -1 & 0 & 1 \\
1 & 0 & 0 & -1 & 0 & -1 & -1 \\
0 & 1 & & & & & \\
0 & 1 & & & & & \\
0 & -1 & & & & & \\
0 & -1 & & & & &
\end{array}
$$

By $L.2$ we must have either $a_{53} = -1$ or $a_{54} = -1$ so, since the cases are equivalent, we may suppose $a_{53} = -1$. By $L.3$ $a_{73} = 0 = a_{83}$.

Now if $a_{74} = 0 = a_{84}$ as well, a_{7j} and a_{8j} $(j = 5, 6, 7)$ must all be units by $L.1$ and, since $a_{72} = -1 = a_{82}$, this is impossible by $L.3$ and $L.4$.

Thus at least one of a_{74} and a_{84} is a unit and by symmetry we may suppose a_{74} is. By $L.3$ $a_{74} \neq -1$ so $a_{74} = 1$. Thus by $L.3$ $a_{64} \neq -1$ so by $L.2$ on $R.1$ $a_{63} = -1$. Hence by $L.6$ with $r_0 = 3$ and symmetry we may suppose $a_{55} = 1 = -a_{67}$. By $L.3$ $a_{75} \neq -1$, $a_{85} \neq -1$, so by $L.2$ on $R.2$ $a_{76} = -1 = a_{86}$. By $L.3$ $a_{87} \neq 1$ so by $L.2$ on $R.4$ $a_{84} = 1$ which is impossible by $L.4$. Hence (A) cannot arise.

(B) By symmetry we may suppose that $a_{52} = 1 = a_{62} = a_{72}$, $a_{82} = -1$ so that

$$
\begin{array}{rrrrrrr}
1 & 1 & 1 & 1 & 0 & 0 & 0 \\
1 & -1 & 0 & 0 & 1 & 1 & 0 \\
1 & 0 & -1 & 0 & -1 & 0 & 1 \\
1 & 0 & 0 & -1 & 0 & -1 & -1 \\
0 & 1 & & & & & \\
0 & 1 & & & & & \\
0 & 1 & & & & & \\
0 & -1 & & & & & \\
\end{array}
$$

By $L.2$ one of a_{j3} and a_{j4} must be a (-1) for each j $(j = 5, 6, 7)$. By $L.5$ both $a_{j3} = -1$ $(j = 5, 6, 7)$ and $a_{j4} = -1$ $(j = 5, 6, 7)$ are impossible so by symmetry we may suppose that $a_{53} = -1 = a_{63} = a_{74}$. Thus by $L.3$ $a_{83} = 0 = a_{84}$. Hence by $L.6$ with $r_0 = 3$ and symmetry, we may suppose that $a_{55} = 1 = -a_{67}$. Now by $L.1$ a_{8j} $(j = 5, 6, 7)$ are all units. By $L.3$ $a_{85} \neq -1$ and $a_{87} \neq 1$ so $a_{85} = 1$ and $a_{87} = -1$. However, this is impossible by $L.3$.

Thus, (B) cannot arise either and the lemma is proved.

We require the following definition.

DEFINITION. Let A be a matrix representation of an n-con and B a submatrix of A, then a column l of A is called a tem-column w. r. t. B if B contains at least one $(+1)$ and at least one (-1) in $C.l$.

LEMMA 11. If A is a matrix representation of a 9-con then each column of A contains at most seven units.

Proof. Suppose the Lemma is false. By $L.7$ nine units cannot occur in a column of A so we need only consider the case when eight do. By $L.7$ four of the units must be $(+1)$s and four (-1)s so we may clearly suppose that $a_{j1} = 1$ $(j = 1, \ldots 4)$, $a_{l1} = -1$ $(l = 5, \ldots 8)$ and $a_{91} = 0$. Thus the first four rows of A will be equivalent to one of the F_i $(i = 1, \ldots 4)$ and so will the second four rows. Denote the first four rows by F_p and the second four by F_q. By inspection of the F_i $(i = 1, \ldots 4)$ we see that at least three of the units of $R.9$ must be used to ensure that $R.9$ and F_p obey $L.2$. Similarly at least three of the units of $R.9$ must be used to ensure that $R.9$ and F_q obey $L.2$. Now if $C.k$ is a tem-column w. r. t. F_p, by $L.3$ we must have $a_{lk} = 0$ for $l = 5, \ldots 8$

and similarly if $C.k$ is a tem-column w. r. t. F_q, then $a_{ik} = 0$ $(i = 1, \ldots 4)$.

Hence from the above we have the following result.

LEMMA 11 A. $R.9$ can contain at most one unit in the columns which are tem-columns w. r. t. F_p and at most one unit in the columns which are tem-columns w. r. t. F_q.

By $L.8$ $T.9$ must have an intersection of positive area with the plane, $P = 0$ say, that is represented by $C.1$. Thus $T^1.9$ must be either a triangle or quadrilateral.

Suppose $T^1.9$ is a triangle, then one face of $T.9$ must lie completely in $P \geqslant 0$ or $P \leqslant 0$, say $P \geqslant 0$ for definiteness. Hence, the intersection T of $T.9$ and $P \leqslant 0$ is a tetrahedron. Since $T.9$ and F_q possessed Crum's Property and $T.9$ did not have a face in $P = 0$ it is clear that T and F_q will also possess Crum's Property and so be a 5-con. However, if we consider its matrix representation, we see that the column representing $P = 0$ contains five (-1)s and this is impossible by $L.7$.

We therefore have the following result.

LEMMA 11 B. The intersection of $T.9$ with $P = 0$ is a quadrilateral.

We now consider the $F_i (i = 1, \ldots 4)$ in turn to see if they can occur either as F_p or F_q. Suppose one or both of F_p and F_q is equivalent to F_1. By elementary transformations we may assume that $F_p = F_1$ so we have

x	y	z	w	A	B	C	D
1	1	1	1	0	0	0	0
1	−1	0	0	1	0	1	0
1	−1	0	0	−1	0	0	1
1	1	−1	0	0	1	0	0

With the coordinate system shown, the configuration on $x = 0$ is shown in FIG. 4, p. 20.

$C^1 = 0$ and $D^1 = 0$ may meet $y^1 = 0$ in different positions relative to $w^1 = 0$ and $B^1 = 0$, and $A^1 = 0$ may also have a non-negative gradient but these changes do not affect the arguments used below.

(i) Suppose a_{92} is a unit, then by the symmetry of F_1 we need only consider the case when $a_{92} = 1$. Hence by Lemma

11A $a_{93} = 0 = a_{95}$ so by $L.2$ we must have $a_{94} = -1 = a_{96}$. Choose the above coordinate system, then from the diagram it is clear that $y^1 = 0$ does not occur in $T^1.9$ since $T^1.9$ contains $w^1 \leqslant 0$, $B^1 \leqslant 0$. Thus $T^1.9$ must be a triangle and this is impossible by Lemma 11B. Hence $a_{92} = 0$.

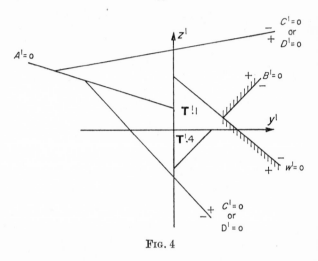

Fig. 4

(ii) Suppose a_{95} is a unit; by symmetry we need only consider the case when $a_{95} = -1$. By Lemma 11A $a_{93} = 0$ so by $L.2$ we must have $a_{94} = -1 = a_{98} = a_{96}$. Choose the above coordinate system. Then from the diagram $T^1.9$ must lie in $y^1 > 0$ since $T^1.9$ contains $w^1 \leqslant 0$, $B^1 \leqslant 0$. However, the diagram also shows that the $A^1 = 0$ portion of $A^1 \leqslant 0$, $D^1 \leqslant 0$ must lie in $y^1 < 0$ so that $A^1 = 0$ cannot occur in $T^1.9$. Thus $T^1.9$ is a triangle and this is impossible by Lemma 11B. Thus $a_{95} = 0$.

The case when a_{93} is a unit is clearly equivalent to (ii) so we may further suppose $a_{93} = 0$. Hence by $L.2$ only one possibility for $T.9$ remains, namely $a_{94} = -1 = a_{96} = a_{97} = a_{98}$. Choose the above coordinate system. Then the diagram shows that $T^1.9$ can only be in $y^1 > 0$ since it contains $B^1 \leqslant 0$, $w^1 \leqslant 0$ and also that $T^1.9$ can only lie in $y^1 < 0$ since it contains $C^1 \leqslant 0$, $D^1 \leqslant 0$. Hence $T^1.9$ does not exist and $L.8$ is contradicted.

Hence F_1 is not a possibility for F_p or F_q.

Now suppose that one or both of F_p and F_q is equivalent to F_2. By elementary transformations we may assume that $F_p = F_2$

so we have

x	y	w	z	A	B	C
1	1	1	1	0	0	0
1	-1	0	1	1	0	0
1	-1	0	0	-1	0	1
1	1	-1	0	0	1	0

With the coordinate system shown, the configuration on $x = 0$ is:

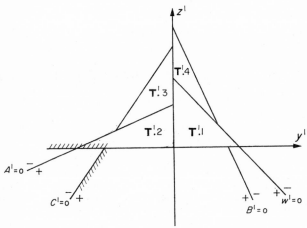

FIG. 5

Some of the lines may be in different positions relative to each other, but these changes do not affect the arguments used below.

(i) Suppose a_{92} is a unit, then by the symmetry of F_2, we need only consider the case when $a_{92} = 1$. By Lemma 11A $a_{93} = 0$ and by $L.3$ $a_{94} \neq -1$ so $R.1$ and $R.9$ contradict $L.2$. Thus $a_{92} = 0$.

(ii) Suppose a_{93} is a unit, then by Lemma 11A $a_{95} = 0$. Thus by $L.2$ on $R.2$ we must have $a_{94} = -1$. By $L.3$ $a_{93} \neq -1$ so $a_{93} = 1$. Finally by $L.2$ on $R.3$ $a_{97} = -1$. Choose the above coordinate system. Then the diagram shows that $T^1.9$ must lie in $y^1 < 0$ since it contains $z^1 \leqslant 0$, $C^1 \leqslant 0$. However, the diagram also shows that the $w^1 = 0$ portion of $w^1 \geqslant 0$, $z^1 \leqslant 0$ must lie in $y^1 > 0$ so that $w^1 = 0$ cannot occur in $T^1.9$. Thus $T^1.9$ is a triangle and this is impossible by Lemma 11B. Hence $a_{93} = 0$.

The case when a_{95} is a unit is clearly equivalent to (ii) so we may further suppose $a_{95} = 0$. Hence by $L.2$ the only possibility for $R.9$ is $a_{94} = -1 = a_{96} = a_{97}$. Choose the above coordinate system. Then the diagram shows that $\mathbf{T}^1.9$ can only lie in $y^1 < 0$ since it contains $z^1 \leqslant 0$, $C^1 \leqslant 0$ and also that $\mathbf{T}^1.9$ can only lie in $y^1 > 0$ since it contains $z^1 \leqslant 0$, $B^1 \leqslant 0$. Hence $\mathbf{T}^1.9$ does not exist and $L.8$ is contradicted.

Thus F_2 is not a possibility for F_p or F_q.

We now suppose that one or both of F_p and F_q is equivalent to F_3. By elementary transformations we may assume that F_p is equivalent to F_3 and that we have

x	y	z	A	w	B	C
1	1		1	1	0	0	0
1	1	1	0	1	0	0
1	1	0	0	-1	1	0
1	0	-1	0	1	0	1

the second column of F_3 having been multiplied by (-1).

(i) Suppose a_{92} is a unit then by Lemma 11A $a_{93} = 0 = a_{95}$ so by $L.2$ on $R.2$ we must have $a_{92} = -1$. Thus by $L.2$ on $R.1$ and $R.4$ $a_{94} = -1 = a_{97}$. Choose the above coordinate system. Then the configuration on $x = 0$ is:

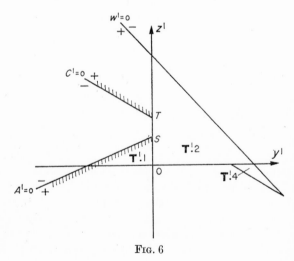

Fig. 6

Now $OT > OS$ for, if it is not, $y^1 = 0$ will not appear in
$\mathbf{T}^1.9$ since $\mathbf{T}^1.9$ contains $C^1 \leqslant 0$, $A^1 \leqslant 0$; this would mean that
$\mathbf{T}^1.9$ is a triangle, which is impossible by Lemma 11 B. Hence
$\mathbf{T}^1.1$ lies in $C^1 < 0$. Now by $L.3$ $a_{j2} = 0$ $(j = 5, \ldots 8)$ so, since
at least three of the units of $R.9$ must be used to ensure that
$R.9$ and F_q obey $L.2$, at least one of a_{j7} $(j = 5, \ldots 8)$ is a $(+1)$.
Thus we may assume $a_{57} = 1$. Clearly $\mathbf{T}^1.5$ will be a triangle
and will lie in $C^1 \geqslant 0$. Hence $\mathbf{T}^1.5$ and $\mathbf{T}^1.1$ will not have an area
in common so that $\mathbf{T}.5$ and $\mathbf{T}.1$ will not possess Crum's Property.
Thus a_{92} is not a unit and $a_{92} = 0$.

The cases when a_{93} is a unit and when a_{95} is a unit are clearly
equivalent to (i) so we may further suppose that $a_{93} = 0 = a_{95}$.
However, $R.9$ and $R.2$ now contradict $L.2$.

Hence F_3 is not a possibility for F_p or F_q.

By Lemmas 9 and 10 we must therefore have that both F_p and
F_q are equivalent to F_4. By elementary transformations we may
suppose that $F_p = F_4$ so we have

x	y	z	w	A	B	C
1	1	1	1	0	0	0
1	−1	1	0	1	0	0
1	−1	0	0	−1	1	0
1	0	−1	0	0	−1	1

For $R.2$ and $R.9$ to obey $L.2$, $R.9$ must have a unit in a tem-
column w. r. t. F_p and the same holds for $R.3$ and $R.9$. By Lemma
11 A this tem-column w. r. t. F_p must be the same for both, so
by inspection we can only have $a_{92} = 1$. Thus by Lemma 11 A
$a_{93} = 0 = a_{95} = a_{96}$. Hence by $L.2$ we have $a_{94} = -1 = a_{97}$.

Choosing the coordinate system shown, the configuration
on $x = 0$ is shown in FIG. 7, p. 24.

Some of the lines may be in different positions relative to each
other, but these changes do not affect the arguments used below.

Now both $y^1 = 0$ and $w^1 = 0$ must occur in $\mathbf{T}^1.9$ for, if one
of them did not, $\mathbf{T}^1.9$ would be a triangle, and this is impossible
by Lemma 11 B. Thus $C^1 = 0$ cannot have a negative gradient
for, if it did, the $y^1 = 0$ portion of $y^1 \geqslant 0$, $C^1 \leqslant 0$ would lie in
$z^1 < 0$, whilst the $y^1 = 0$ portion of $y^1 \geqslant 0$, $w^1 \leqslant 0$ would lie
in $z^1 > 0$, so that $y^1 = 0$ would not occur in $\mathbf{T}^1.9$. As $C^1 = 0$
clearly cannot have a gradient of zero, $C^1 = 0$ must have a positive gradient and so $OJ < OK$. Furthermore, $OK < OL$, for,

if it was not, $w^1 = 0$ would not occur in $\mathbf{T}^1.9$ since $\mathbf{T}^1.9$ contains $y^1 \geqslant 0$, $C^1 \leqslant 0$.

Just as $R.9$ had to contain a unit in a tem-column w. r. t. F_p, it must similarly contain a unit in a tem-column w. r. t. F_q. By $L.3$ this tem-column w. r. t. F_q cannot be $C.4$ or $C.7$, so we may suppose that it is $C.8$ and that $a_{98} = 1$. Let the equation of the

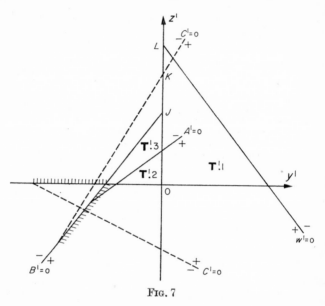

Fɪɢ. 7

D_m-plane represented by $C.8$ be $D = 0$. Clearly $D^1 = 0$ must close $\mathbf{T}^1.9$ so, since $\mathbf{T}^1.9$ is a quadrilateral, $D^1 = 0$ must join $C^1 = 0$ to $y^1 = 0$ and it must meet $y^1 = 0$ in a point M where $OM > OL$. Hence if $D^1 = 0$ has a non-negative gradient, $\mathbf{T}^1.1$ lies in $D^1 > 0$ whilst if $D^1 = 0$ has a negative gradient $\mathbf{T}^1.2$ lies in $D^1 > 0$. Since $C.8$ is a tem-column w. r. t. F_q at least one of $R.h.$ $(h = 5, \ldots 8)$ has a (-1) in $C.8$, say $R.5$ for definiteness. Thus $\mathbf{T}^1.5$ lies in $D^1 \leqslant 0$ and so does not have an area in common with at least one of the $\mathbf{T}^1.k$ $(k = 1, \ldots 4)$. Thus $\mathbf{T}.5$ and at least one of the $\mathbf{T}.k$ $(k = 1, \ldots 4)$ do not possess Crum's Property and the Lemma is proved.

Lᴇᴍᴍᴀ 12. If A is a matrix representation of a 9-con then it does not contain a minor equivalent to F_2.

Proof. Suppose the lemma is false, then by elementary transformations we may suppose that the units of the first four rows are

x	y	z	w	A	B	C
1	1	1	1	0	0	0
1	−1	0	1	1	0	0
1	−1	0	0	−1	0	1
1	1	−1	0	0	1	0

By Lemma 11 at least two of a_{j1} $(j = 5, \ldots 9)$ are zeros so we may assume $a_{51} = 0 = a_{61}$. We now consider the possibilities for $R.l$ where $a_{l1} = 0$.

Suppose $a_{l2} = -1$, then by $L.3$ $a_{l4} \neq -1$, so by $L.2$ we must have $a_{l5} = -1$ and $a_{l7} = -1$. Thus we have (i) $a_{l2} = -1 = a_{l5} = a_{l7}$.

Suppose $a_{l3} = -1$, then by $L.3$ $a_{l2} \neq -1$, so by $L.2$ $a_{l6} = -1$. By $L.2$ on $R.2$ either $a_{l2} = 1$ or $a_{l5} = -1$, since $a_{l4} \neq -1$ by $L.3$. Thus for the former we have (ii) $a_{l2} = 1$, $a_{l3} = -1 = a_{l6}$. For the latter, by $L.2$ we have $a_{l7} = -1$ so (iii) $a_{l3} = -1 = a_{l5} = a_{l6} = a_{l7}$.

Now if $a_{l2} \neq -1$ and $a_{l3} \neq -1$ by $L.2$ on $R.1$ we must have $a_{l4} = -1$. Thus by $L.3$ $a_{l2} = 0$. By $L.2$ on $R.3$ either $a_{l5} = 1$ or $a_{l7} = -1$ and by $L.2$ on $R.4$ either $a_{l3} = 1$ or $a_{l6} = -1$. Hence, we have another four possibilities so that the complete set of possibilities for $R.l$ is

(i) $a_{l2} = -1 = a_{l5} = a_{l7}$ (ii) $a_{l2} = 1, a_{l3} = -1 = a_{l6}$

(iii) $a_{l3} = -1 = a_{l5} = a_{l6} = a_{l7}$ (iv) $a_{l3} = 1 = a_{l5}, a_{l4} = -1$

(v) $a_{l3} = 1, a_{l4} = -1 = a_{l7}$ (vi) $a_{l5} = 1, a_{l4} = -1 = a_{l6}$

(vii) $a_{l4} = -1 = a_{l6} = a_{l7}$

By $L.4$ the same possibility cannot occur in two different rows so in order to prove the lemma, we need to show that each possibility cannot occur with any of the others.

With the above coordinate system we have from boundedness: from $T.2$ $a_2 > 0$, $a_3 > 0$; from $T.3$ $c_2 > 0$, $c_3 > 0$; from $T.4$ $b_2 < 0$, $b_3 > 0$.

Thus, if $R.l$ is the possibility (iii) $T.l$ will be unbounded in the z-direction so (iii) cannot occur.

Next suppose that $R.5$ is the possibility (vi) so that $a_{55} = 1$, $a_{54} = -1 = a_{56}$. By $L.3$ $a_{52} = 0 = a_{53}$ and $a_{57} \neq -1$. Choose the above coordinate system. Then if $a_{57} = 1$, $T.5$ is unbounded in the y-direction. Thus, $a_{57} = 0$ and we may suppose $a_{58} = 1$. If $D = 0$ is the equation of the plane represented by $C.8$ then from the boundedness of $T.5$ we have $d_2 < 0$.

Now if (vi) and (iv) occur together we may suppose $a_{63} = 1 = a_{65}$, $a_{64} = -1$; by $L.2$ we must then have either $a_{66} = 1$ or $a_{68} = -1$. However, if $a_{66} = 1$ $T.6$ is unbounded in the z-direction whilst if $a_{68} = -1$ $T.6$ is unbounded in the y-direction. Thus (vi) and (iv) cannot occur together.

Also if (vi) and (ii) occur together we may suppose $a_{62} = 1$, $a_{63} = -1 = a_{66}$; by $L.3$ $a_{65} = 0$ so by $L.2$ either $a_{64} = 1$ or $a_{68} = -1$. However, if $a_{64} = 1$ $T.6$ is unbounded in the z-direction whilst if $a_{68} = -1$ $T.6$ is unbounded in the y-direction. Thus (vi) and (ii) cannot occur together.

Now the cases when (v) and (iv) occur together and when (i) and (v) occur together are respectively equivalent to those when (vi) and (iv) occur together (by interchanging columns 3 and 5; columns 6 and 7; rows 1 and 2; rows 3 and 4 and multiplying column 2 by (-1)) and when (ii) and (vi) occur together (by interchanging columns 6 and 7; rows 1 and 2; rows 3 and 4; columns 3 and 5 and multiplying column 2 by (-1)). Hence (v) and (iv) cannot occur together and neither can (i) and (v). Thus, at most three of the possibilities can occur with (vi), so that if (vi) occurs at least one of the a_{j1} $(j = 5, \ldots 9)$ is a (-1). Similarly, if (v) occurs at least one of the a_{j1} $(j = 5, \ldots 9)$ is a (-1). However, if neither (v) nor (vi) occurs at most four of the possibilities can occur so again at least one of the a_{j1} $(j = 5, \ldots 9)$ is a (-1).

Hence in every case at least one of the a_{j1} $(j = 5, \ldots 9)$ is a (-1) so that $C.1$ is a tem-column. Thus by $L.8$ every tetrahedron of the 9-con must have an intersection of positive area with the plane represented by $C.1$.

With the above coordinate system the configuration on $x = 0$ is shown in FIG. 8, p. 27.

Some of the lines may have different positions relative to each other but this will be taken into account in the arguments used below. However, it is clear that $w^1 \leqslant 0$, $C^1 \leqslant 0$ must lie in $y^1 < 0$, $z^1 > 0$.

Consider (vii); if its section (vii)^1 exists it must occur in $y^1 < 0$, $z^1 > 0$ since (vii)^1 contains $w^1 \leqslant 0$, $C^1 \leqslant 0$. But $y^1 < 0$, $z^1 > 0$ lies in $B^1 > 0$ so, since (vii)^1 contains $B^1 \leqslant 0$, (vii)^1 cannot exist. Hence (vii) cannot occur.

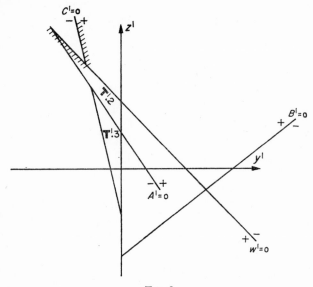

FIG. 8

Now suppose (vi) and (v) occur together. We may suppose $R.5$ is (vi) and $R.6$ is (v), then by our previous consideration of (vi) we may assume $a_{58} = 1$. By $L.3$ $a_{65} = 0$ so by $L.2$ we must have either $a_{66} = 1$ or $a_{68} = -1$. Consider the sections on $x = 0$; from the diagram it is clear that $B^1 \leqslant 0$, $w^1 \leqslant 0$ lies in $A^1 > 0$ and also in $y^1 > 0$. Thus $A^1 = 0$ cannot occur in $\mathbf{T}^1.5$ so that $D^1 = 0$ must join $B^1 = 0$ to $w^1 = 0$ and it must meet $w^1 = 0$ in a point which lies in $y^1 > 0$. Since $w^1 \leqslant 0$, $C^1 \leqslant 0$ occurs in $z^1 > 0$, $y^1 < 0$ it is clear that $z^1 = 0$ does not occur in $\mathbf{T}^1.6$. As $z^1 > 0$, $y^1 < 0$ lies in $B^1 > 0$, $B^1 = 0$ cannot close $\mathbf{T}^1.6$ so $a_{66} \neq 1$. Thus, we must have $a_{68} = -1$. Now if $D^1 = 0$ is to close $\mathbf{T}^1.6$ it must join $C^1 = 0$ to $w^1 = 0$ and it must meet $w^1 = 0$ in a point which lies in $y^1 < 0$. From the above this is impossible since $D^1 = 0$ meets $w^1 = 0$ in $y^1 > 0$. Thus (vi) and (v) cannot occur together.

Consider (v); let its remaining unit be $a_{lm} = 1$ and let $D = 0$ be the equation of the plane represented by $C.m$. As in the above $z^1 = 0$ does not occur in $(v)^1$ so $D^1 = 0$ must join $w^1 = 0$ to $C^1 = 0$ in such a way that $w^1 \leqslant 0$, $D^1 \geqslant 0$, $C^1 \leqslant 0$ is a triangle. Hence it follows that $w^1 \geqslant 0$, $C^1 \geqslant 0$ must lie in $D^1 > 0$. Now if $C^1 = 0$ meets $w^1 = 0$ in $A^1 \geqslant 0$ $T^1.3$ must lie in $w^1 \geqslant 0$, $C^1 \geqslant 0$ whilst if $C^1 = 0$ meets $w^1 = 0$ in $A^1 \leqslant 0$ $T^1.2$ lies in $w^1 \geqslant 0$, $C^1 \geqslant 0$. Hence at least one of $T^1.3$ and $T^1.2$ must lie in $D^1 > 0$ and we have the following result.

LEMMA 12A. If (v) occurs in the matrix and $R.p$ is such that $a_{p1} = -1$ then $a_{pm} \neq -1$.

Proof. Suppose $a_{pm} = -1$ then $T^1.p$ lies in $D^1 \leqslant 0$ and so does not have an area in common with at least one of $T^1.2$ and $T^1.3$. Thus $T.p$ and at least one of $T.2$ and $T.3$ do not possess Crum's Property.

From the above results the only possibility that can occur with (v) is (ii) so we now consider whether or not this case can occur. We may suppose that $R.5$ is (v) and $R.6$ is (ii) so, since none of the other possibilities can occur, we must have $a_{j1} = -1$ $(j = 7, 8, 9)$. By $L.3$ $a_{52} = 0 = a_{55} = a_{65} = a_{64} = a_{67} = a_{56}$ so we may further suppose that $a_{68} = 1$ and we have

$$
\begin{array}{cccccccc}
1 & 1 & 1 & 1 & 0 & 0 & 0 & 0 \\
1 & -1 & 0 & 1 & 1 & 0 & 0 & 0 \\
1 & -1 & 0 & 0 & -1 & 0 & 1 & 0 \\
1 & 1 & -1 & 0 & 0 & 1 & 0 & 0 \\
0 & 0 & 1 & -1 & 0 & 0 & -1 & \\
0 & 1 & -1 & 0 & 0 & -1 & 0 & 1 \\
-1 & 0 & 0 & & 0 & & & \\
-1 & 0 & 0 & & 0 & & & \\
-1 & 0 & 0 & & 0 & & &
\end{array}
$$

If a_{5m} is the remaining unit of $R.5$ by Lemma 12A we have $a_{jm} \neq -a_{5m}$ $(j = 7, 8, 9)$. Further by $L.5$ both $a_{j4} = 1$ $(j = 7, 8, 9)$ and $a_{j7} = 1$ $(j = 7, 8, 9)$ are impossible so by $L.2$ on $R.5$ only two effective cases arise, namely (a) $a_{74} = 1 = a_{84} = a_{97}$ and (b) $a_{74} = 1 = a_{87} = a_{97}$.

(a) Suppose $a_{74} = 1 = a_{84} = a_{97}$. By $L.6$ with $r_0 = 6$ we may therefore suppose that $a_{76} = 1$ and $a_{88} = -1$. By $L.3$ $a_{94} = 0 =$

$a_{86} = a_{77} = a_{87}$. Thus by $L.2$ on $R.6$ either $a_{96} = 1$ or $a_{98} = -1$. However by $L.6$ with $r_0 = 9$, $a_{96} \neq 1$ so $a_{98} = -1$. By $L.3$ $a_{96} = 0$ and by $L.2$ we may suppose $a_{89} = 1 = -a_{99}$. By $L.2$ on $R.7$ we can only have $a_{78} = 1$. Thus the matrix is

x	y	z	w	A	B	C	D	E
1	1	1	1	0	0	0	0	0
1	−1	0	1	1	0	0	0	0
1	−1	0	0	−1	0	1	0	0
1	1	−1	0	0	1	0	0	0
0	0	1	−1	0	0	−1		
0	1	−1	0	0	−1	0	1	0
−1	0	0	1	0	1	0	1	0
−1	0	0	1	0	0	0	−1	1
−1	0	0	0	0	0	1	−1	−1

Choosing the coordinate system shown, we know from the above that $b_2 < 0$. Hence from the boundedness of T.6 $d_2 < 0$. However, T.7 is now unbounded in the y-direction so (a) cannot occur.

(b) Suppose $a_{74} = 1 = a_{87} = a_{97}$. By $L.6$ with $r_0 = 6$ we may therefore suppose that $a_{86} = 1$ and $a_{98} = -1$. By $L.3$ $a_{84} = 0 = a_{94} = a_{96} = a_{77}$. Thus by $L.2$ on $R.6$ either $a_{76} = 1$ or $a_{78} = -1$. However by $L.6$ with $r_0 = 7$, $a_{76} \neq 1$ so $a_{78} = -1$. By $L.3$ $a_{76} = 0$ and by $L.2$ we may suppose $a_{79} = 1 = -a_{99}$. By $L.2$ on $R.8$ we can only have $a_{88} = 1$. Thus the matrix is

x	y	z	w	A	B	C	D	E
1	1	1	1	0	0	0	0	0
1	−1	0	1	1	0	0	0	0
1	−1	0	0	−1	0	1	0	0
1	1	−1	0	0	1	0	0	0
0	0	1	−1	0	0	−1		
0	1	−1	0	0	−1	0	1	0
−1	0	0	1	0	0	0	−1	1
−1	0	0	0	0	1	1	1	0
−1	0	0	0	0	0	1	−1	−1

Choosing the coordinate system shown, we know from the above that $b_3 > 0$ and $c_3 > 0$. Hence from the boundedness of T.6 $d_3 > 0$. However T.8 is now unbounded in the z-direction, so (b) cannot occur. Thus (v) and (ii) cannot occur together.

Hence (v) cannot occur with any of the other possibilities and, since (vi) is equivalent to (v), neither can (vi). Thus only three possibilities remain namely, (i), (ii) and (iv).

Suppose (ii) and (iv) occur together then we may suppose $R.5$ is (ii) and $R.6$ is (iv). By $L.3$ $a_{62} = 0 = a_{54} = a_{55} = a_{66}$ and $a_{57} \neq -1$. With the usual coordinate system $a_{57} \neq 1$ for, if it was, $\mathbf{T}.5$ would be unbounded in the y-direction. Hence $a_{57} = 0$ and we may suppose $a_{58} = 1$. Let $D = 0$ be the equation of the plane represented by $C.8$, then from the boundedness of $\mathbf{T}.5$ $d_2 < 0$, $d_3 > 0$. By $L.3$ $a_{67} \neq -1, a_{68} \neq -1$. Also $a_{67} \neq 1, a_{68} \neq 1$ for, if either was, $\mathbf{T}.6$ would be unbounded in the z-direction. Thus, $a_{67} = 0 = a_{68}$ and we may suppose $a_{69} = 1$. Now the only other possibility that can occur is (i) so at least two of the a_{j1} $(j = 7, 8, 9)$ are (-1)s and we may assume $a_{71} = -1 = a_{81}$. Thus we have

x	y	z	w	A	B	C	D	E
1	1	1	1	0	0	0	0	0
1	-1	0	1	1	0	0	0	0
1	-1	0	0	-1	0	1	0	0
1	1	-1	0	0	1	0	0	0
0	1	-1	0	0	-1	0	1	0
0	0	1	-1	1	0	0	0	1
-1	0	0		0				
-1	0	0		0				

From the boundedness of $\mathbf{T}.6$ we have $e_2 < 0$, $e_3 < 0$.

Suppose $R.9$ is (i), then by $L.3$ $a_{93} = 0 = a_{94} = a_{96}$, $a_{98} \neq -1$, $a_{99} \neq -1$. Further $a_{98} \neq 1$, $a_{99} \neq 1$ for if either was, $\mathbf{T}.9$ would be unbounded in the y-direction. Thus $a_{98} = 0 = a_{99}$ and we may assume $a_{9.10} = 1$. Now by $L.2$ on $R.5$ one of $a_{76} = 1$ and $a_{78} = -1$ holds and one of $a_{86} = 1$ and $a_{88} = -1$ holds; by $L.2$ on $R.6$ one of $a_{74} = 1$ and $a_{79} = -1$ holds and one of $a_{84} = 1$ and $a_{89} = -1$ holds; by $L.2$ on $R.9$ one of $a_{77} = 1$ and $a_{7.10} = -1$ holds and one of $a_{87} = 1$ and $a_{8.10} = -1$ holds. Hence $R.7$ and $R.8$ must contradict $L.2$ and so $R.9$ cannot be (i).

Thus $a_{91} = -1$ so by $L.3$ $a_{92} = 0 = a_{93} = a_{95}$. By $L.5$ both $a_{j4} = 1 (j = 7, 8, 9)$ and $a_{j9} = -1$ $(j = 7, 9, 8)$ are impossible so by $L.2$ on $R.6$ only two effective cases arise, namely (a) $a_{74} = a_{84} = 1$, $a_{99} = -1$ and (b) $a_{74} = 1$, $a_{89} = -1 = a_{99}$.

(a) Suppose $a_{74} = 1 = a_{84}$, $a_{99} = -1$. By $L.6$ with $r_0 = 5$ we may therefore suppose that $a_{76} = 1$ and $a_{88} = -1$.

By $L.3$ $a_{94} = 0 = a_{86}$ and $a_{96} \neq -1$. Thus if a_{7m} is the remaining unit of $R.7$, by $L.2$ $a_{8m} = a_{9m} = -a_{7m}$. By $L.3$ $a_{77} \neq -1$, $a_{87} \neq -1$, $a_{89} \neq -1$ so $m \neq 7$ and $m \neq 9$. Also $a_{78} \neq 1$ for if it was $T.7$ would be unbounded in the y-direction. Thus $m \neq 8$ and we may suppose $m = 10$. By $L.2$ on $R.8$ we must have $a_{98} = 1$. However, $R.5$ and $R.9$ now contradict $L.2$ since $a_{96} = 0$ by $L.1$. Thus (a) does not arise.

(b) Suppose $a_{74} = 1$, $a_{89} = -1 = a_{99}$. By $L.6$ with $r_0 = 5$ we may therefore suppose that $a_{86} = 1$ and $a_{98} = -1$. By $L.3$ $a_{84} = 0 = a_{94} = a_{96}$ and $a_{88} \neq -1$. However, $a_{88} \neq 1$ for, if it was, $T.8$ would be unbounded in the z-direction. Thus $a_{88} = 0$. By $L.3$ $a_{87} \neq -1$, $a_{97} \neq -1$ so by $L.2$ we may suppose $a_{8.10} = 1 = -a_{9.10}$. By $L.2$ on $R.5$ one of $a_{76} = 1$ and $a_{78} = -1$ holds so by $L.2$ on $R.7$ with $R.8$ and $R.9$ we must have $a_{79} = 1$. However, if $a_{76} = 1$ $T.7$ is unbounded in the y-direction whilst if $a_{78} = -1$ $T.7$ is unbounded in the z-direction. Thus (b) cannot arise either.

Hence (ii) and (iv) cannot occur together. As the case when (i) and (iv) occur together is equivalent to this one, we also have that (i) and (iv) cannot occur together. Hence (iv) cannot occur with any of the other possibilities, so that in order to prove the lemma, we now only have to show that (i) and (ii) cannot occur together.

Suppose they do, then we may suppose that $R.5$ is (i) and $R.6$ is (ii). By $L.3$ $a_{53} = 0 = a_{56} = a_{65} = a_{67}$. Since the other possibilities have been eliminated, we have $a_{j1} = -1$ $(j = 7, 8, 9)$ so the matrix is

x	y	z	w	A	B	C
1	1	1	1	0	0	0
1	-1	0	1	1	0	0
1	-1	0	0	-1	0	1
1	1	-1	0	0	1	0
0	-1	0		-1	0	-1
0	1	-1		0	-1	0
-1	0	0		0		
-1	0	0		0		
-1	0	0		0		

By $L.3$ $a_{54} \neq -1$. Also $a_{54} \neq 1$ for if it was **T**.5 would be unbounded in the y-direction. Thus $a_{54} = 0$ and we may assume
$a_{58} = 1$. Let $D = 0$ be the equation of the plane represented by $C.8$
then from the boundedness of **T**.5 $d_2 > 0, d_3 > 0$. By $L.3$ $a_{64} \neq -1$,
$a_{68} \neq -1$. Also $a_{64} \neq 1$ for if it was **T**.6 would be unbounded in the
z-direction, whilst $a_{68} \neq 1$ for, if it was, **T**.6 would be unbounded
in the y-direction. Thus, $a_{64} = 0 = a_{68}$ and we may suppose
$a_{69} = 1$. Let $E = 0$ be the equation of the plane represented by
$C.9$. By $L.5$ both $a_{j6} = 1$ $(j = 7, 8, 9)$ and $a_{j7} = 1$ $(j = 7, 8, 9)$
are impossible, so by $L.2$ at least one of the a_{j8} $(j = 7, 8, 9)$ is
a (-1) and at least one of the a_{j9} $(j = 7, 8, 9)$ is a (-1). Consider
the configuration on $x = 0$.

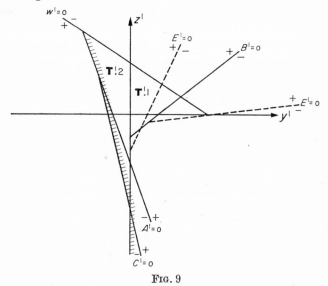

Fig. 9

Some of the lines may be in different positions relative to each
other, but these changes do not affect the arguments used below.

Now at least one of the **T**.m $(m = 7, 8, 9)$ lies in $E \leqslant 0$ so if
it and **T**.2 are to possess Crum's Property, $\mathbf{T}^1.2$ must have
an area in $E^1 \leqslant 0$. Thus it is clear from the diagram that we
must have $a_4/a_3 < e_4/e_3 < 0$ since $E^1 = 0$ closes $\mathbf{T}^1.6$. Further
since $D^1 = 0$ closes $\mathbf{T}^1.5$, $D^1 = 0$ must have a negative gradient
and $d_4/d_3 < a_4/a_3$ must hold. Since $a_4/a_3 < 0$ the quadrant $y^1 > 0$,
$z^1 > 0$ therefore lies in $D^1 > 0$ and *a fortiori* so does $\mathbf{T}^1.1$.

Since one of the $T^1.m$ ($m = 7, 8, 9$) lies in $D^1 \leqslant 0$, it and $T^1.1$ do not have an area in common and therefore the corresponding tetrahedra do not possess Crum's Property.

Thus (i) and (ii) cannot occur together and the lemma is proved.

LEMMA 13. *If A is a matrix representation of a 9-con, then it does not contain a minor equivalent to F_3.*

Proof. Suppose the lemma is false, then by elementary transformations we may suppose that the units of the first four rows are

x	y	z	A	w	B	C
1	−1	1	1	0	0	0
1	1	1	0	1	0	0
1	1	0	0	−1	1	0
1	0	−1	0	1	0	1

For convenience we have multiplied $C.2$ of F_3 by (-1).

By Lemma 11 at least two of a_{j1} ($j = 5 \ldots 9$) are zeros so we may assume $a_{51} = 0 = a_{61}$. We now consider the possibilities for $R.l$ where $a_{l1} = 0$.

Suppose $a_{l2} = -1$ then by $L.3$ $a_{l3} \neq -1$ so by $L.2$ on $R.1$ $a_{l4} = -1$. By $L.3$ $a_{l5} \neq -1$ so by $L.2$ on $R.4$ we have the following two possibilities: (i) $1 = a_{l3}, -1 = a_{l4} = a_{l2}$ and (ii) $a_{l7} = -1 = a_{l2} = a_{l4}$.

Suppose $a_{l3} = -1$ then by $L.3$ $a_{l5} \neq -1$ so by $L.2$ on $L.4$ $a_{l7} = -1$. By $L.3$ $a_{l2} \neq -1$ so by $L.2$ on $R.3$ we have two further possibilities namely, (iii) $a_{l5} = 1$, $a_{l3} = -1 = a_{l7}$ and (iv) $a_{l6} = -1 = a_{l3} = a_{l7}$.

Now if $a_{l2} \neq -1$ and $a_{l3} \neq -1$ by $L.2$ on $R.2$ we must have $a_{l5} = -1$. By $L.3$ $a_{l2} \neq -1$ so by $L.2$ on $R.3$ $a_{l6} = -1$. By $L.3$ $a_{l3} \neq -1$ so by $L.2$ on $R.1$ we have either (v) $a_{l2} = 1$, $a_{l5} = -1 = a_{l6}$ or (vi) $a_{l4} = -1 = a_{l5} = a_{l6}$.

For convenience we now tabulate these possibilities.

(i) $a_{l3} = 1$, $a_{l2} = -1 = a_{l4}$ (ii) $a_{l2} = -1 = a_{l4} = a_{l7}$

(iii) $a_{l5} = 1$, $a_{l3} = -1 = a_{l7}$ (iv) $a_{l3} = -1 = a_{l6} = a_{l7}$

(v) $a_{l2} = 1$, $a_{l5} = -1 = a_{l6}$ (vi) $a_{l4} = -1 = a_{l5} = a_{l6}$

By $L.4$ the same possibility cannot occur in two different rows so in order to prove the lemma we need to show that each possibility cannot occur with any of the others.

With the above coordinate system we have from boundedness:

From T.1 $a_2 > 0$, $a_3 < 0$; from T.3 $b_2 < 0$, $b_3 < 0$; from T.4 $c_2 > 0$, $c_3 > 0$.

Suppose (i) occurs then we may assume that R.5 is (i) so $a_{53} = 1$ $a_{52} = -1 = a_{54}$. By L.3 $a_{55} = 0$, $a_{56} \neq -1$, $a_{57} \neq -1$. Further $a_{56} \neq 1$ for if it was T.5 would be unbounded in the y-direction whilst $a_{57} \neq 1$ for, if it was, T.5 would be unbounded in the z-direction. Thus $a_{56} = 0 = a_{57}$ and we may suppose $a_{58} = 1$. Let $D = 0$ be the equation of the plane represented by C.8, then from the boundedness of T.5 we have $d_2 > 0$, $d_3 < 0$.

If (ii) occurs with (i) we may suppose R.6 is (ii) so $a_{62} = -1 = a_{64} = a_{67}$. Now $a_{63} \neq -1$, $a_{68} \neq -1$ for if either was T.6 would be unbounded in the y-direction. Hence R.5 and R.6 contradict L.2 and so (i) and (ii) cannot occur together.

If (vi) occurs with (i) we may suppose R.6 is (vi) so $a_{64} = -1 = a_{65} = a_{66}$. By L.3 $a_{63} = 0 = a_{62}$. Also $a_{68} \neq -1$ for if it was T.6 would be unbounded in the z-direction. Hence R.5 and R.6 contradict L.2 and so (i) and (vi) cannot occur together.

Since the case when (v) and (iv) occur together is equivalent to the case when (i) and (vi) occur together, (iv) and (v) cannot occur together either.

Consider the case when (i) and (v) occur together. Then we may suppose R.6 is (v) so $a_{62} = 1$, $a_{65} = -1 = a_{66}$. By L.3 $a_{63} = 0 = a_{64}$, $a_{67} \neq -1$, $a_{68} \neq -1$. Also $a_{67} \neq 1$, $a_{68} \neq 1$ for if either was T.6 would be unbounded in the y-direction. Thus $a_{67} = 0 = a_{68}$ so we may suppose $a_{69} = 1$. Since (iv) cannot occur with (v) the only other possibility that can occur with both (i) and (v) is (iii). Hence at least two of the a_{j1} ($j = 7, 8, 9$) are (-1)s and we may suppose $a_{71} = -1 = a_{81}$. Thus we have

x	y	z	A	w	B	C	D	E
1	−1	1	1	0	0	0	0	0
1	1	1	0	1	0	0	0	0
1	1	0	0	−1	1	0	0	0
1	0	−1	0	1	0	1	0	0
0	−1	1	−1	0	0	0	1	0
0	1	0	0	−1	−1	0	0	1
−1	0	0	0					
−1	0	0	0					

From the boundedness of T.6 we have $e_2 < 0$, $e_3 < 0$. Suppose $R.9$ is (iii) then $a_{95} = 1$, $a_{93} = -1 = a_{97}$. By $L.3$ $a_{92} = 0 = a_{94} = a_{96}$, $a_{98} \neq -1$, $a_{99} \neq -1$. Also $a_{98} \neq 1$, $a_{99} \neq 1$, for if either was T.9 would be unbounded in the z-direction. Thus $a_{98} = 0 = a_{99}$ and we may suppose $a_{9.10} = 1$. Now for each l ($l = 7, 8$): by $L.2$ on $R.5$ one of $a_{l4} = 1$ and $a_{l8} = -1$ holds; by $L.2$ on $R.6$ one of $a_{l6} = 1$ and $a_{l9} = -1$ holds and by $L.2$ on $R.9$ one of $a_{l7} = 1$ and $a_{l.10} = -1$ holds. Hence $R.7$ and $R.8$ must contradict $L.2$ so that $R.9$ cannot be (iii).

Thus $a_{91} = -1$ and by $L.3$ $a_{92} = 0 = a_{93} = a_{95}$. By $L.5$ both $a_{j4} = 1$ ($j = 7, 8, 9$) and $a_{j8} = -1$ ($j = 7, 8, 9$) are impossible, so by $L.2$ on $R.5$ only two effective cases arise namely, (a) $a_{74} = 1 = a_{84}$, $a_{98} = -1$ and (b) $a_{74} = 1$, $a_{88} = -1 = a_{98}$.

(a) Suppose $a_{74} = 1 = a_{84}$, $a_{98} = -1$. By $L.6$ with $r_0 = 6$ we may therefore suppose that $a_{76} = 1$ and $a_{89} = -1$. By $L.3$ $a_{94} = 0 = a_{86}$, $a_{96} \neq -1$. Thus, if a_{7m} is the remaining unit of $R.7$, by $L.2$ we must have $a_{8m} = a_{9m} = -a_{7m}$. By $L.3$ $a_{77} \neq -1$, $a_{87} \neq -1$, $a_{88} \neq -1$ so $m \neq 7$ and $m \neq 8$. If $a_{79} = 1$, T.7 is unbounded in the z-direction, so $m \neq 9$. Thus, we may suppose $m = 10$. By $L.2$ on $R.8$ $a_{99} = 1$. By $L.1$ $a_{96} = 0$ and so $R.6$ and $R.9$ contradict $L.2$. Thus (a) does not arise.

(b) Suppose $a_{74} = 1$, $a_{88} = -1 = a_{98}$. By $L.6$ with $r_0 = 6$ we may therefore suppose that $a_{86} = 1$ and $a_{99} = -1$. By $L.3$ $a_{84} = 0 = a_{94} = a_{96}$. Now $a_{89} \neq 1$ for if it was, T.8 would be unbounded in the y-direction. Since by $L.3$ $a_{87} \neq -1$, $a_{97} \neq -1$, by $L.2$ we may suppose that $a_{8.10} = 1 = -a_{9.10}$. By $L.2$ on $R.6$ one of $a_{76} = 1$ and $a_{79} = -1$ holds, so by $L.2$ on $R.7$ we can only have $a_{78} = 1$. Now if $a_{76} = 1$, T.7 is unbounded in the z-direction, whilst if $a_{79} = -1$ T.7 is unbounded in the y-direction. Thus (b) does not arise either.

Hence (i) and (v) cannot occur together.

Now the cases when (v) and (iii) occur together and when (v) and (vi) occur together are respectively equivalent to those when (i) and (v) occur together and when (i) and (ii) occur together so neither of the two former cases can arise. Thus it follows that if (v) is to occur it must occur with (ii).

Suppose $R.5$ is (v) and $R.6$ is (ii) then $a_{52} = 1$, $a_{55} = -1 = a_{56} = a_{62} = a_{64} = a_{67}$. By $L.3$ $a_{53} = 0 = a_{63} = a_{54} = a_{65} = a_{66} = a_{57}$. Thus we may suppose $a_{58} = 1$. As none of the other possibi-

3*

lities can occur with (v) we must have $a_{j1} = -1$ $(j = 7, 8, 9)$ so the matrix is

x	y	z	A	w	B	C	D	E
1	-1	1	1	0	0	0	0	0
1	1	1	0	1	0	0	0	0
1	1	0	0	-1	1	0	0	0
1	0	-1	0	1	0	1	0	0
0	1	0	0	-1	-1	0	1	0
0	-1	0	-1	0	0	-1		
-1	0	0	0					
-1	0	0	0					
-1	0	0	0					

The signs of a_2, a_3, b_2, b_3, c_2 and c_3 are the same as above. From the boundedness of **T**.5 we have $d_2 < 0$, $d_3 < 0$. By **L**.3 $a_{68} \neq -1$. Also $a_{68} \neq 1$ for if it was, **T**.6 would be unbounded in the y-direction. Thus $a_{68} = 0$ and we may suppose $a_{69} = 1$. From the boundedness of **T**.6 $e_2 > 0$. By **L**.5 $a_{j6} = 1$ $(j = 7, 8, 9)$ is impossible so by **L**.2 at least one of the a_{j8} $(j = 7, 8, 9)$ is a (-1).

Now C.1 is a tem-column so by **L**.8 every tetrahedron has an intersection of positive area with $x = 0$. Thus consider the configuration on $x = 0$.

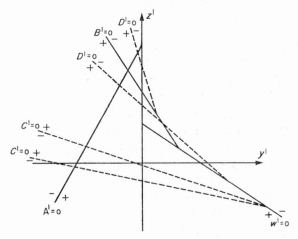

FIG. 10

Some of the lines may be in different positions relative to each other, but these changes do not affect the arguments used below.

Since $D^1 = 0$ closes $T^1.5$ it must have a negative gradient and $d_4/d_3 > 1$ must hold. Since at least one of the a_{j8} $(j = 7, 8, 9)$ is a (-1) at least one of the $T.m$ $(m = 7, 8, 9)$ lies in $D \leqslant 0$ so if it and $T.1$ are to possess Crum's Property $T^1.1$ must have an area in $D^1 \leqslant 0$. Thus we have $a_4/a_3 > d_4/d_3 > 1$. Hence it is clear from the diagram that $A^1 \leqslant 0$, $C^1 \leqslant 0$ must lie in $y^1 < 0$ and so $y^1 = 0$ does not occur in $T^1.6$. Thus $E^1 = 0$ must join $A^1 = 0$ to $C^1 = 0$ in such a way that $A^1 \leqslant 0$, $C^1 \leqslant 0$, $E^1 \geqslant 0$ is a triangle. Hence $A^1 \geqslant 0$, $C^1 \geqslant 0$ lies in $E^1 > 0$. Now if $A^1 = 0$ meets $C^1 = 0$ in $z^1 \geqslant 0$. $T^1.4$ lies in $A^1 \geqslant 0$, $C^1 \geqslant 0$ whilst if $A^1 = 0$ meets $C^1 = 0$ in $z^1 \leqslant 0$, $T^1.1$ lies in $A^1 \geqslant 0$, $C^1 \geqslant 0$. Thus at least one of the $T^1.l$ $(l = 1, \ldots 4)$ lies in $A^1 \geqslant 0$, $C^1 \geqslant 0$ and *a fortiori* in $E^1 > 0$. Hence none of the a_{j9} $(j = 7, 8, 9)$ is a (-1) for if one was, say $a_{79} = -1$ for definiteness, $T^1.7$ would lie in $E^1 \leqslant 0$; thus $T^1.7$ would not have an area in common with at least one of the $T^1.l$ $(l = 1, \ldots 4)$ and so the corresponding tetrahedra would not possess Crum's Property. By $L.5$ both $a_{j4} = 1$ $(j = 7, 8, 9)$ and $a_{j7} = 1$ $(j = 7, 8, 9)$ are impossible so by $L.2$ on $R.6$ only two effective cases arise namely, (a) $a_{74} = 1 = a_{84} = a_{97}$ and (b) $a_{74} = a_{87} = a_{97} = 1$.

(a) Suppose $a_{74} = 1 = a_{84} = a_{97}$. By $L.6$ with $r_0 = 5$ we may therefore suppose that $a_{76} = 1$ and $a_{88} = -1$. By $L.3$ $a_{94} = 0 = a_{86} = a_{77}$, $a_{96} \neq -1$ so if a_{7m} is the remaining unit of $R.7$, by $L.2$ we must have $a_{8m} = a_{9m} = -a_{7m}$. If $a_{78} = 1$, $T.7$ is unbounded in the z-direction so $m \neq 8$. By $L.3$ $a_{79} \neq -1$, $a_{89} \neq -1$ so $m \neq 9$ and we may therefore suppose $m = 10$. By $L.2$ on $R.8$ $a_{98} = 1$ so by $L.1$ $a_{96} = 0$ and $R.5$ and $R.9$ thus contradict $L.2$. Hence (a) cannot arise.

(b) Suppose $a_{74} = a_{87} = a_{97} = 1$. By $L.6$ with $r_0 = 5$ we may therefore suppose that $a_{86} = 1$ and $a_{98} = -1$. By $L.3$ $a_{84} = 0 = a_{94} = a_{96} = a_{77}$. By $L.2$ on $R.5$ either $a_{76} = 1$ or $a_{78} = -1$. However, if $a_{76} = 1$ let the remaining unit of $R.7$ be a_{7m} then by $L.2$ $a_{8m} = a_{9m} = -a_{7m}$; this is impossible by $L.4$ since $m \neq 7$ because $a_{77} = 0$. Thus $a_{78} = -1$. By $L.3$ $a_{79} \neq -1$, $a_{99} \neq -1$ so by $L.2$ we may suppose $a_{7.10} = 1 = -a_{9.10}$. Let $F = 0$ be the equation of the plane represented by $C.10$, then from the boundedness of $T.7$ $f_2 < 0$. However $T.9$ is now unbounded in the y-direction. Thus (b) cannot arise either.

Hence (v) and (ii) cannot occur together and so (v) cannot occur with any of the other possibilities. As (i) and (iii) are both equivalent to (v), the same holds for (i) and (iii) so we are left with only three possibilities, namely (ii), (iv) and (vi).

Suppose (ii) and (vi) occur together, then we may assume $R.5$ is (ii) and $R.6$ is (vi) so $a_{52} = -1 = a_{54} = a_{57} = a_{64} = a_{65} = a_{66}$. By $L.3$ $a_{53} = 0 = a_{55} = a_{62} = a_{63}$. As the only other possibility that can occur is (iv), at least two of the a_{j1} $(j = 7, 8, 9)$ are (-1)s so we may suppose $a_{71} = -1$. Thus

x	y	z	A	w	B	C	D
1	−1	1	1	0	0	0	0
1	1	1	0	1	0	0	0
1	1	0	0	−1	1	0	0
1	0	−1	0	1	0	1	0
0	−1	0	−1	0		−1	
0	0	0	−1	−1	−1		
−1							

Now $a_{56} \neq 1$ for if it was **T.5** would be unbounded in the y-direction whilst $a_{67} \neq 1$ for if it was **T.6** would be unbounded in the z-direction. Thus by $L.2$ we may suppose $a_{58} = 1 = -a_{68}$. From boundedness we have: from **T.5** $d_2 > 0$ and from **T.6** $d_3 > 0$.

Now $C.1$ is a tem-column so by $L.8$ every tetrahedron has an intersection of positive area with $x = 0$. Thus consider the configuration on $x = 0$.

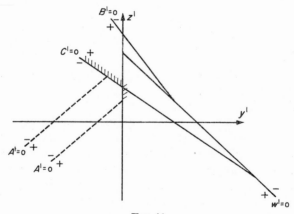

FIG. 11

Some of the lines may be in different relative positions to each other but these changes do not affect the arguments used below.

Since $d_2 > 0, d_3 > 0, D^1 = 0$ has a negative gradient and so it cannot close $T^1.5$ by joining $A^1 = 0$ to $y^1 = 0$. Hence in order to close $T^1.5$ $D^1 = 0$ must meet $C^1 = 0$ in $y^1 < 0, A^1 < 0$ and it must also have a gradient less than that of $C^1 = 0$ so $d_4/d_3 < c_4/c_3 < 1$.

Since $D^1 = 0$ meets $C^1 = 0$ in $y^1 < 0, A^1 < 0, D^1 = 0$ meets $A^1 = 0$ in $C^1 < 0$ and so the $A^1 = 0$ portion of $A^1 \leqslant 0, D^1 \leqslant 0$ lies in $C^1 < 0$ and a fortiori in $w^1 > 0$. Thus $A^1 = 0$ does not occur in $T^1.6$ so $D^1 = 0$ must close $T^1.6$ in such a way that $w^1 \leqslant 0, B^1 \leqslant 0, D^1 \leqslant 0$ is a triangle. Hence from the diagram $d_4/d_3 > 1$ and we have a contradiction to the above.

Hence (ii) and (vi) cannot occur together. As the case when (iv) and (ii) occur together is equivalent to this one, it cannot arise either. Thus (ii) cannot occur with any of the other possibilities and since (iv) and (vi) are both equivalent to (ii) the same holds for them and the Lemma is proved.

LEMMA 14. If A is a matrix representation of a 9-con, then it does not contain a minor equivalent to F_4.

Proof. Suppose the lemma is false then by elementary transformations we may suppose that the units of the first four rows are

x	y	z	A	w	B	C
1	−1	1	1	0	0	0
1	1	1	0	1	0	0
1	1	0	0	−1	1	0
1	0	−1	0	0	−1	1

For convenience we have multiplied $C.2$ of F_4 by (-1).

By Lemma 11 at least two of the a_{j1} $(j = 5, \ldots 9)$ are zeros so we may assume $a_{51} = 0 = a_{61}$. We now consider the possibilities for $R.l$ where $a_{l1} = 0$.

Suppose $a_{l2} = -1$ then by $L.3$ $a_{l3} \neq -1$ so by $L.2$ we must have $a_{l4} = -1$. By $L.2$ on $R.4$ one of $a_{l3} = 1, a_{l6} = 1$ and $a_{l7} = -1$ must hold, so we have the first three possibilities tabulated below.

Suppose $a_{l3} = -1$ then by $L.3$ $a_{l2} = 0$. By $L.2$ on $R.3$ one of $a_{l5} = 1$ and $a_{l6} = -1$ must hold and by $L.2$ on $R.4$ one of $a_{l6} = 1$

and $a_{17} = -1$ must hold. We therefore have the possibilities (iv) to (vi) below.

Now if $a_{12} \neq -1$, $a_{13} \neq -1$, by $L.2$ on $R.2$ we must have $a_{15} = -1$. By $L.3$ $a_{12} \neq -1$ so by $L.2$ on $R.3$ $a_{16} = -1$. Thus by $L.2$ on $R.4$ one of $a_{13} = 1$ and $a_{17} = -1$ must hold. By $L.3$ $a_{13} \neq -1$ so by $L.2$ on $R.1$ one of $a_{12} = 1$ and $a_{14} = -1$ must hold. Hence we have the possibilities (vii) to (x) below.

Thus the possibilities are:

$$\text{(i)} \quad a_{12} = -1 = a_{14}, \, a_{13} = 1$$

$$\text{(ii)} \quad a_{12} = -1 = a_{14}, \, a_{16} = 1$$

$$\text{(iii)} \quad a_{12} = -1 = a_{14} = a_{17}$$

$$\text{(iv)} \quad a_{13} = -1, \, a_{15} = 1 = a_{16}$$

$$\text{(v)} \quad a_{13} = -1 = a_{17}, \, a_{15} = 1$$

$$\text{(vi)} \quad a_{13} = -1 = a_{16} = a_{17}$$

$$\text{(vii)} \quad a_{15} = -1 = a_{16}, \, a_{13} = 1 = a_{12}$$

$$\text{(viii)} \quad a_{15} = -1 = a_{16} = a_{14}, \, a_{13} = 1$$

$$\text{(ix)} \quad a_{15} = -1 = a_{16} = a_{17}, \, a_{12} = 1$$

$$\text{(x)} \quad a_{15} = -1 = a_{16} = a_{17} = a_{14}$$

By $L.4$ the same possibility cannot occur in two different rows so in order to prove the lemma we need to show that each possibility cannot occur with any of the others.

With the above coordinate system we have from boundedness: from $T.1$ $a_1 < 0$, $a_2 > 0$; from $T.3$ $b_1 < 0$, $b_2 < 0$; from $T.4$ $c_1 < 0$, $c_2 < 0$.

Hence it is clear that none of (vii), (viii), (ix) and (x) can occur, for they are all unbounded in the x-direction. Furthermore, (iii) cannot occur for, if it did, rows 2, 3, 4 and l would contradict $L.9A$.

LEMMA 14A. If (iv) occurs in the matrix, then at most two of the a_{j1} $(j = 7, 8, 9)$ are (-1)s.

Proof. We may suppose $R.5$ is (iv) and that the remaining unit of $R.5$ is a_{5m} so that $a_{53} = -1$, $a_{55} = 1 = a_{56}$. If $a_{j1} = -1$, then by $L.3$ on the first four rows we have $a_{j2} = 0 = a_{j3} = a_{j5} = a_{j6}$, so by $L.2$ on $R.5$ we can only have $a_{jm} = -a_{5m}$, i.e. $a_{j1} = -1$ implies $a_{jm} = -a_{5m} \neq 0$. Hence by $L.5$ j can take at most two different values and the lemma is proved.

Suppose (ii) occurs, then we may suppose $R.5$ is (ii) so $a_{52} = -1 = a_{54}$, $a_{56} = 1$. By $L.3$ $a_{53} = 0 = a_{55}$, $a_{57} \neq -1$. Also, $a_{57} \neq 1$ for if it was, $T.5$ would be unbounded in the y-direction. Thus $a_{57} = 0$ and we may suppose $a_{58} = 1$. Let $D = 0$ be the equation of the plane represented by $C.8$, then from the boundedness of $T.5$ $d_2 > 0$.

If (i) occurs with (ii) we may suppose $R.6$ is (i) so $a_{62} = -1 = a_{64}$, $a_{63} = 1$. By $L.3$ $a_{66} \neq -1$ so by $L.2$ on $R.5$ we must have $a_{68} = -1$. However $T.6$ is now unbounded in the y-direction so (i) and (ii) cannot occur together.

If (iv) occurs with (ii) we may suppose $R.6$ is (iv) so $a_{63} = -1$, $a_{65} = 1 = a_{66}$. By $L.3$ $a_{62} = 0$. Also $a_{64} \neq 1$ for if it was, $T.6$ would be unbounded in the x-direction. Thus by $L.2$ on $R.5$ we must have $a_{68} = -1$. However, $T.6$ is now unbounded in the y-direction so (ii) and (iv) cannot occur together either.

Hence if (ii) does occur at most two of the possibilities can occur with it, and so at least one of the a_{j1} $(j = 7, 8, 9)$ is a (-1).

However if (ii) does not occur, then at most four possibilities can occur and so at least one of the a_{j1} $(j = 7, 8, 9)$ is a (-1). Thus in both cases at least one (-1) occurs in $C.1$ and so $C.1$ is a tem-column. Therefore, by $L.8$ every tetrahedron has an intersection of positive area with $x = 0$. Thus consider the configuration on $x = 0$.

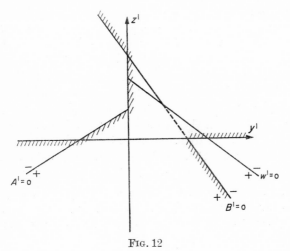

Fig. 12

Some of the lines may be in different positions relative to each other, but these changes do not affect the arguments used below.

LEMMA 14B. If (i) occurs in the matrix then at most two of the a_{j1} ($j = 7, 8, 9$) are (-1)s.

Proof. We may assume $R.5$ is (i) and that the remaining unit of $R.5$ is a_{5m}. Thus $a_{52} = -1 = a_{54}$, $a_{53} = 1$. By $L.3$ $a_{55} = 0 = a_{56}$, $a_{57} \neq -1$, so we may further assume $a_{5m} = 1$. Let $M = 0$ be the equation of the plane represented by $C.m$. Since $M^1 = 0$ must close $T^1.5$ it is clear from the diagram that $T^1.4$ must lie in $M^1 > 0$. Thus if $a_{j1} = -1$ we cannot have $a_{jm} = -1$ for if we did, $T^1.j$ would lie in $M^1 \leqslant 0$ and so would not have an area in common with $T^1.4$. Thus $T.4$ and $T.j$ would not possess Crum's Property. Further, if $a_{j1} = -1$, by $L.3$ on the first four rows $a_{j2} = 0 = a_{j3}$ and so by $L.2$ on $R.5$ we must have $a_{j4} = 1$, i.e. $a_{j1} = -1$ implies $a_{j4} = 1$. Hence by $L.5$ j can take at most two different values, and the lemma is proved.

LEMMA 14C. If (ii) occurs in the matrix then at most two of the a_{j1} ($j = 7, 8, 9$) are (-1)s.

Proof. We may assume $R.5$ is (ii) and that the remaining unit of $R.5$ is a_{5m}. Thus $a_{52} = -1 = a_{54}$, $a_{56} = 1$. By $L.3$ $a_{53} = 0 = a_{55}$, $a_{57} \neq -1$ so we may further assume $a_{5m} = 1$. Let $M = 0$ be the equation of the plane represented by $C.m$.

If $M^1 = 0$ has a non-negative gradient, it clearly cannot close $T^1.5$ by joining $B^1 = 0$ to $y^1 = 0$. Thus in order to close $T^1.5$ $M^1 = 0$ must meet $A^1 = 0$ in $y^1 < 0$ and it must also have a gradient greater than that of $A^1 = 0$. Hence $T^1.4$ clearly lies in $M^1 > 0$.

If $M^1 = 0$ has a negative gradient it clearly cannot close $T^1.5$ by joining $A^1 = 0$ to $y^1 = 0$. Thus in order to close $T^1.5$, $M^1 = 0$ must meet $B^1 = 0$ in $y^1 < 0$ and it must also have a gradient less than that of $B^1 = 0$. Hence $T^1.4$ lies in $M^1 > 0$.

Thus in either case, $T^1.4$ lies in $M^1 > 0$. Hence as in Lemma 14B if $a_{j1} = -1$ then $a_{jm} \neq -1$.

Further, if $a_{j1} = -1$, by $L.3$ $a_{j2} = 0 = a_{j6}$ and so by $L.2$ on $R.5$ we must have $a_{j4} = 1$, i.e. $a_{j1} = -1$ implies $a_{j4} = 1$. Hence by $L.5$ j can take at most two different values and the lemma is proved.

Suppose (v) occurs, then we may suppose $R.5$ is (v) so $a_{53} = -1 = a_{57}$, $a_{55} = 1$. By $L.3$ $a_{52} = 0 = a_{56}$. We now find it convenient to multiply $C.5$ by (-1) and use the following coordinate system

x	y	A	B	w	z	C
1	−1	1	1	0	0	0
1	1	1	0	−1	0	0
1	1	0	0	1	1	0
1	0	−1	0	0	−1	1
0	0	−1		−1	0	−1

From boundedness we have: from $T.2$ $a_2 < 0$; from $T.1$ $b_2 > 0$; from $T.4$ $c_2 < 0$.

Now if $a_{54} = 1$, $T.5$ would be unbounded in the y-direction so $a_{54} \neq 1$. By $L.3$ $a_{54} \neq -1$ so $a_{54} = 0$ and we may suppose $a_{58} = 1$. Let $D = 0$ be the equation of the plane represented by $C.8$ then from the boundedness of $T.5$ $d_2 < 0$.

If (iv) and (v) occur together we may suppose $R.6$ is (iv) so $a_{66} = 1$, $a_{63} = -1 = a_{65}$ (since $C.5$ has been multiplied by -1). Now $a_{68} \neq -1$ for if it was, $T.6$ would be unbounded in the y-direction, so by $L.2$ on $R.5$ we must have $a_{67} = 1$. From the above we know that $C.1$ contains at least one (-1) so let $a_{71} = -1$. By $L.3$ $a_{73} = 0 = a_{75} = a_{76}$ and $a_{77} \neq -1$. Thus $R.6$ and $R.7$ contradict $L.2$ and so (iv) and (v) cannot occur together.

If (v) and (vi) occur together, we may suppose $R.6$ is (vi) so $a_{63} = -1 = a_{66} = a_{67}$. By $L.3$ $a_{65} = 0$ so by $L.2$ on $R.5$ $a_{68} = -1$. However, $T.6$ is now unbounded in the y-direction so (v) and (vi) cannot occur together either.

Thus if (v) occurs, it can only occur with (i) or (ii) or both. From the above (i) and (ii) cannot occur together so it follows that if (v) does occur in the matrix then $a_{j1} = -1$ ($j = 7$, 8, 9). Hence by Lemmas 14B and 14C (v) cannot occur with either (i) or (ii). Thus (v) cannot occur with any of the other possibilities.

Consider (ii): from the above it cannot occur with (i), (iii), (iv) or (v), so it can only occur with (vi). Thus if (ii) occurs in the matrix we must have $a_{j1} = -1$ ($j = 7$, 8, 9). This contradicts Lemma 14C, so (ii) cannot occur with any of the other possibilities.

Hence we are only left with three possibilities, namely (i), (iv) and (vi) so at least two of the a_{j1} ($j = 7, 8, 9$) are (-1)s, and we may suppose $a_{71} = -1 = a_{81}$. By $L.3$ $a_{j2} = 0 = a_{j3} = a_{j5} = a_{j6}$ ($j = 7, 8$).

We revert to our original matrix and coordinate system. Suppose (i) and (iv) occur together, then we may assume $R.5$ is (i) and $R.6$ is (iv) so $a_{52} = -1 = a_{54} = a_{63}$, $a_{53} = 1 = a_{65} = a_{66}$. Now in the course of the proof of Lemma 14B we proved that if $R.5$ is (i) then $a_{j1} = -1$ implies $a_{j4} = 1$. We use this now so that $a_{74} = 1 = a_{84}$. Let a_{6m} be the remaining unit of $R.6$, then by $L.2$ $a_{7m} = a_{8m} = -a_{6m} \neq 0$. By $L.3$ $a_{64} \neq -1$ so $m \neq 4$ and $a_{61} = 0$ so $m \neq 1$. Hence, $R.7$ and $R.8$ contradict $L.4$ so (i) and (iv) cannot occur together.

Thus (vi) can only occur with either (i) or (iv) so we must have $a_{j1} = -1$ ($j = 7, 8, 9$). Hence by Lemmas 14B and 14A (vi) cannot occur with either. Thus (vi) cannot occur with any of the other possibilities and clearly the same now holds for (i) and (iv) so the Lemma is proved.

Remark. From the analysis at the beginning of the Chapter and Lemmas 10, 12, 13 and 14, we see that if four units of the same sign occur in a column of a matrix representation of a 9-con, then the four rows containing these units must be equivalent to F_1.

LEMMA 15. If A is a matrix representation of a 9-con, then A does not contain a minor equivalent to F_1.

Proof. Suppose the lemma is false, then by elementary transformations we may suppose that the units of the first four rows are

$$
\begin{array}{cccccccc}
1 & 1 & 1 & 1 & 0 & 0 & 0 & 0 \\
1 & -1 & 0 & 0 & 1 & 0 & 1 & 0 \\
1 & -1 & 0 & 0 & -1 & 0 & 0 & 1 \\
1 & 1 & -1 & 0 & 0 & 1 & 0 & 0
\end{array}
$$

By Lemma 11 at least two of the a_{j1} ($j = 5, \ldots 9$) are zeros, so we may assume $a_{51} = 0 = a_{61}$. We now consider possibilities for $R.l$ where $a_{l1} = 0$.

Suppose $a_{l2} = -1$, then by $L.2$ on $R.2$ one of $a_{l5} = -1$ and $a_{l7} = -1$ must hold, and by $L.2$ on $R.3$ one of $a_{l5} = 1$ and $a_{l8} = -1$ must hold. Thus we have the first three possibilities tabulated below.

Suppose $a_{12} = 1$ then by $L.2$ on $R.1$ one of $a_{13} = -1$ and $a_{14} = -1$ must hold and by $L.2$ on $R.4$ one of $a_{13} = 1$ and $a_{16} = -1$ must hold. We therefore have the possibilities (iv) to (vi) below.

Thus we need now only consider the cases when $a_{12} = 0$.

Suppose $a_{13} = -1$ then by $L.2$ on $R.4$ $a_{16} = -1$. By $L.2$ on $R.2$ one of $a_{15} = -1$ and $a_{17} = -1$ must hold and by $L.2$ on $R.3$ one of $a_{15} = 1$ and $a_{18} = -1$ must hold. Hence we have possibilities (vii) to (ix) below.

Now if $a_{12} = 0$, $a_{13} \neq -1$ by $L.2$ on $R.1$ we must have $a_{14} = -1$. By $L.2$ on $R.4$ one of $a_{13} = 1$ and $a_{16} = -1$ must hold, by $L.2$ on $R.2$ one of $a_{15} = -1$ and $a_{17} = -1$ must hold and by $L.2$ on $R.3$ one of $a_{15} = 1$ and $a_{18} = -1$ must hold.

Thus we have possibilities (x) to (xv) below.

Hence the possibilities for $R.1$ are:

(i) $a_{12} = -1 = a_{15} = a_{18}$ (ii) $a_{12} = -1 = a_{17}, a_{15} = 1$

(iii) $a_{12} = -1 = a_{17} = a_{18}$ (iv) $a_{12} = 1, a_{13} = -1 = a_{16}$

(v) $a_{12} = 1 = a_{13}, a_{14} = -1$ (vi) $a_{12} = 1, a_{14} = -1 = a_{16}$

(vii) $a_{13} = -1 = a_{16} = a_{15} = a_{18}$ (viii) $a_{13} = -1 = a_{16} = a_{17}, a_{15} = 1$

(ix) $a_{13} = -1 = a_{16} = a_{17} = a_{18}$ (x) $a_{14} = -1 = a_{15} = a_{18}, a_{13} = 1$

(xi) $a_{14} = -1 = a_{17}, a_{13} = 1 = a_{15}$ (xii) $a_{14} = -1 = a_{17} = a_{18}, a_{13} = 1$

(xiii) $a_{14} = -1 = a_{16} = a_{15} = a_{18}$ (xiv) $a_{14} = -1 = a_{16} = a_{17}, a_{15} = 1$

(xv) $a_{14} = -1 = a_{16} = a_{17} = a_{18}$

By $L.4$ the same possibility cannot occur in two different rows, so in order to prove the Lemma we need to show that each possibility cannot occur with any of the other possibilities.

LEMMA 15A. At most one of (i), (ii) and (iii) and at most one of (iv), (v) and (vi) can occur in the matrix.

Proof. Because the cases are equivalent, we need only prove the former. Suppose at least two of (i), (ii) and (iii) do occur, then since all three of them have $a_{12} = -1$ we may suppose $a_{52} = -1 = a_{62}$ and so $C.2$ contains four (-1)s. Consider the matrix obtained from the rows 2, 3, 5 and 6, then from the above Remark it must be equivalent to F_1. However, by inspection, it is clearly not so, since $a_{21} = 1 = a_{31}$, $a_{51} = 0 = a_{61}$. Thus the case cannot arise and the lemma is proved.

Suppose (xiv) occurs, then we may assume that $R.5$ is (xiv) and so we have

x	y	z	w	A	B	C	D
1	1	1	1	0	0	0	0
1	-1	0	0	1	0	$\overset{\cdot}{1}$	0
1	-1	0	0	-1	0	0	1
1	1	-1	0	0	1	0	0
0	0	0	-1	1	-1	-1	0

By $L.2$ (xiv) cannot occur with any of (viii), (ix), (xi), (xii) and (xv).

Choosing the coordinate system shown, from boundedness we have: from $T.4$ $b_1 < 0$, $b_2 < 0$, $b_3 > 0$; from $T.2$ at least one of $a_1 < 0$ and $c_1 < 0$ must hold, and at least one of $a_2 > 0$ and $c_2 > 0$ must hold; from $T.5$ at least one of $a_1 < 0$ and $c_1 > 0$ must hold and at least one of $a_2 < 0$ and $c_2 > 0$ must hold.

Thus we must have $a_1 < 0$ and $c_2 > 0$. From $T.3$ $d_1 < 0$.

Hence none of (vii), (x) and (xiii) can occur with (xiv) for if they did they would all be unbounded in the x-direction.

Suppose (iv) occurs with (xiv) then we may suppose $R.6$ is (iv) so $a_{62} = 1$, $a_{63} = -1 = a_{66}$. By $L.3$ $a_{65} = 0$, so by $L.2$ on $R.5$ we must have either $a_{64} = 1$ or $a_{67} = 1$. However, $a_{64} \neq 1$ for if it was, $T.6$ would be unbounded in the z-direction whilst $a_{67} \neq 1$ for if it was, $T.6$ would be unbounded in the y-direction. Thus (xiv) and (iv) cannot occur together.

Suppose (v) occurs with (xiv) then we may assume $R.6$ is (v) so $a_{62} = 1 = a_{63}$, $a_{64} = -1$. By $L.3$ $a_{65} = 0$ so by $L.2$ on $R.5$ we must have either $a_{66} = 1$ or $a_{67} = 1$. However, $a_{66} \neq 1$ for if it was, $T.6$ would be unbounded in the z-direction, whilst $a_{67} \neq 1$ for if it was, $T.6$ would be unbounded in the y-direction. Thus (xiv) and (v) cannot occur together.

Suppose (vi) occurs with (xiv) then we may assume $R.6$ is (vi) so $a_{62} = 1$, $a_{64} = -1 = a_{66}$. By $L.3$ $a_{65} = 0$ so by $L.2$ on $R.5$ we must have $a_{67} = 1$. However, $T.6$ is now unbounded in the y-direction so (xiv) and (vi) cannot occur together.

Hence (xiv) can only occur with possibilities (i), (ii) and (iii). By Lemma 15A therefore (xiv) can occur with only one of (i),

(ii) and (iii) so we may suppose $a_{j1} = -1$ $(j = 7, 8, 9)$. By $L.3$ $a_{j2} = 0 = a_{j3} = a_{j5}$ $(j = 7, 8, 9)$. Thus $C.1$ is a tem-column and so by $L.8$ every tetrahedron must have an intersection of positive area with $x = 0$. Hence consider the configuration on $x = 0$.

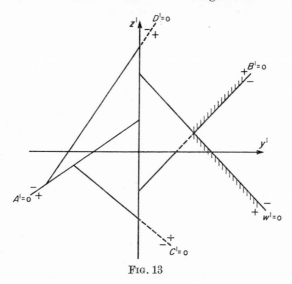

FIG. 13

The diagram may be radically altered and still represent a possible configuration on $x = 0$ but it is useful to illustrate various arguments used below.

From the diagram it is clear that $T^1.5$ must lie in $y^1 > 0$ since $T^1.5$ contains $w^1 \leqslant 0$, $B^1 \leqslant 0$. However, the $A^1 = 0$ portion of $A^1 \geqslant 0$, $C^1 \leqslant 0$ must lie in $y^1 < 0$ so that $A^1 = 0$ cannot occur in $T^1.5$. Hence $C^1 = 0$ must join $w^1 = 0$ to $B^1 = 0$ in such a way that $w^1 \leqslant 0$, $B^1 \leqslant 0$, $C^1 \leqslant 0$ is a triangle. Thus $w^1 \geqslant 0$, $B^1 \geqslant 0$ must lie in $C^1 < 0$. Now at least one of $T^1.1$ and $T^1.4$ lies completely in $w^1 \geqslant 0$, $B^1 \geqslant 0$ so at least one of them lies in $C^1 < 0$, say it is $T^1.l$.

Now suppose at least one of the a_{j7} $(j = 7, 8, 9)$ is a $(+1)$, say $a_{77} = 1$ for definiteness, then $T^1.7$ lies in $C^1 \geqslant 0$. Hence it does not have an area in common with $T^1.l$ and so the corresponding tetrahedra do not possess Crum's Property.

Thus $a_{j7} \neq 1$ $(j = 7, 8, 9)$. By $L.3$ $a_{j7} \neq -1$ $(j = 7, 8, 9)$ so $a_{j7} = 0$ $(j = 7, 8, 9)$.

Suppose (ii) occurs with (xiv) then we may assume $R.6$ is (ii) so $a_{62} = -1 = a_{67}$, $a_{65} = 1$. From the above $a_{j2} = 0 = a_{j5} = a_{j7}$ ($j = 7, 8, 9$). Thus if a_{6m} is the remaining unit of $R.6$ then by $L.2$ on $R.6$ $a_{jm} = -a_{6m}$ ($j = 7, 8, 9$) and this is impossible by $L.5$. Thus (xiv) and (ii) cannot occur together.

Suppose (iii) occurs with (xiv) then we may assume $R.6$ is (iii) so $a_{62} = -1 = a_{67} = a_{68}$. By $L.3$ $a_{65} = 0$. Thus by $L.2$ on $R.5$ one of $a_{64} = 1$ and $a_{66} = 1$ must hold. However by $L.3$ and the above $a_{j4} \neq -1$, $a_{j6} \neq -1$, $a_{j2} = 0 = a_{j5} = a_{j7}$ ($j = 7, 8, 9$). Thus by $L.2$ on $R.6$ $a_{j8} = 1$ ($j = 7, 8, 9$) which is impossible by $L.5$. Thus (xiv) and (iii) cannot occur together.

Finally suppose (i) and (xiv) occur together then we may assume $R.6$ is (i) so $a_{62} = -1 = a_{65} = a_{68}$. By $L.3$ $a_{63} = 0 = a_{64} = a_{66} = a_{67}$, so we may suppose $a_{69} = 1$. Let $E = 0$ be the equation of the plane represented by $C.9$ then from the boundedness of $T.6$ $e_1 < 0$. Now $a_{j5} = 0 = a_{j7}$ ($j = 7, 8, 9$) and by $L.5$ both $a_{j4} = 1$ ($j = 7, 8, 9$) and $a_{j6} = 1$ ($j = 7, 8, 9$) are impossible. Thus by $L.2$ on $R.5$ we may assume $a_{74} = 1 = a_{84} = a_{96}$ since the case when $a_{74} = 1 = a_{86} = a_{96}$ is equivalent to it. By $L.3$ $a_{94} = 0 = a_{76} = a_{86}$. By $L.6$ with $r_0 = 6$ we may suppose $a_{78} = 1$, $a_{89} = -1$. By $L.3$ $a_{88} = 0$. Now $a_{79} \neq 1$ for if $a_{79} = 1$, $T.7$ is unbounded in the x-direction. By $L.3$ $a_{79} \neq -1$ so $a_{79} = 0$. By $L.2$ we may therefore assume $a_{7.10} = 1 = -a_{8.10}$. By $L.2$ on $R.6$ we must have either $a_{98} = 1$ or $a_{99} = -1$.

Now if $a_{98} = 1$ then by $L.2$ on $R.7$ $a_{9.10} = -1$ so that $R.8$ and $R.9$ contradict $L.2$.

Thus $a_{99} = -1$. By $L.2$ on $R.8$ $a_{9.10} = 1$ and then $R.7$ and $R.9$ contradict $L.2$.

Hence (xiv) and (i) cannot occur together.

Thus (xiv) cannot occur with any of the other possibilities and so (xiv) cannot arise. As (ix), (xii) and (xiii) are all equivalent to (xiv) none of them can arise either.

Suppose (viii) occurs, then we may suppose $R.5$ is (viii) and we have

x	y	z	w	A	B	C	D
1	1	1	1	0	0	0	0
1	-1	0	0	1	0	1	0
1	-1	0	0	-1	0	0	1
1	1	-1	0	0	1	0	0
0	0	-1	0	1	-1	-1	0

By $L.2$ (viii) cannot occur with (xv) and by $L.3$ (viii) cannot occur with (x).

Choose the coordinate system shown. From boundedness we have: from $T.4$ $b_2 < 0$, $b_3 > 0$; from $T.2$ at least one of $a_2 > 0$ and $c_2 > 0$ holds, also $a_3 c_3 < 0$; from $T.5$ at least one of $a_2 < 0$ and $c_2 > 0$ holds, also at least one of $a_3 > 0$ and $c_3 < 0$ holds.

Hence $c_2 > 0$, $a_3 > 0$ and $c_3 < 0$. From $T.3$ $d_3 > 0$.

Thus neither (vii) nor (xi) can occur with (viii) for, if one of them did, it would be unbounded in the z-direction.

Suppose (ii) occurs with (viii) then we may assume $R.6$ is (ii) so $a_{62} = -1 = a_{67}$, $a_{65} = 1$. By $L.3$ $a_{63} = 0$ so by $L.2$ on $R.5$ $a_{66} = 1$. However, $T.6$ is now unbounded in the z-direction so (ii) and (viii) cannot occur together.

Suppose (iv) occurs with (viii) then we may assume $R.6$ is (iv) so $a_{62} = 1$, $a_{63} = -1 = a_{66}$. By $L.3$ $a_{65} = 0$ so by $L.2$ on $R.5$ $a_{67} = 1$. However $T.6$ is now unbounded in the z-direction so (iv) and (viii) cannot occur together.

Suppose (vi) occurs with (viii) then we may assume $R.6$ is (vi) so $a_{62} = 1$, $a_{64} = -1 = a_{66}$. By $L.3$ $a_{63} = 0 = a_{65}$ so by $L.2$ on $R.5$ $a_{67} = 1$. However, $T.6$ is now unbounded in the y-direction so (vi) and (viii) cannot occur together.

The case when (iii) occurs with (viii) is equivalent to the case when (vi) occurs with (viii) as can easily be seen by multiplying columns 2, 3, and 5 by (-1) and rearranging.

Thus (viii) can only possibly occur with (i) and (v) so we may assume $a_{81} = -1 = a_{91}$. By $L.3$ $a_{j2} = 0 = a_{j5} = a_{j3}$ $(j = 8, 9)$.

Suppose (i) occurs with (viii) then we may assume $R.6$ is (i) so $a_{62} = -1 = a_{65} = a_{68}$. Now $a_{64} \neq 1$ for, if it is, $T.6$ is unbounded in the z-direction. By $L.3$ $a_{64} \neq -1$ so $a_{64} = 0$. By $L.3$ $a_{63} = a_{65} = a_{67} = 0$. Let $a_{6.9} = 1$ and let $E = 0$ be the equation of the plane represented by $C.9$. From the boundedness of $T.6$ $e_3 > 0$.

Now suppose $R.7$ is (v) then we have $a_{72} = 1 = a_{73}$, $a_{74} = -1$. By $L.3$ $a_{75} = 0 = a_{76} = a_{77} = a_{78}$. Now $a_{79} \neq 1$, for if $a_{79} = 1$, $T.7$ is unbounded in the z-direction. By $L.3$ $a_{79} \neq -1$ so $a_{79} = 0$. Let $a_{7.10} = 1$. For each j $(j = 8, 9)$, by $L.2$ on $R.5$ one of $a_{j6} = 1$ and $a_{j7} = 1$ holds, on $R.6$ one of $a_{j8} = 1$ and $a_{j9} = -1$ holds, on $R.7$ one of $a_{j4} = 1$ and $a_{j.10} = -1$ holds. However, $R.8$ and $R.9$ must now contradict $L.2$.

Thus $R.7$ is not (v) so we must have $a_{71} = -1$ and by $L.3$ $a_{72} = 0 = a_{73} = a_{75}$. By $L.2$ on $R.5$ two effective cases arise: (a) $a_{76} = 1 = a_{86} = a_{97}$ and (b) $a_{76} = 1 = a_{87} = a_{97}$.

(a) Suppose $a_{76} = 1 = a_{86} = a_{97}$. By $L.6$ with $r_0 = 6$ we may further assume $a_{78} = 1$, $a_{89} = -1$. By $L.3$ $a_{96} = 0$, $a_{77} = 0 = a_{87} = a_{88}$. If $a_{79} = 1$ $T.7$ is unbounded in the z-direction. Thus $a_{79} \neq 1$ so by $L.2$ we may suppose $a_{7.10} = 1 = -a_{8.10}$. By $L.2$ on $R.6$ one of $a_{98} = 1$ and $a_{99} = -1$ holds. However, $R.9$ with one of $R.7$ and $R.8$ now contradicts $L.2$ so (a) cannot arise.

Thus, (b) suppose $a_{76} = 1 = a_{87} = a_{97}$. By $L.6$ with $r_0 = 6$ we may further assume $a_{88} = 1$, $a_{99} = -1$. By $L.3$ $a_{86} = 0 = a_{96} = a_{77} = a_{98}$.

If $a_{78} = 1$, let a_{7m} be the remaining unit of $R.7$ then by $L.2$ $a_{8m} = a_{9m} = -a_{7m}$ which is impossible by $L.4$. Thus, by $L.2$ on $R.6$ $a_{79} = -1$. By $L.2$ we may therefore suppose $a_{7.10} = 1 = -a_{9.10}$. By $L.2$ on $R.8$ we must have $a_{89} = 1$. Hence

x	y	A	B	z	C	D	E	F	G
1	1	1	1	0	0	0	0	0	0
1	−1	0	0	1	0	1	0	0	0
1	−1	0	0	−1	0	0	1	0	0
1	1	−1	0	0	1	0	0	0	0
0	0	−1	0	1	−1	−1	0	0	0
0	−1	0	0	−1	0	0	−1	1	0
−1	0	0	0	0	1	0	0	−1	1
−1	0	0	0	0	0	1	1	1	0
−1	0	0	0	0	0	1	0	−1	1

Choose the coordinate system shown. From boundedness we have: from $T.3$ $e_1 < 0$; from $T.6$ $f_1 < 0$; from $T.8$ $d_1 > 0$. However, $T.2$ is now unbounded so (b) cannot arise.

Hence (i) and (viii) cannot occur together.

The case when (v) occurs with (viii) is equivalent to the case when (i) occurs with (viii) as can easily be seen by multiplying columns 2, 3 and 5 by (−1) and rearranging.

Hence (viii) cannot occur with any of the other possibilities and so (viii) cannot arise. As (vii), (x) (xi) are all equivalent to (viii) none of them arise either.

We can therefore have possibilities (i), (ii), (iii), (iv), (v), (vi) and (xv). By Lemma 15A at most three of them can occur together so $C.1$ contains at least two (-1)s. Thus let $a_{51} = -1 = a_{61}$.

Suppose (xv) occurs, then we may assume

x	y	z	w	A	B	C	D
1	1	1	1	0	0	0	0
1	-1	0	0	1	0	1	0
1	-1	0	0	-1	0	0	1
1	1	-1	0	0	1	0	0
-1							
-1							
0	0	0	-1	0	-1	-1	-1

Choose the coordinate system shown. Since $C.1$ is a tem-column, $\mathbf{T^1}.7$ must have an intersection of positive area with $x = 0$. To consider the configuration on $x = 0$ we may clearly use the diagram above. Since $\mathbf{T^1}.7$ contains $w^1 \leqslant 0$, $B^1 \leqslant 0$ it can only be in $y^1 > 0$, but as it also contains $C^1 \leqslant 0$, $D^1 \leqslant 0$ it can only lie in $y^1 < 0$. Hence $\mathbf{T^1}.7$ does not have an intersection with $x = 0$ which is impossible.

Thus (xv) cannot occur. Hence by Lemma 15A we may further suppose $a_{71} = -1$. By $L.3$ $a_{j2} = 0 = a_{j3} = a_{j5}$ $(j = 5, 6, 7)$.

Suppose (vi) occurs, then we may assume $R.8$ is (vi) so $a_{82} = 1$, $a_{84} = -1 = a_{86}$. By $L.3$ $a_{83} = 0 = a_{85}$. If a_{8l} is the remaining unit of $R.8$ then by $L.9A$ on rows 1, 4 and 8 we cannot have $a_{jl} = -a_{8l}$ $(j = 5, 6, 7)$. Thus by $L.2$ on $R.8$ for each j $(j = 5, 6, 7)$ we must have either $a_{j4} = 1$ or $a_{j6} = 1$. By $L.5$ both $a_{j4} = 1$ $(j = 5, 6, 7)$ and $a_{j6} = 1$ $(j = 5, 6, 7)$ are impossible, so by symmetry we may suppose $a_{54} = 1 = a_{64} = a_{76}$. By $L.3$ $a_{74} = 0 = a_{56} = a_{66}$.

Now suppose $R.9$ is (iii) then $a_{92} = -1 = a_{97} = a_{98}$. By $L.3$ $a_{93} = 0 = a_{94} = a_{95} = a_{96} = a_{87} = a_{88}$. If a_{9m} is the remaining unit of $R.9$ then by $L.9A$ on rows 2, 3 and 9 we cannot have $a_{jm} = -a_{9m}$ $(j = 5, 6, 7)$. Thus by $L.2$ on $R.9$ for each j $(j = 5, 6, 7)$ we must have either $a_{j7} = 1$ or $a_{j8} = 1$. By $L.5$ both $a_{j7} = 1$ $(j = 5, 6, 7)$ and $a_{j8} = 1$ $(j = 5, 6, 7)$ are impossible so by symmetry we may suppose that two of the a_{j7} and one of the a_{j8} are $(+1)$s $(j = 5, 6, 7)$. By $L.4$ $a_{57} = a_{67} = 1$ is impossible, so we may assume $a_{57} = a_{77} = a_{68} = 1$. By $L.3$ $a_{58} = 0 = a_{78} = a_{67}$.

4*

Let $a_{59} = 1$, then by $L.2$ $a_{69} = -1 = a_{79}$. However, $R.6$ and $R.7$ now contradict $L.2$ and so $R.9$ cannot be (iii).

Now suppose $R.9$ is (i) then $a_{92} = -1 = a_{95} = a_{98}$. By $L.3$ $a_{93} = 0 = a_{94} = a_{96} = a_{88}$. By $L.5$ $a_{j8} = 1$ ($j = 5, 6, 7$) is impossible so if a_{9m} is the remaining unit of $R.9$ then by $L.2$ $a_{jm} = -a_{9m}$ holds for at least one value of j ($j = 5, 6, 7$) By $L.3$ $a_{k7} \neq -1$ ($k \geqslant 5$) so $m \neq 7$. Thus we may suppose $a_{99} = 1$. By $L.6$ with $r_0 = 9$ we may therefore suppose $a_{58} = 1, a_{69} = -1$. Then by $L.3$ $a_{68} = 0$.

If $a_{78} = 1$, let a_{5p} be the remaining unit of $R.5$. Then by $L.2$ $a_{6p} = a_{7p} = -a_{5p}$. However, $R.6$ and $R.7$ now contradict $L.2$.

Thus $a_{78} \neq 1$ so by $L.2$ on $R.9$ $a_{79} = -1$. By $L.3$ $a_{78} = 0$. By $L.6$ with $r_0 = 5$ we must now have $a_{59} = 1$ so by $L.2$ we may suppose $a_{6.10} = 1 = -a_{7.10}$ and we therefore have

x	y	z	A	B	C	D	E	F	G
1	1	1	1	0	0	0	0	0	0
1	−1	0	0	1	0	1	0	0	0
1	−1	0	0	−1	0	0	1	0	0
1	1	−1	0	0	1	0	0	0	0
−1	0	0	1	0	0	0	1	1	0
−1	0	0	1	0	0	0	0	−1	1
−1	0	0	0	0	1	0	0	−1	−1
0	1	0	−1	0	−1				
0	−1	0	0	−1	0	0	−1	1	0

Choose the coordinate system shown. From boundedness we have: from $T.1$ $a_1 < 0$; from $T.4$ $c_1 < 0$. If $f_1 \geqslant 0$ then from $T.6$ $g_1 > 0$ and $T.7$ is then unbounded.

Thus $f_1 < 0$. From $T.5$ $e_1 > 0$; from $T.9$ $b_1 < 0$. However, $T.3$ is now unbounded so $R.9$ cannot be (i).

As the case when $R.9$ is (ii) is equivalent to that when $R.9$ is (i), by Lemma 15 A (vi) cannot occur with any of the other possibilities. Hence (vi) cannot arise and since (iii) is equivalent to (vi) neither can (iii).

We shall find the following lemma useful.

LEMMA 15 B. *If A is a matrix representation of a 9-con, then it does not contain a minor equivalent to*

$$
\begin{array}{rrrrrr}
1 & & -1 & & & \\
1 & -1 & & & & \\
1 & 1 & 1 & 1 & & \\
-1 & 0 & 0 & 1 & 0 & -1 \\
-1 & 0 & 0 & 0 & 1 & -1 \\
& 1 & 1 & -1 & -1 &
\end{array}
$$

Proof. Suppose such a minor occurs, then by $L.2$ on $R.4$ and $R.5$ we may assume

$$
\begin{array}{ccccccc}
x & y & z & w & A & B & C \\
1 & & -1 & & & & \\
1 & -1 & & & & & \\
1 & 1 & 1 & 1 & & & \\
-1 & 0 & 0 & 1 & 0 & -1 & 1 \\
-1 & 0 & 0 & 0 & 1 & -1 & -1 \\
& 1 & 1 & -1 & -1 & &
\end{array}
$$

Choose the coordinate system shown. As $C.1$ is a tem-column each tetrahedron must have an intersection of positive area with $x = 0$, so consider the configuration on $x = 0$.

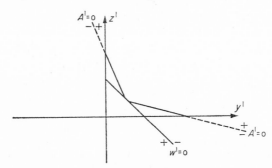

FIG. 14

If $A^1 = 0$ has a gradient $>$ that of $w^1 = 0$ then in order that $T^1.6$ should have positive area, we must have $a_4/a_2 > w_4/w_2$. Hence $A^1 = 0$ meets $w^1 = 0$ in $z^1 > 0$ and $w^1 \geqslant 0$, $A^1 \geqslant 0$ lies in $z^1 > 0$.

If $A^1 = 0$ has a gradient $<$ that of $w^1 = 0$ then in order that $T^1.6$ should have positive area, we must have $a_4/a_3 > w_4/w_3$. Hence $A^1 = 0$ meets $w^1 = 0$ in $y^1 > 0$ and $A^1 \geqslant 0$, $w^1 \geqslant 0$ lies in $y^1 > 0$.

Now at least one of $T^1.4$ and $T^1.5$ must lie completely in $A^1 \geqslant 0$, $w^1 \geqslant 0$, say it is $T^1.l$. Thus in the former case $T^1.l$ does not have an area in common with $T^1.1$ and in the latter, it does not have an area in common with $T^1.2$. Hence in both cases $T.l$ does not possess Crum's Property with one of $T.1$ and $T.2$.

Thus the only possibility is that the gradients of $A^1 = 0$ and $w^1 = 0$ should be equal. However in this case in order that $T^1.6$ should have positive area $w^1 \geqslant 0$, $A^1 \geqslant 0$ must have zero area. This is impossible, since $T^1.l$ lies in $w^1 \geqslant 0$, $A^1 \geqslant 0$ and the lemma is proved.

Suppose (v) and (i) occur together then we may assume $R.5$ is (v) and $R.6$ is (i) so that $a_{52} = 1 = a_{53}$, $a_{54} = -1 = a_{62} = a_{65} = a_{68}$. By $L.3$ $a_{55} = 0 = a_{58} = a_{63} = a_{64}$. Now $a_{j6} \neq -1$, $a_{j7} \neq -1$ ($j \geqslant 5$). Thus if $a_{56} = 1$ or $a_{57} = 1$ then by $L.2$ on $R.5$ $a_{j4} = 1$ ($j = 7, 8, 9$) which is impossible by $L.5$. Similarly, if $a_{66} = 1$ or $a_{67} = 1$ then by $L.2$ on $R.6$ $a_{j8} = 1$ ($j = 7, 8, 9$) which is also impossible by $L.5$. Thus $a_{56} = 0 = a_{66} = a_{57} = a_{67}$. Let $a_{59} = 1$. Two cases now arise: (a) $a_{69} = 1$ and (b) $a_{69} \neq 1$.

(a) Suppose $a_{69} = 1$. By $L.5$ $a_{j9} = -1$ ($j = 7, 8, 9$) is impossible, so we may assume $a_{99} \neq -1$ then by $L.2$ on $R.5$ and $R.6$ $a_{94} = 1 = a_{98}$. Now if $a_{j9} \neq -1$ for $j = 7$ or 8 then by $L.2$ $a_{j4} = 1 = a_{j8}$ and this is impossible by $L.4$. Thus $a_{79} = -1 = a_{89}$. By $L.3$ $a_{j4} \neq -1$, $a_{j8} \neq -1$ ($j = 7, 8$) so if a_{9l} is the remaining unit of $R.9$, by $L.2$ we must have $a_{7l} = a_{8l} = -a_{9l}$. If $l \neq 9$ we have a contradiction to $L.4$, so $l = 9$ and thus $a_{99} = 1$. Hence we have

x	y	z	A	B	C	D	E	F
1	1	1	1	0	0	0	0	0
1	−1	0	0	1	0	1	0	0
1	−1	0	0	−1	0	0	1	0
1	1	−1	0	0	1	0	0	0
0	1	1	−1	0	0	0	0	1
0	−1	0	0	−1	0	0	−1	1
−1	0	0		0				−1
−1	0	0		0				−1
−1	0	0	1	0	0	0	1	1

Choose the coordinate system shown. From boundedness we have: from T.1 $a_1 < 0$; from T.5 $f_1 < 0$; from T.9 $e_1 > 0$; from T.6 $b_1 < 0$. However, T.3 is now unbounded so (a) cannot arise.

Thus (b) $a_{69} \neq 1$. By L.3 $a_{69} \neq -1$ so $a_{69} = 0$. Let $a_{6.10} = 1$.

(b$_1$) Suppose $a_{74} = 1 = a_{84}$ then by L.5 $a_{94} \neq 1$ and by L.3 $a_{94} \neq -1$ so $a_{94} = 0$. Thus by L.2 on R.5 $a_{99} = -1$. By L.6 with $r_0 = 6$ we may therefore assume $a_{78} = 1$, $a_{8.10} = -1$. By L.3 $a_{88} = 0$, $a_{98} \neq -1$ so if a_{7l} is the remaining unit of R.7 then $a_{8l} = a_{9l} = -a_{7l}$.

If $l \geqslant 11$ we may suppose $a_{8.11} = a_{9.11} = -a_{7.11} \neq 0$. Then by L.2 on R.8 $a_{9.10} = 1$. However R.6 and R.9 now contradict L.2.

Thus $l < 11$. Since $a_{89} \neq -1$, $l \neq 9$ so we can only have $l = 10$ and therefore $a_{7.10} = 1 = -a_{9.10}$. Now $a_{89} \neq 0$ for, if it was, rows 1, 2, 4, 5, 8, and 9 contradict Lemma 15B. By L.3 $a_{89} \neq -1$ so $a_{89} = 1$ and we have

x	y	z	w	A	B	C	D	E	F
1	1	1	1	0	0	0	0	0	0
1	-1	0	0	1	0	1	0	0	0
1	-1	0	0	-1	0	0	1	0	0
1	1	-1	0	0	1	0	0	0	0
0	1	1	-1	0	0	0	0	1	0
0	-1	0	0	-1	0	0	-1	0	1
-1	0	0	1	0	0	0	1	0	1
-1	0	0	1	0	0	0	0	1	-1
-1	0	0	0	0				-1	-1

Choose the coordinate system shown. From boundedness we have: from T.5 $e_1 < 0$; from T.8 $f_1 < 0$; from T.7 $d_1 > 0$; from T.6 $a_1 < 0$. However, T.3 is now unbounded.

Hence (b$_1$) cannot arise.

Thus at most one of the a_{j4} ($j = 7, 8, 9$) is a $(+1)$. By L.5 $a_{j9} = -1$ ($j = 7, 8, 9$) is impossible so by L.2 on R.5 we may suppose $a_{74} = 1$, $a_{89} = -1 = a_{99}$. Now the case when two of the a_{j8} ($j = 7, 8, 9$) are $(+1)$s is equivalent to (b$_1$) so we may suppose at most one of the a_{j8} ($j = 7, 8, 9$) is a $(+1)$. By L.5 $a_{j.10} = -1$ ($j = 7, 8, 9$) is impossible so by L.2 on R.6 we must have two of the $a_{j.10}$ ($j = 7, 8, 9$) are (-1)s and one of the a_{j8} ($j = 7, 8, 9$) is a $(+1)$. By L.4 $a_{8.10} = -1 = a_{9.10}$ is impossible so we may suppose $a_{7.10} = -1 = a_{8.10}$, $a_{98} = 1$. By $L.3$ $a_{84} = 0 = a_{94} = a_{78} = a_{88}$.

Now if $a_{9.10} = 1$ then by $L.3$ $a_{7.9} = 0$ and we have a contradiction to Lemma 15 B in rows 1, 2, 4, 5, 7 and 8.

Thus $a_{9.10} \neq 1$ so by $L.3$ $a_{9.10} = 0$. However, we now have a contradiction to Lemma 15 B in rows 1, 2, 3, 6, 8 and 9.

Hence (v) and (i) cannot occur together. As the case when (iv) and (i) occur together is equivalent to that when (v) and (i) occur together, by Lemma 15 A, (i) cannot occur with any of the other possibilities, and so (i) cannot arise.

Since (ii), (iv) and (v) are all equivalent to (i) they cannot arise either, and the lemma is proved.

From the analysis at the beginning of the Chapter and Lemmas 10, 12, 13, 14 and 15 it follows that if A is a matrix representation of a 9-con, then no column of A can contain four units of the same sign. Now suppose that B is a matrix representation of an n-con for $n > 9$ and that one of its columns. $C.l$ say, contains four units of the same sign. By $L.7$ $C.l$ can contain at most eight units, so $C.l$ contains at least $(n-8)$ zeros. Thus by omitting $(n-9)$ of the rows that have zeros in $C.l$ we have a matrix representation of a 9-con one of whose columns contains four units of the same sign. As this is impossible, we have:

LEMMA 16. If A is a matrix representation of an n-con $(n \geqslant 9)$ then no column of A can contain four units of the same sign.

For a positive integer n suppose an n-con exists and let A be one of its matrix representations. By elementary transformations we can arrange that $a_{1j} = 1$ $(j = 1, \ldots 4)$ and $a_{1j} = 0$ $(j > 4)$. Therefore by $L.2$ every row r with $r \geqslant 2$ must contain a (-1) in the first four columns. Since by $L.16$ $C.1$, $C.2$, $C.3$, and $C.4$, can each contain at most three (-1)s if $n \geqslant 9$, it follows that there can be at most 13 rows in the matrix and *a fortiori* at most 13 tetrahedra in the n-con. We therefore have the following theorem:

THEOREM 2. An n-con can exist only if $n \leqslant 13$.

CHAPTER THREE

ON A PROPERTY OF THE COLUMNS OF A MATRIX REPRESENTATION OF A 9-CON

AFTER introducing some definitions, we show that there are only four types of tetrahedra that can occur in a 9-con, the way in which they are characterised in a matrix representation being given by Lemma 17. We then define an operation on the tetrahedra of a 9-con which leads to a function defined over the D_m-planes of the 9-con. An equality involving this function is obtained and this enables us to analyse the possible sets of D_m-planes that can occur in a 9-con. By this means and with the help of a number of lemmas, we arrive at the main result of the chapter, namely, Theorem 3. If A is a matrix representation of a 9-con then at most one column of A can contain six units.

We require the following notation and definitions.

Notation. A, B, ... P will be used to denote distinct tetrahedra, no pair of which are overlapping. The faces of A, B, C, ... will be denoted by a_i, b_i, c_i ... $(i = 1, \ldots 4)$.

We write A, B ... F/G, H ... P in V if each of the tetrahedra A, ... F has a common area in the plane V with each of G, .. P where A, ...F lie in one closed half-space defined by V and G, ... P lie in the other.

DEFINITIONS. Consider a matrix representation of an n-con, then:

A unit with the property that three units of the opposite sign lie in the same column is called a tript.

A unit with the property that two and only two units of the opposite sign lie in the same column is called a dopt.

A unit with the property that one and only one unit of the opposite sign lies in the same column is called a sipt.

A unit with the property that no units of the opposite sign lie in the same column is called a nopt.

DEFINITIONS. A D_1-plane is called a uno.

A D_2-plane, D^1, such that there exists A and B with A/B in D^1 is called a unun. Otherwise a D_2-plane is called a nodo.

A D_3-plane, D^1, such that there exists A, B and C with AB/C in D^1 is called a doun. Otherwise a D_3-plane is called a notre.

A D_4-plane, D^1, such that there exists A, B, C and D with A B C/D in D^1 is called a treun. A D_4-plane, D^1, such that there exists A, B, C and D with A B/C D is called a dodo.

A D_5-plane is called a dotre.

A D_6-plane is called a tetre.

By $L.16$ a column of a matrix representation of an n-con ($n \geqslant 9$) cannot contain four units of the same sign so the above planes are the only possible D_m-planes for an n-con ($n \geqslant 9$). Furthermore it follows that dotres and tetres in an n-con ($n \geqslant 9$) are uniquely defined apart from an interchange of letters.

If a 9-con exists, consider one of its tetrahedra, A say, with faces a_i ($i = 1, \ldots 4$); let x_i be the D_m-plane corresponding to a_i. Each of the remaining eight tetrahedra has an area in common with one of the faces of A and by $L.16$ this can effectively be done in only four ways, namely,

(1) A/BCD in x_1, A/EFG in x_2 and A/HI in x_3. A is then called a naik.

(2) A/BCD in x_1, A/EFG in x_2, A/H in x_3 and A/I in x_4. A is then called a dhoat.

(3) A/BCD in x_1, A/EF in x_2, A/GH in x_3 and A/I in x_4. A is then called a thaik.

(4) A/BC in x_1, A/DE in x_2, A/FG in x_3 and A/HI in x_4. A is then called a chardho.

LEMMA 17. If $R.l$ is a row of a matrix representation of a 9-con then the four units of $R.l$ must be either (1) two tripts, one dopt and a nopt in which case $T.l$ is a naik, or (2) two tripts and two sipts in which case $T.l$ is a dhoat, or (3) one tript, two dopts and a sipt in which case $T.l$ is a thaik or (4) four dopts in which case $T.l$ is a chardho.

Proof. From the above, only four types of tetrahedra can occur in a 9-con and (1), (2), (3) and (4) are simply the conditions that $T.l$ should be one of those types.

LEMMA 18. The number of nopts in the matrix representation of a 9-con is equal to the number of naiks in the 9-con.

Proof. From $L.17$ each row of the matrix can contain at most one nopt and if a row does contain a nopt then by $L.17$ it can only represent a naik. As a row representing a naik must contain a nopt the result follows.

DEFINITION. If a face a_1 of A has a positive area in common with a face b_1 of B we say that a_1 has A-contract with b_1, and write $a_1 \text{ A } b_1$.

Clearly if A/BCD in x_1, then $a_1 \text{ A } b_1$, $a_1 \text{ A } c_1$, $a_1 \text{ A } d_1$ where a_1, b_1, c_1 and d_1 all lie in x_1.

Suppose a 9-con exists; if more than one does, choose any one. Taking any tetrahedron A of this 9-con we define an algebraic operation on A as follows:

If A has a face, a_1 say, such that $a_1 \text{ A } b_1$, $a_1 \text{ A } c_1$, $a_1 \text{ A } d_1$, then there exists a face a_2 of A such that a_2 has A-contact with at most one face of the 9-con. We now operate so that a_1 has algebraic or ∇-contact with b_1 and c_1 and a_2 has ∇-contact with d_1 and we write $a_1 \nabla b_1$, $a_1 \nabla c_1$, $a_2 \nabla d_1$. We say that there has been a "subtraction" from x_1, and an "addition" to x_2 where x_i is the D_m-plane corresponding to a_i. For the faces of A which have A-contact with at most two faces of the 9-con the operation takes A-contact into ∇-contact.

If A has two faces, a_1 and a_3 say, with $a_1 \text{ A } b_1$, $a_1 \text{ A } c_1$, $a_1 \text{ A } d_1$ and $a_3 \text{ A } e_1$, $a_3 \text{ A } f_1$, $a_3 \text{ A } g_1$, then operate on a_1, a_2 and a_4 as above. Thus we have a_3 unchanged and one other face a_j ($j = 2$ or 4) with only one ∇-contact. We now operate on a_3 so that $a_3 \nabla e_1$, $a_3 \nabla f_1$ and $a_j \nabla g_1$.

If A is such that each of its faces has A-contact with two faces of the 9-con then the operation takes A-contact into ∇-contact.

We therefore arrive at the situation where each of the faces of A has ∇-contact with two and only two of the faces of the 9-con. Neglecting the effect of the operation on A we now repeat the operation on another tetrahedron B of the 9-con. The process is then repeated until all nine tetrahedra have been operated upon.

We now consider the effect of these operations on the D_m-planes of the 9-con. Consider any D_m-plane, D say; let i tetrahedra be completely contained in one of the closed half-spaces defined by D and j in the other. Thus $i + j = m$ since each of the i tetrahedra must have a positive area in common with each of the j tetrahedra.

The i-algebraic total for D is defined as $\frac{1}{2}m \pm$ the number of $\begin{Bmatrix} \text{additions to} \\ \text{subtractions from} \end{Bmatrix}$ the plane D when the operation has only been performed on the i tetrahedra.

The j-algebraic total for D is defined similarly.

Hence we have:

If $j = 3$ the i-algebraic total for D is $\frac{1}{2}m - i$ since there is a subtraction from D for each of the i tetrahedra. If $j = 2$ the i-algebraic total D is $\frac{1}{2}m$.

If $j = 1$ the i-algebraic total for D is $\frac{1}{2}m + i$, since there is an addition to D for each of the i tetrahedra. If $j = 0$ the i-algebraic total for D is $\frac{1}{2}m + 2i$ since there are two additions to D for each of the i tetrahedra.

Clearly exactly similar results hold for the j-algebraic total when we range over the values of i.

DEFINITION. The algebraic total for D is the sum of the i- and j-algebraic totals.

DEFINITION. The surplus for D is the algebraic total for $D - 3$. Hence, we have the following table:

Plane	Algebraic Total	Surplus
Uno	3	0
Unun	4	1
Nodo	6	3
Doun	5	2
Notre	9	6
Treun	6	3
Dodo	4	1
Dotre	3	0
Tetre	0	−3

Now $\sum\limits_{D_m}$ Algebraic total for $D_m = 36$, the number of faces of the 9-con, since whenever a subtraction is made from one plane, an addition is made to another and conversely. Hence if the 9-con contains a total of l D_m-planes, (m not necessarily being a fixed integer) then the D_m-planes must be such that the sum of their surpluses is $36 - 3l$.

We now obtain an upper bound for the number of tetres appearing in a 9-con. If two tetres occur in a 9-con we may suppose that they are represented by $C.1$ and $C.2$ in its matrix representation. Hence we may assume $a_{j1} = 1$ $(j = 1, 2, 3)$, $a_{j1} = -1$ $(j = 4, 5, 6)$, $a_{j1} = 0$ $(j = 7, 8, 9)$. Now if $a(+1)$ and $a(-1)$ occur in the first six rows of $C.2$, by $L.3$ they must both lie in either rows 1, 2 and 3 or rows 4, 5 and 6. By $L.3$ we have in the former case $a_{j2} = 0$ $(j = 4, 5, 6)$ and in the latter, $a_{j2} = 0$ $(j = 1, 2, 3)$. As $C.2$ only contains three units of the same sign, it is clear that only three units can occur in the first six rows of $C.2$. Hence only two effective cases arise: (A) $a_{12} = 1 = a_{22} = a_{42}$, $a_{72} = -1 = a_{82} = a_{92}$ and (B) $a_{12} = 1 = a_{22} = a_{72}$, $a_{32} = -1 = a_{82} = a_{92}$. (We note that $a_{12} = a_{22} = a_{32} \neq 0$ is impossible by $L.5$.)

However (A) and (B) are equivalent, so only one effective case occurs. Hence:

LEMMA 19. If a 9-con contains two tetres then we may suppose that the first two columns of its matrix representation are

$$
\begin{array}{rr}
1 & 1 \\
1 & 1 \\
1 & 0 \\
-1 & 1 \\
-1 & 0 \\
-1 & 0 \\
0 & -1 \\
0 & -1 \\
0 & -1
\end{array}
$$

Suppose a third tetre occurs in the 9-con, then we may assume that it is represented by $C.3$ and that $C.1$ and $C.2$ are as in $L.19$. By $L.17$ a row in a matrix representation of a 9-con can contain at most two tripts so $a_{13} = 0 = a_{23} = a_{43}$. Hence the remaining spaces of $C.3$ are all units and by $L.3$ $a_{53} = a_{33} = a_{63}$. Thus we must have $a_{73} = a_{83} = a_{93}$ which is impossible by $L.5$. Hence:

LEMMA 20. At most two tetres occur in a 9-con.

We find the following lemmas useful.

LEMMA 21. If two dotres occur in a 9-con then their units in the matrix representation fall in at least seven distinct rows.

Proof. Suppose their units fall in at most six distinct rows. Let $C.1$ and $C.2$ represent the dotres, then for the first column we may suppose $a_{j1} = 1$ $(j = 1, 2, 3)$, $a_{j1} = -1$ $(j = 4, 5)$, $a_{j1} = 0$ $(j > 5)$.

If $a_{12} = -1$ then by $L.3$ $a_{42} \neq 1$, $a_{52} \neq 1$, so we may assume $a_{42} = -1$ since one of a_{42} and a_{52} must be a unit by our supposition. Thus by $L.3$ $a_{22} \neq 1$, $a_{32} \neq 1$ and so there is at most one $(+1)$ in $C.2$ which is impossible. Hence $a_{12} \neq -1$.

By the same argument $a_{12} \neq 1$ so $a_{12} = 0$. By symmetry $a_{22} = 0 = a_{32}$ and we have a contradiction.

LEMMA 22. If two dodos occur in a 9-con, then their units in the matrix representation fall in at least six distinct rows.

Proof. Suppose their units fall in at most five distinct rows. Let $C.1$ and $C.2$ represent the dodos then for the first column we may suppose $a_{j1} = 1$ $(j = 1, 2)$, $a_{j1} = -1$ $(j = 3, 4)$, $a_{j1} = 0$ $(j > 4)$. Now at least three units must occur in the first four rows of $C.2$ and so $a(+1)$ and $a(-1)$ must occur in these rows. Thus by $L.3$ either $a_{12} = 1 = -a_{22}$ in which case $a_{32} = 0 = a_{42}$ by $L.3$ or $a_{32} = 1 = -a_{42}$ so that $a_{12} = 0 = a_{22}$ by $L.3$. Hence we have a contradiction and the lemma is proved.

LEMMA 23. If a dotre and a dodo occur in a 9-con, then their units in the matrix representation fall in at least six distinct rows. Furthermore if their units do fall in only six distinct rows, then the columns representing the dotre and dodo contain a minor equivalent to

$$
\begin{array}{rr}
1 & 1 \\
1 & 1 \\
1 & -1 \\
-1 & 0 \\
-1 & 0 \\
0 & -1
\end{array}
$$

Proof. Suppose their units fall in at most six distinct rows. Let $C.1$ represent the dotre and $C.2$ the dodo, then for the first column we may suppose $a_{j1} = 1$ $(j = 1, 2, 3)$, $a_{j1} = -1$ $(j = 4, 5)$ $a_{j1} = 0$ $(j > 5)$. Now at least three units must occur in the first five rows of $C.2$ and so $a(+1)$ and $a(-1)$ must occur in these rows. However if $a_{42} = 1$ by $L.3$ $a_{j2} \neq -1$ $(j = 1, 2, 3)$ so we must have $a_{52} = -1$; hence by $L.3$ $a_{j2} = 0$ $(j = 1, 2, 3)$ and this is impossible. Thus $a_{42} \neq 1$. By the same argument $a_{42} \neq -1$ so $a_{42} = 0$. By symmetry we also have $a_{52} = 0$. Hence the a_{j2} $(j = 1, 2, 3)$ must all be units and we have the given matrix or one equivalent to it.

LEMMA 24. Suppose a matrix representation of a 9-con contains a minor $\begin{pmatrix} a_{il} & a_{im} \\ a_{jl} & a_{jm} \end{pmatrix}$ where $a_{il} = a_{jl} \neq 0$, $a_{im} = a_{jm} \neq 0$ and a_{il} and a_{im} are both tripts, then $R.i$ and $R.j$ contain zeros in the columns representing dotres and dodos.

Further if neither $R.i$ nor $R.j$ contains a nopt then $T.i/T.j$ is a unun.

Proof. We may clearly suppose that the a_{ij} $(i,j = 1, 2)$ are all $(+1)$s and tripts; thus we may also assume $a_{l1} = -1$ $(l = 3, 4, 5)$. By $L.3$ $a_{l2} \neq -1$ $(l = 3, 4, 5)$ so we may therefore suppose $a_{m2} = -1$ $(m = 6, 7, 8)$.

(A) Let $C.3$ represent a dotre or dodo then, if a_{13} is a unit say $a_{13} = 1$, it must be a dopt or a tript. By $L.3$ $a_{l3} \neq -1$ $(l = 3, \dots 8)$ so a_{13} is a dopt and $a_{23} = -1 = a_{93}$. However, by $L.3$ $a_{l3} = 0$ $(l = 3, \dots 8)$ so $C.3$ does not represent a dotre or dodo and the first part of the lemma is proved.

(B) By $L.2$ we may suppose $a_{13} = 1 = -a_{23}$. If neither $R.1$ nor $R.2$ contains a nopt then by $L.17$ both a_{13} and a_{23} must be sipts and so $C.3$ is a unun.

We now consider the possibility of two tetres occurring in a 9-con.

LEMMA 25. If two tetres occur in a 9-con then at most one dotre occurs.

Proof. Suppose two dotres occur. Let $C.1$ and $C.2$ represent the tetres and $C.3$ and $C.4$ the dotres. By $L.19$ and $L.24$ we may therefore suppose that

$$
\begin{array}{rr}
1 & 1 \quad 0 \quad 0 \\
1 & 1 \quad 0 \quad 0 \\
1 & 0 \\
-1 & 1 \\
-1 & 0 \\
-1 & 0 \\
0 & -1 \\
0 & -1 \\
0 & -1
\end{array}
$$

By $L.21$ at least one of a_{43} and a_{44} is a unit, so let $a_{43} = 1$. By $L.17$ $a_{44} = 0$ and by $L.3$ $a_{j3} \neq -1$ $(j = 3, 7, 8, 9)$ so we must have $a_{53} = -1 = a_{63}$. By $L.3$ $a_{33} \neq 0$ so we may suppose $a_{73} = 1 = a_{83}$. By $L.21$ a_{34} is a unit, so let $a_{34} = 1$. By $L.3$ $a_{54} \neq -1$, $a_{64} \neq -1$ so at least one of a_{74} and a_{84} is a (-1). Hence by $L.3$ $a_{54} = 0 = a_{64}$ and so $C.4$ contains five zeros. Thus $C.4$ is not a dotre and the lemma is proved.

Suppose a dotre does occur with two tetres in a 9-con. Let $C.1$ and $C.2$ represent the tetres and $C.3$ the dotre. By $L.19$ and $L.24$ we may therefore suppose

$$
\begin{array}{rr}
1 & 1 & 0 \\
1 & 1 & 0 \\
1 & 0 \\
-1 & 1 \\
-1 & 0 \\
-1 & 0 \\
0 & -1 \\
0 & -1 \\
0 & -1
\end{array}
$$

We shall assume that there are three $(+1)$s in $C.3$ and consider the various possible positions of the two (-1)s. By $L.17$ $a_{43} \neq -1$. Now we cannot have $a_{33} = -1 = a_{53}$, since by $L.3$ we then have $a_{73} = 1 = a_{83} = a_{93}$ which is impossible by $L.5$. By symmetry $a_{33} = -1 = a_{63}$ is also impossible. Thus, if $a_{33} = -1$ by $L.3$ $a_{43} = 0 = a_{53} = a_{63}$ and so $C.3$ contains five zeros. Thus $a_{33} \neq -1$ and therefore only three effective cases arise:

(E_1) $a_{53} = -1 = a_{63}$. By $L.3$ $a_{33} = 0$, and by $L.5$ the a_{j3} $(j = 7, 8, 9)$ are not all $(+1)$s so we may suppose $a_{43} = 1 = a_{73} = a_{83}$, $a_{93} = 0$.

(E_2) $a_{53} = -1 = a_{73}$. By $L.3$ $a_{33} = 0 = a_{43}$ so $a_{63} = 1 = a_{83} = a_{93}$.

(E_3) $a_{73} = -1 = a_{83}$. By $L.3$ $a_{43} = 0$. Hence:

Lemma 26. If a 9-con contains two tetres and a dotre its matrix representation must contain a minor equivalent to one of the following:

(E$_1$)			(E$_2$)			(E$_3$)		
1	1	0	1	1	0	1	1	0
1	1	0	1	1	0	1	1	0
1	0	0	1	0	0	1	0	
−1	1	1	−1	1	0	−1	1	0
−1	0	−1	−1	0	−1	−1	0	
−1	0	−1	−1	0	1	−1	0	
0	−1	1	0	−1	−1	0	−1	−1
0	−1	1	0	−1	1	0	−1	−1
0	−1	0	0	−1	1	0	−1	

LEMMA 27. It is not possible for two tetres, a dotre and a dodo to occur in a 9-con.

Proof. Suppose the lemma is false. By $L.26$ we may suppose that the first three columns of the matrix representation have one of the forms (E_1), (E_2) and (E_3). Let $C.4$ be the dodo, then by $L.24$ $a_{14} = 0 = a_{24}$.

Firstly consider the case when (E_2) occurs. If a_{44} is a unit, say $a_{44} = 1$, then by $L.3$ $a_{j4} \neq -1$ $(j = 3, 7, 8, 9)$ so we must have $a_{54} = -1 = a_{64}$; by $L.3$ $a_{j4} = 0$ $(j = 3, 7, 8, 9)$ and so $C.4$ contains only three units. Thus $a_{44} = 0$. By $L.23$ $a_{54} = 0 = a_{74}$ so the remaining spaces of $C.4$ are units. By $L.3$ we must have $a_{34} = a_{64}$. Hence $a_{84} = a_{94}$ which is impossible by $L.4$. Thus (E_2) cannot occur.

Secondly, consider the case when (E_1) occurs. By $L.17$ $a_{44} = 0$ so $C.3$ and $C.4$ do not possess a minor equivalent to the matrix of $L.23$. Hence the units of $C.3$ and $C.4$ fall in at least seven distinct rows and we may therefore suppose $a_{34} = 1$. By $L.3$ $a_{54} \neq -1$, $a_{64} \neq -1$, so two of the a_{j4} $(j = 7, 8, 9)$ are (-1)s. By $L.4$ $a_{74} = a_{84} = -1$ is impossible so by the symmetry of $R.7$ and $R.8$ we may suppose $a_{84} = -1 = a_{94}$. By $L.3$ $a_{54} = 0 = a_{64}$. Hence $a_{74} = 1$ and we have

1	1	0	0
1	1	0	0
1	0	0	1
−1	1	1	0
−1	0	−1	0
−1	0	−1	0
0	−1	1	1
0	−1	1	−1
0	−1	0	−1

By $L.1$ we may suppose $a_{35} = 1 = a_{36}$, $a_{3l} = 0$ $(l > 6)$. By $L.6$ with $r_0 = 3$ we may therefore assume $a_{15} = -1 = a_{26}$ and, by the symmetry of $R.1$ and $R.2$, by $L.2$ we may further suppose that $a_{75} = -1$. Hence by $L.3$ the remaining spaces of $C.5$ and $C.6$, except possibly a_{16}, are zeros. Thus by $L.1$ we may suppose $a_{97} = -1 = a_{98}$, $a_{9l} = 0$ $(l > 8)$. By $L.6$ with $r_0 = 9$ we may therefore assume $a_{57} = 1 = a_{68}$ and, by the symmetry of $R.5$ and $R.6$, by $L.2$ we may further suppose that $a_{87} = 1$. Thus by $L.3$ the remaining spaces of $C.7$ and $C.8$, except possibly for a_{58}, are zeros. Hence we have

1	1	0	0	−1		0	0
1	1	0	0	0	−1	0	0
1	0	0	1	1	1	0	0
−1	1	1	0	0	0	0	0
−1	0	−1	0	0	0	1	
−1	0	−1	0	0	0	0	1
0	−1	1	1	−1	0	0	0
0	−1	1	−1	0	0	1	0
0	−1	0	−1	0	0	−1	−1

(i) Consider the case when $a_{58} = 0$. By $L.2$ we may therefore suppose $a_{59} = 1 = -a_{69}$ and then the remaining spaces of $C.9$ are zeros by $L.3$. Thus

A	x	y	z	B	C	D	E	F
1	1	0	0	−1		0	0	0
1	1	0	0	0	−1	0	0	0
1	0	0	1	1	1	0	0	0
−1	1	1	0	0	0	0	0	0
−1	0	−1	0	0	0	1	0	1
−1	0	−1	0	0	0	0	1	−1
0	−1	1	1	−1	0	0	0	0
0	−1	1	−1	0	0	1	0	0
0	−1	0	−1	0	0	−1	−1	0

Choose the coordinate system shown. Now $y = 0$ is a tem-plane so each tetrahedron of the 9-con must have an intersection of positive area with $y = 0$. Thus consider the configuration on $y = 0$ shown in Fig. 15, p. 67.

Consider $T^1.5$ and $T^1.6$, clearly at least one of them must lie in the sector $D^1 \geqslant 0$, $E^1 \geqslant 0$. Since each of $T^1.4$, $T^1.7$ and $T^1.8$

must have an area in common with both $T^1.5$ and $T^1.6$ the sector $D^1 \geqslant 0$, $E^1 \geqslant 0$ must have an area in $x^1 > 0$, $x^1 < 0$, $z^1 > 0$ and $z^1 < 0$.

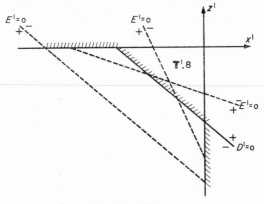

FIG. 15

Now if $E^1 = 0$ has a gradient $\geqslant$ that of $D^1 = 0$ then in order that $T^1.9$ should be closed and have positive area, we must have $e_4/e_1 < d_4/d_1$. Thus $E^1 = 0$ meets $D^1 = 0$ in $z^1 < 0$ and therefore $D^1 \geqslant 0$, $E^1 \geqslant 0$ does not have an area in $z^1 > 0$.

Thus $E^1 = 0$ must have a gradient $<$ that of $D^1 = 0$. In order that $T^1.9$ should be closed and have positive area, we must have $e_4/e_3 < d_4/d_3$. Thus $E^1 = 0$ meets $D^1 = 0$ in $x^1 < 0$ and therefore $D^1 \geqslant 0$, $E^1 \geqslant 0$ does not have an area in $x^1 > 0$.

Hence (i) cannot arise and so a_{58} is a unit. By $L.3$ $a_{58} \neq 1$ so $a_{58} = -1$.

(ii) Consider the case when $a_{16} = 1$. We have

x	y	A	B	C	z	D	E
1	1	0	0	−1	1	0	0
1	1	0	0	0	−1	0	0
1	0	0	1	1	1	0	0
−1	1	1	0	0	0	0	0
−1	0	−1	0	0	0	1	−1
−1	0	−1	0	0	0	0	1
0	−1	1	1	−1	0	0	0
0	−1	1	−1	0	0	1	0
0	−1	0	−1	0	0	−1	−1

Choose the coordinate system shown. From boundedness we have: from T.1 $c_1 > 0$; from T.3 $b_1 < 0$; from T.7 $a_1 > 0$; from T.8 $d_1 < 0$; from T.9 $e_1 > 0$. However, T.5 is now unbounded. Thus (ii) cannot arise and so $a_{16} \neq 1$. By L.3 $a_{16} \neq -1$ so $a_{16} = 0$. By L.2 we may therefore suppose $a_{19} = 1 = -a_{29}$. By L.3 the remaining spaces of C.9 are zeros so we have

A	x	y	B	z	C	D	E	F
1	1	0	0	−1	0	0	0	1
1	1	0	0	0	−1	0	0	−1
1	0	0	1	1	1	0	0	0
−1	1	1	0	0	0	0	0	0
−1	0	−1	0	0	0	1	−1	0
−1	0	−1	0	0	0	0	1	0
0	−1	1	1	−1	0	0	0	0
0	−1	1	−1	0	0	1	0	0
0	−1	0	−1	0	0	−1	−1	0

Choose the coordinate system shown. From boundedness we have: from T.7 $b_1 > 0$; from T.8 $d_1 > 0$; from T.9 $e_1 < 0$; from T.5 $a_1 > 0$; from T.3 $c_1 < 0$; from T.2 $f_1 > 0$. However, T.1 is now unbounded. Hence (E_1) cannot occur.

Finally consider the case when (E_3) occurs. We have

$$
\begin{matrix}
1 & 1 & 0 & 0 \\
1 & 1 & 0 & 0 \\
1 & 0 & & \\
-1 & 1 & 0 & \\
-1 & 0 & & \\
-1 & 0 & & \\
0 & -1 & -1 & \\
0 & -1 & -1 & \\
0 & -1 & &
\end{matrix}
$$

Now if a_{74} or a_{84} is a unit, say $a_{74} = 1$, then as three of the a_{j3} $(j = 3, 5, 6, 9)$ are $(+1)$s by L.3 at most one of the a_{j4} $(j = 3, 4, 5, 6, 9)$ is a (-1) and so we must have $a_{84} = -1$. Hence by L.3 at least four of the a_{j4} $(j = 3, 4, 5, 6, 9)$ are zeros and therefore C.4 does not represent a dodo. Thus, $a_{74} = 0 = a_{84}$. If a_{34} is a unit, say $a_{34} = 1$, then by L.3 there is only one possible place for a (-1) in C.4 so $a_{34} = 0$ also. Hence, the remaining spaces of $C.4$ are units and by $L.3$ we must have $a_{44} = a_{94}$. Thus let $a_{44} = 1 = a_{94}$ then $a_{54} = a_{64} = -1$. By $L.4$ $a_{53} = a_{63} \neq 0$ is impossible, so we may suppose $a_{33} = 1 = a_{53} = a_{93}$, $a_{63} = 0$. By $L.1$ we may suppose $a_{65} = -1 = a_{66}$, $a_{6l} = 0$ $(l > 6)$. By $L.6$ with $r_0 = 6$ we may therefore assume that $a_{75} = 1 = a_{86}$ and by the symmetry of $R.7$ and $R.8$, by $L.2$ we may further suppose $a_{55} = 1$. Thus by $L.3$ the remaining spaces of $C.5$ and $C.6$ are zeros, except possibly for a_{76}. By $L.1$ we may suppose $a_{37} = -1 = a_{38}$, $a_{3l} = 0$ $(l > 8)$. By $L.6$ with $r_0 = 3$ we may therefore assume that $a_{17} = 1 = a_{28}$ and by the symmetry of $R.1$ and $R.2$, by $L.2$ we may further suppose $a_{97} = 1$. Thus by $L.3$ the remaining spaces of $C.7$ and $C.8$ are zeros except possibly for a_{18}.

Now $a_{18} \neq 0$ for if $a_{18} = 0$ we have a contradiction to $L.9$. By $L.3$ $a_{18} \neq 1$ so $a_{18} = -1$. By $L.1$ we may suppose $a_{89} = 1$ so we have

x	A	B	y	C	z	D	E	F
1	1	0	0	0	0	1	-1	
1	1	0	0	0	0	0	1	
1	0	1	0	0	0	-1	-1	
-1	1	0	1	0	0	0	0	
-1	0	1	-1	1	0	0	0	
-1	0	0	-1	-1	-1	0	0	
0	-1	-1	0	1		0	0	
0	-1	-1	0	0	1	0	0	1
0	-1	1	1	0	0	1	0	

Choose the coordinate system shown. From boundedness we have: from $T.6$ $c_2 < 0$; from $T.5$ $b_2 > 0$. Now suppose $a_2 \geqslant 0$ then from $T.8$ $f_2 > 0$. Hence $a_{76} \neq -1$ and $a_{79} \neq -1$ for, if either was, $T.7$ would be unbounded in the y-direction. $R.7$ and $R.8$ therefore contradict $L.2$ and so we must have $a_2 < 0$. Thus from $T.9$ $d_2 < 0$; from $T.3$ $e_2 > 0$. However, $T.1$ is now unbounded.

Hence (E_3) cannot occur and the lemma is proved.

LEMMA 28. It is not possible for two tetres, a dotre and a treun to occur in a 9-con.

Proof. Suppose the lemma is false. By $L.26$ we may suppose that the first three columns of the matrix representation have one of the forms (E_1), (E_2) and (E_3). Let $C.4$ represent the treun; we assume that there are three $(+1)$s in $C.4$.

Firstly consider the case when (E_1) occurs, then we have

$$
\begin{array}{rrr}
1 & 1 & 0 \\
1 & 1 & 0 \\
1 & 0 & 0 \\
-1 & 1 & 1 \\
-1 & 0 & -1 \\
-1 & 0 & -1 \\
0 & -1 & 1 \\
0 & -1 & 1 \\
0 & -1 & 0
\end{array}
$$

By $L.17$ $a_{44} = 0$ and $a_{j4} \neq -1$ $(j = 1, 2, 5, 6)$ so there are only three effective possibilities for the (-1) of $C.4$, namely: (a) a_{34}; (b) a_{74} or a_{84}; (c) a_{94}.

(a) Suppose $a_{34} = -1$ then by $L.3$ $a_{54} = 0 = a_{64}$. By $L.4$ we cannot have either $a_{14} = a_{24} = 1$ or $a_{74} = a_{84} = 1$ so by symmetry we may suppose $a_{14} = 1 = a_{84} = a_{94}$. Let $a_{85} = 1$ then by $L.2$ $a_{95} = -1 = a_{75}$. By $L.3$ $a_{55} = 0 = a_{65}$ and we have a contradiction to $L.6$ when $r_0 = 9$.

(b) By symmetry we may suppose $a_{74} = -1$ then by $L.3$ we can only have $a_{34} = 1 = a_{84} = a_{94}$. Let $a_{85} = 1$, then by $L.2$ $a_{35} = -1 = a_{95}$. By $L.3$ $a_{55} = 0 = a_{65}$ and we have a contradiction to $L.6$ when $r_0 = 9$.

(c) Suppose $a_{94} = -1$ then by $L.3$ $a_{14} = 0 = a_{24} = a_{44}$. By $L.4$ we cannot have either $a_{54} = a_{64} = 1$ or $a_{74} = a_{84} = 1$ so we may suppose $a_{34} = 1 = a_{54} = a_{74}$. Let $a_{75} = 1$, then by $L.2$ $a_{35} = -1 = a_{85}$. By $L.3$ $a_{15} = 0 = a_{25}$ and we have a contradiction to $L.6$ when $r_0 = 3$.

Hence (E_1) does not occur.

Secondly consider the case when (E_2) occurs, then we have

$$
\begin{array}{rrr}
1 & 1 & 0 \\
1 & 1 & 0 \\
1 & 0 & 0 \\
-1 & 1 & 0 \\
-1 & 0 & -1 \\
-1 & 0 & 1 \\
0 & -1 & -1 \\
0 & -1 & 1 \\
0 & -1 & 1
\end{array}
$$

By $L.17$ $a_{j4} \neq -1$ ($j = 1, 2, 4, 5, 7$) so there are only three effective possibilities for the (-1) of $C.4$, namely: (a) a_{34}; (b) a_{64}; (c) a_{84} or a_{94}.

(a) Suppose $a_{34} = -1$ then by $L.3$ $a_{44} = 0 = a_{54} = a_{64}$. By $L.4$ we cannot have either $a_{14} = a_{24} = 1$ or $a_{84} = a_{94} = 1$ so we may suppose $a_{14} = a_{74} = a_{84} = 1$. Let $a_{85} = 1$, then by $L.2$ $a_{65} = -1 = a_{95}$ and by $L.3$ the remaining spaces of $C.5$ are zeros. Let $a_{96} = 1$, then by $L.2$ $a_{36} = -1 = a_{66}$ and by $L.3$ $a_{46} = 0$. However, $R.4$ and $R.6$ now contradict $L.2$ and so (a) cannot arise.

(b) Suppose $a_{64} = -1$ then by $L.3$ $a_{14} = 0 = a_{24} = a_{34} = a_{54} = a_{74}$. Hence $a_{84} = 1 = a_{94}$ which is impossible by $L.4$.

(c) By symmetry we may suppose $a_{84} = -1$ then by $L.3$ we can only have $a_{34} = 1 = a_{64} = a_{94}$. Let $a_{95} = 1$ then by $L.2$ $a_{35} = -1 = a_{65}$ and by $L.3$ $a_{45} = 0$. However, $R.4$ and $R.6$ now contradict $L.2$ so (c) cannot arise.

Hence (E_2) does not occur.

Finally consider the case when (E_3) occurs, then we have

$$
\begin{array}{rrr}
1 & 1 & 0 \\
1 & 1 & 0 \\
1 & 0 & \\
-1 & 1 & 0 \\
-1 & 0 & \\
-1 & 0 & \\
0 & -1 & -1 \\
0 & -1 & -1 \\
0 & -1 &
\end{array}
$$

By $L.17$ $a_{j4} \neq -1$ ($j = 1, 2, 4, 7, 8$) so there are only three effective possibilities for the (-1) of $C.4$, namely (a) a_{34}; (b) a_{54} or a_{64}; (c) a_{94}.

(a) Suppose $a_{34} = -1$ then by $L.3$ $a_{44} = a_{54} = a_{64} = 0$. By $L.4$ we cannot have either $a_{14} = a_{24} = 1$ or $a_{74} = a_{84} = 1$ so we may suppose $a_{14} = 1 = a_{74} = a_{94}$. Thus by $L.3$ $a_{33} = 0$ and so $a_{53} = a_{63} = a_{93} = 1$. We therefore have a contradiction to $L.6$ when $r_0 = 9$.

(b) By symmetry we may suppose $a_{54} = -1$ then by $L.3$ $a_{14} = 0 = a_{24} = a_{34}$. By $L.4$ at least one of a_{74} and a_{84} is zero, say $a_{84} = 0$. Two cases now arise, either (i) $a_{53} = 0$ or (ii) $a_{53} = 1$.

(i) Let $a_{53} = 0$ then we must have $a_{33} = a_{63} = a_{93} = 1$.

Now if $a_{94} = 1$ then letting $a_{95} = 1$ by $L.2$ we must have $a_{35} = -1 = a_{65}$. By $L.3$ $a_{15} = a_{25} = 0$ and we have a contradiction to $L.6$ when $r_0 = 3$.

Thus $a_{94} \neq 1$ so $a_{94} = 0$; hence $a_{44} = 1 = a_{64} = a_{74}$. Let $a_{65} = 1$ then by $L.2$ $a_{45} = -1 = a_{95}$ and by $L.3$ the remaining spaces of $C.5$ are zeros. Let $a_{96} = 1$ then by $L.2$ $a_{36} = -1 = a_{56}$. By $L.3$ $a_{16} = 0 = a_{26}$ and we have a contradiction to $L.6$ when $r_0 = 3$. Thus (i) cannot arise.

(ii) Let $a_{53} = 1$ then by $L.3$ $a_{74} = 0$. Thus we must have $a_{44} = 1 = a_{64} = a_{94}$.

Now if $a_{93} = 0$ then $a_{33} = 1 = a_{63}$. Let $a_{65} = 1$ then by $L.2$ $a_{45} = -1 = a_{95}$. By $L.3$ $a_{75} = a_{85} = 0$ and we have a contradiction to $L.6$ when $r_0 = 9$.

Thus $a_{93} \neq 0$ so $a_{93} = +1$. Let $a_{95} = -1$ then by $L.2$ $a_{35} = 1 = a_{65}$ and by $L.3$ $a_{15} = a_{25} = a_{45} = 0$. Hence, if $a_{33} = 1$ we have a contradiction to $L.6$ when $r_0 = 3$. Thus $a_{33} = 0$ and so $a_{63} = 1$. However, $R.4$ and $R.6$ now contradict $L.2$. Thus (ii) cannot arise and so neither can (b).

(c) Suppose $a_{94} = -1$ then by $L.3$ $a_{14} = a_{24} = a_{44} = 0$. By $L.4$ at least one of a_{74} and a_{84} is a zero, say $a_{84} = 0$. Now if $a_{74} = 1$ then by $L.3$ $a_{93} = 0$ so $a_{33} = 1 = a_{53} = a_{63}$. Hence if $a_{34} = 1$ we have a contradiction to $L.6$ when $r_0 = 3$. Thus $a_{34} = 0$ and we must have $a_{54} = a_{64} = 1$ which is impossible by $L.4$.

Thus $a_{74} \neq 1$ so $a_{74} = 0$ and therefore $a_{34} = a_{54} = a_{64} = 1$. Hence if $a_{33} = 1$ we have a contradiction to $L.6$ when $r_0 = 3$. Thus $a_{33} = 0$ and we must have $a_{53} = a_{63} = 1$, which is impossible by $L.4$.

Hence (c) cannot occur and so neither can (E_3) and the lemma is proved.

LEMMA 29. It is impossible for two tetres and two dodos to occur in a 9-con.

Proof. Suppose the lemma is false. Let $C.1$ and $C.2$ represent the tetres and $C.3$ and $C.4$ the dodos, then by $L.19$ and $L.24$ we may suppose we have

$$
\begin{array}{rrrr}
1 & 1 & 0 & 0 \\
1 & 1 & 0 & 0 \\
1 & 0 & & \\
-1 & 1 & & \\
-1 & 0 & & \\
-1 & 0 & & \\
0 & -1 & & \\
0 & -1 & & \\
0 & -1 & &
\end{array}
$$

(a) Suppose that $a_{43} = 1$ then by $L.17$ $a_{44} = 0$. By $L.3$ the only places for the (-1)s of $C.3$ are $a_{53} = -1 = a_{63}$ so $a_{33} = 0$ by $L.3$. Thus we may suppose that $a_{73} = 1$. Now by $L.4$ we cannot have $a_{54} = a_{64} \neq 0$, so three effective cases arise, namely: (a_1) $a_{54} = 1$, $a_{64} = 0$; (a_2) $a_{54} = 1 = -a_{64}$; (a_3) $a_{54} = 0 = a_{64}$.

(a_1) Suppose $a_{54} = 1$, $a_{64} = 0$ then by $L.3$ $a_{34} \neq -1$, $a_{74} \neq -1$ so we must have $a_{84} = -1 = a_{94}$. Let $a_{55} = 1$ then by $L.2$ $a_{65} = -1$ and by $L.3$ $a_{15} = 0 = a_{25} = a_{35} = a_{45} = a_{75}$, $a_{85} \neq -1$, $a_{95} \neq -1$. Now $a_{85} = a_{95} = 1$ is impossible by $L.4$. However, if $a_{85} = a_{95} = 0$ we have a contradiction to $L.6$ when $r_0 = 6$. Thus we may suppose that $a_{85} = 1$, $a_{95} = 0$. Let $a_{86} = 1$ then by $L.2$ $a_{96} = -1$ and by $L.3$ $a_{16} = a_{26} = a_{46} = a_{56} = 0$. Since only one of a_{34} and a_{74} is 1 and the other is zero by $L.2$ one of a_{36} and a_{76} is -1. Hence by $L.3$ $a_{66} = 0$. Thus let $a_{97} = 1$, then by $L.2$ $a_{67} = -1$.

If $a_{74} = 0$ then $a_{34} = 1$ and by $L.2$ on $R.7$ with $R.8$ and $R.9$ we have $a_{76} = -1 = a_{77}$. By $L.3$ $a_{36} = 0 = a_{37}$ so $R.3$ and $R.7$ contradict $L.2$.

Thus $a_{74} = 1$ and $a_{34} = 0$. Thus by $L.2$ on $R.3$ with $R.8$ and $R.9$ we have $a_{36} = -1 = a_{37}$. By $L.3$ $a_{17} = 0 = a_{27}$ and we have a contradiction to $L.6$ when $r_0 = 3$.

Thus (a_1) cannot arise.

(a_2) Suppose $a_{54} = 1 = -a_{64}$ then by $L.3$ $a_{34} = 0 = a_{74}$ so by symmetry we may further assume $a_{84} = 1 = -a_{94}$. Let $a_{55} = 1$ then by $L.2$ $a_{85} = -1$ and by $L.3$ $a_{j5} = 0$ $(j = 1, 2, 4, 6, 9)$. Let $a_{66} = 1$ then by $L.2$ $a_{96} = -1$ and by $L.3$ $a_{j6} = 0$ $(j = 1, 2, 4, 5, 8)$. Now if both a_{35} and a_{36} are units, we have a contradiction to $L.6$ when $r_0 = 3$ so at least one of a_{35} and a_{36} is a zero. Since the case when $a_{35} = 0$ is equivalent to the case when $a_{36} = 0$ we may assume $a_{36} = 0$. Let $a_{97} = -1$ then by $L.2$ $a_{37} = 1$ and by $L.3$ $a_{j7} = 0$ $(j = 4, 5, 6)$.

Thus we have

$$
\begin{array}{cccccccc}
1 & 1 & 0 & 0 & 0 & 0 & & \\
1 & 1 & 0 & 0 & 0 & 0 & & \\
1 & 0 & 0 & 0 & & 0 & 1 & \\
-1 & 1 & 1 & 0 & 0 & 0 & 0 & \\
-1 & 0 & -1 & 1 & 1 & 0 & 0 & \\
-1 & 0 & -1 & -1 & 0 & 1 & 0 & \\
0 & -1 & 1 & 0 & & & & \\
0 & -1 & 0 & 1 & -1 & 0 & & \\
0 & -1 & 0 & -1 & 0 & -1 & -1 &
\end{array}
$$

Now if $a_{75} = 1$ by $L.2$ on $R.7$ and $R.9$ one of a_{76} and a_{77} is a $(+1)$ and hence $R.3$ and $R.7$ contradict $L.2$ since $a_{35} \neq -1$ by $L.3$. Thus $a_{75} \neq 1$. By $L.3$ $a_{75} \neq -1$ so $a_{75} = 0$.

If $a_{87} = 0$ then let $a_{88} = 1$ so by $L.2$ $a_{78} = -1$ and by $L.3$ $a_{18} = 0 = a_{28}$. By $L.2$ on $R.7$ and $R.9$ one of a_{76} and a_{77} is a $(+1)$ so by $L.2$ on $R.3$ and $R.7$ we must have $a_{38} = 1$. Hence by $L.2$ on $R.8$ and $R.3$ we must have $a_{35} = 1$ which contradicts $L.6$ when $r_0 = 3$.

Thus $a_{87} \neq 0$ and so by $L.3$ $a_{87} = -1$; then by $L.2$ on $R.7$ and $R.8$ $a_{77} = 1$ so by $L.3$ $a_{17} = 0 = a_{27} = a_{35} = a_{76}$. Let $a_{38} = 1 = a_{39}$ then by $L.6$ with $r_0 = 3$ we may suppose that $a_{18} = -1 = a_{29}$. By the symmetry of $R.1$ and $R.2$ by $L.2$ we may further assume that $a_{78} = -1$. By $L.3$ the remaining spaces of $C.8$ and $C.9$ are zeros except possibly a_{19}.

Now $a_{19} \neq 0$ for, if $a_{19} = 0$ we have a contradiction to $L.9$. By $L.3$ $a_{19} \neq -1$ so $a_{19} = 1$ and we have

x	A	y	z	B	C	D	E	F
1	1	0	0	0	0	0	-1	1
1	1	0	0	0	0	0	0	-1
1	0	0	0	0	0	1	1	1
-1	1	1	0	0	0	0	0	0
-1	0	-1	1	1	0	0	0	0
-1	0	-1	-1	0	1	0	0	0
0	-1	1	0	0	0	1	-1	0
0	-1	0	1	-1	0	-1	0	0
0	-1	0	-1	0	-1	-1	0	0

Choose the coordinate system shown. From boundedness we have: from T.5 $b_3 < 0$; from T.6 $c_3 > 0$.

Now if $a_3 = 0$ then from T.8 $d_3 > 0$ and T.9 is therefore unbounded. Thus $a_3 \neq 0$.

If $a_3 > 0$ then from T.9 $d_3 < 0$, from T.7 $e_3 < 0$ and from T.3 $f_3 > 0$.

If $a_3 < 0$ then from T.8 $d_3 > 0$, from T.7 $e_3 > 0$ and from T.3 $f_3 < 0$. Hence in both cases T.1 is unbounded.

Thus (a_2) cannot arise.

(a_3) Suppose finally $a_{54} = 0 = a_{64}$. Since the a_{j4} $(j = 3, 7, 8, 9)$ are all units, we may clearly suppose $a_{34} = 1$.

Now if $a_{74} = -1$ then we may assume $a_{84} = -1 = -a_{94}$. Let $a_{75} = 1$ then by L.2 $a_{85} = -1$. By L.3 $a_{55} \neq -1$, $a_{65} \neq -1$ and by L.4 we cannot have $a_{55} = a_{65} = 1$. Further, if $a_{55} = a_{65} = 0$ we have a contradiction to L.6 when $r_0 = 8$ so by symmetry we may suppose $a_{55} = 1$, $a_{65} = 0$. By L.3 the remaining spaces of $C.5$ are zeros. Let $a_{56} = 1$ then by L.2 $a_{66} = -1 = a_{96}$ and by L.3 the remaining spaces of $C.6$ are zeros. Let $a_{67} = 1$ then by L.2 $a_{87} = -1 = a_{97}$. By L.3 $a_{37} = 0$ and so R.3 and R.9 contradict L.2.

Thus $a_{74} \neq -1$ so $a_{74} = 1$, $a_{84} = -1 = a_{94}$. Let $a_{85} = 1 = a_{86}$ then by L.6 with $r_0 = 8$ we may suppose $a_{55} = -1 = a_{66}$. By the symmetry of R.5 and R.6 by L.2 we may further assume $a_{95} = -1$. By L.3 and L.4 on R.8 and R.9 $a_{96} = 0$. Let $a_{97} = -1$ then by L.2 $a_{57} = 1$. Now by L.4 $a_{67} \neq 1$ so by L.2 on R.6 and R.9 we must have $a_{65} = 1$. By L.3 the remaining spaces of $C.5$ are zeros so $C.5$ represents a dodo. By interchanging $C.4$ and $C.5$ we clearly have case (a_2). Thus (a_3) cannot arise.

Hence (a) cannot occur. Since the cases when $a_{43} = -1$ and when $a_{44} = \pm 1$ are equivalent to it, we may therefore suppose $a_{43} = 0 = a_{44}$. By L.22 we may now assume $a_{33} = 1$; since by L.3 $a_{53} \neq -1$, $a_{63} \neq -1$ we may suppose $a_{73} = -1 = a_{83}$. If a_{34} is a unit, we have a contradiction to L.6 when $r_0 = 3$ so $a_{34} = 0$. Thus let $a_{35} = 1 = a_{36}$ then by L.6 we may suppose $a_{15} = -1 = a_{26}$. By the symmetry of R.1 and R.2 we may further assume $a_{95} = -1$ by L.2. By L.3 the remaining spaces of $C.5$ and $C.6$

are zeros except possibly for a_{16}. We therefore have the following

$$
\begin{array}{rrrrrr}
1 & 1 & 0 & 0 & -1 & \\
1 & 1 & 0 & 0 & 0 & -1 \\
1 & 0 & 1 & 0 & 1 & 1 \\
-1 & 1 & 0 & 0 & 0 & 0 \\
-1 & 0 & & & 0 & 0 \\
-1 & 0 & & & 0 & 0 \\
0 & -1 & -1 & & 0 & 0 \\
0 & -1 & -1 & & 0 & 0 \\
0 & -1 & & & -1 & 0
\end{array}
$$

Two effective possibilities arise for the remaining $(+1)$ of $C.3$, namely (b) a_{53} or a_{63} and (c) a_{93}.

(b) By symmetry we may clearly suppose $a_{53} = 1$ so that $a_{63} = 0 = a_{93}$. Since $C.4$ represents a dodo we cannot have $a_{74} = 0 = a_{84}$ so we must have either (b_1) one of a_{74} and a_{84} is a unit and the other is a zero, or (b_2) both a_{74} and a_{84} are units.

(b_1) By symmetry we may assume $a_{74} = 1$, $a_{84} = 0$ then by $L.3$ $a_{54} \neq -1$ so $a_{54} = 1$, $a_{64} = -1 = a_{94}$. Let $a_{97} = 1$ then by $L.2$ $a_{87} = -1 = a_{67}$ and the remaining spaces of $C.7$ are zeros by $L.3$. Let $a_{88} = 1$ then by $L.2$ $a_{68} = -1 = a_{98}$ and by $L.3$ $a_{48} = 0$. But now $R.4$ and $R.6$ contradict $L.2$ and so (b_1) cannot occur.

(b_2) By $L.4$ we cannot have $a_{74} = a_{84} \neq 0$ so we may suppose $a_{74} = 1 = -a_{84}$. By $L.3$ $a_{54} = 0$ so by symmetry we may assume $a_{64} = 1 = -a_{94}$. Let $a_{97} = 1$ then by $L.2$ $a_{87} = -1 = a_{57}$ and by $L.3$ the remaining spaces of $C.7$ are zeros. Let $a_{58} = 1$ then by $L.2$ $a_{48} = -1 = a_{68}$ and by $L.3$ the remaining spaces of $C.8$ are zeros. Let $a_{69} = 1$ then by $L.2$ $a_{49} = -1 = a_{79}$ and by $L.3$ the remaining spaces of $C.9$ are zeros. Thus, we have

x	y	A	B	C	D	E	z	F
1	1	0	0	-1		0	0	0
1	1	0	0	0	-1	0	0	0
1	0	1	0	1	1	0	0	0
-1	1	0	0	0	0	0	-1	-1
-1	0	1	0	0	0	-1	1	0
-1	0	0	1	0	0	0	-1	1
0	-1	-1	1	0	0	0	0	-1
0	-1	-1	-1	0	0	-1	0	0
0	-1	0	-1	-1	0	1	0	0

Choose the coordinate system shown. From boundedness we have: from T.4 $f_3 < 0$; from T.6 $b_3 > 0$; from T.7 $a_3 > 0$; from T.5 $e_3 > 0$. Thus T.8 is unbounded.

Hence (b_2) cannot occur and so neither can (b).

(c) Suppose $a_{93} = 1$ then $a_{53} = 0 = a_{63}$. As in (b) we cannot have $a_{74} = a_{84} = 0$ so either (c_1) one of a_{74} and a_{84} is a unit and the other is a zero or (c_2) both a_{74} and a_{84} are units.

(c_1) By symmetry we may assume $a_{74} = 1$, $a_{84} = 0$ then by L.3 $a_{94} \neq -1$ so $a_{94} = 1$, $a_{54} = -1 = a_{64}$. Let $a_{87} = 1 = a_{88}$ then by L.6 with $r_0 = 8$ we may suppose $a_{57} = -1 = a_{68}$. By the symmetry of R.5 and R.6 by L.2 we may further assume $a_{77} = -1$; then by L.3 the remaining spaces of C.7 and C.8, except possibly for a_{48} and a_{58}, are zeros. Now $a_{58} \neq -1$ by L.3. If $a_{58} = 1$ then by L.2 on R.4 and R.5 we must have $a_{48} = -1$ which is impossible by L.3. Thus $a_{58} = 0$. Let $a_{59} = 1$ then by L.2 $a_{49} = -1 = a_{69}$ and by L.3 the remaining spaces of C.9 are zeros. Hence, by L.2 on R.4 and R.6 we must have $a_{48} = 1$. Thus we have

x	y	A	B	C	D	E	F	z
1	1	0	0	-1		0	0	0
1	1	0	0	0	-1	0	0	0
1	0	1	0	1	1	0	0	0
-1	1	0	0	0	0	0	1	-1
-1	0	0	-1	0	0	-1	0	1
-1	0	0	-1	0	0	0	-1	-1
0	-1	-1	1	0	0	-1	0	0
0	-1	-1	0	0	0	1	1	0
0	-1	1	1	-1	0	0	0	0

Choose the coordinate system shown. From boundedness we have: from T.4 $f_3 > 0$; from T.6 $b_3 < 0$; from T.5 $e_3 > 0$; from T.8 $a_3 > 0$. Thus T.7 is unbounded.

Hence (c_1) cannot occur.

(c_2) By L.4 we cannot have $a_{74} = a_{84} \neq 0$, so we may suppose $a_{74} = 1 = -a_{84}$. By L.3 $a_{94} = 0$ so by symmetry we may assume $a_{54} = 1 = -a_{64}$. Let $a_{97} = 1$ then by L.2 we have $a_{57} = -1 = a_{67}$ and by L.3 the remaining spaces of C.7, except possibly for a_{47}, are zeros. Now $a_{47} \neq -1$ by L.5. If $a_{47} = 1$ then C.7 represents a dodo and the case is equivalent to the case (a). Thus

$a_{47} = 0$. Let $a_{58} = 1$ then by $L.2$ $a_{48} = -1 = a_{78}$ and by $L.3$ the remaining spaces of $C.8$ are zeros. Let $a_{69} = 1$ then by $L.2$ $a_{49} = -1 = a_{89}$ and by $L.3$ the remaining spaces of $C.9$ are zeros. Thus we have

x	y	A	B	C	D	E	z	F
1	1	0	0	−1		0	0	0
1	1	0	0	0	−1	0	0	0
1	0	1	0	1	1	0	0	0
−1	1	0	0	0	0	0	−1	−1
−1	0	0	1	0	0	−1	1	0
−1	0	0	−1	0	0	−1	0	1
0	−1	−1	1	0	0	0	−1	0
0	−1	−1	−1	0	0	0	0	−1
0	−1	1	0	−1	0	1	0	0

Choose the coordinate system shown. From boundedness we have: from $T.4$ $f_3 < 0$; from $T.5$ at least one of $b_3 < 0$ and $e_3 > 0$ holds; from $T.6$ at least one of $b_3 < 0$ and $e_3 < 0$ holds. Hence we must have $b_3 < 0$, from $T.7$ $a_3 < 0$. Hence $T.8$ is unbounded and so (c_2) cannot arise.

Hence (c) cannot occur and the lemma is proved.

Consider a 9-con that contains two tetres. By $L.20$ it cannot contain any more. Let there be l D_m-planes (m not necessarily being a fixed integer) in the 9-con besides the two tetres; then we know that the total surplus is $36 - 3l - 6 = 30 - 3l$. Thus the surplus of the l planes, S_l say, is $30 - 3l + 6 = 36 - 3l$. Since there are no tetres amongst them the surplus of each plane is $\geqslant 0$. Thus $36 - 3l \geqslant 0$, i.e. $l \leqslant 12$. Also the l planes must contain $36 - 12 = 24$ faces of the 9-con.

(a) Suppose a dotre does not occur with the two tetres. Since each of the planes contains at most four faces we have $l \geqslant \frac{24}{4} = 6$.

If $l = 12$ then $S_l = 0$ so we must have twelve planes none of which have a positive surplus. From the table it is clear that they must all be unos. This is impossible however, because the planes do not contain 24 faces of the 9-con. Thus the case cannot arise.

If $l = 11$ then $S_l = 3$ so we must have at least eight planes, none of which have a positive surplus, i.e. at least eight unos. Thus the remaining three planes must contain 16 faces which is clearly impossible. Hence the case cannot arise.

If $l = 10$ then $S_l = 6$ and so we have at least four unos. Hence the remaining six planes contain 20 faces and therefore two at least contain four faces. By $L.29$ we cannot have two dodos, so we have at least one treun. As its surplus is 3, we must have at least two more unos. Hence we have at least six unos in all. Thus the four remaining planes must contain 18 faces, which is impossible, since a dotre does not occur. Hence the case cannot arise.

If $l = 9$ then $S_l = 9$. Firstly, suppose a treun occurs. As its surplus is 3 we must have at least two unos occurring. This leaves six planes to contain 18 faces. However, since the least surplus for a D_3-plane is 2, we can have at most $\frac{1}{2}(S_l - 3) = 3$ D_3-planes. Hence we have at least two more D_4-planes occurring. By $L.29$ only one can possibly be a dodo, so if one treun occurs then two do. Now if two treuns, we must have at least four unos so that the three other planes contain 12 faces and hence they must be three D_4-planes. By $L.29$ at least two of these must be treuns, so now we have at least four treuns. Thus if a treun occurs, we must have four treuns occurring and this is clearly impossible, since their surplus is 12. Hence a treun does not occur.

Now since the surplus for a D_3-plane is at least 2, we can have at most four D_3-planes, so at least one D_4-plane occurs. From the above it must be a dodo. By $L.29$ there cannot be another dodo so only one D_4-plane can occur. Hence the remaining eight planes must contain 20 faces, so there must be four D_3-planes which give a surplus of at least 8 and four D_2-planes, which give a surplus of at least 4. Since $S_l = 9$ this is clearly impossible and so the case cannot occur.

If $l = 8$ then $S_l = 12$. We remark firstly that four treuns cannot occur for if they did, their surplus would be $+12$ so that each of the four other planes would have to have a surplus of zero. Hence they would be unos and the eight planes would not contain 24 faces of the 9-con. Now suppose three treuns occur then their surplus is 9. As $S_l = 12$ this means that at least two unos occur. Hence the three other planes must contain 10 faces, so that at least one of them is a D_4-plane. By the above remark it cannot be a treun so it must be a dodo. Therefore, by $L.29$ and the above remark we cannot have any more D_4-planes so the other two planes must be D_3-planes. Now the three treuns give a surplus of 9, and the two D_3-planes a surplus of at least 4 so we have a contradiction to $S_l = 12$. Hence at most, two treuns can occur.

We now remark that there can be at most five D_3-planes for if there were six, the surplus would be at least 12; since $S_l = 12$ the two other planes would have a surplus of zero so they would be unos and in this case the planes do not contain 24 faces of the 9-con. Since there are now at most five D_3-planes, there must be at least two D_4-planes if the planes are to contain 24 faces. By L.29 at least one of them must be a treun. As a treun has a surplus of 3 and five D_3-planes a surplus of at least 10 we see from $S_l = 12$ that at most four D_3-planes can occur. Now suppose there are four D_3-planes, then with the two D_4-planes above we see that the last two planes must contain four faces. Since we cannot have another D_3-plane we must have two D_2-planes. The four D_3-planes give a surplus of at least 8, the two D_4-planes a surplus of at least 4 since one of them is a treun and the two D_2-planes a surplus of at least 2. Hence the total surplus is at least 14, whereas $S_l = 12$. Hence at most three D_3-planes occur. However, in order that the eight planes shall contain 24 faces we must now have at least three D_4-planes. From the above and L.29 at most three D_4-planes can occur, and so we must have two treuns and a dodo. The remaining five planes must contain 12 faces so there must be at least two D_3-planes. However, the two treuns and the dodo give a surplus of 7, and the two D_3-planes a surplus of at least 4. Hence at least two of the planes must have a surplus of zero, i.e. they must be unos. As the eighth plane cannot be a D_4-plane, the planes cannot contain 24 faces of the 9-con and so the case cannot arise.

If $l = 7$ then $S_l = 15$. In order that the planes should contain 24 faces, there must be at least three D_4-planes; by L.29 at least two of them must be treuns.

(i) If only two treuns occur, then we must have a dodo and four D_3-planes. As two treuns and a dodo have a surplus of 7, the D_3-planes must have a surplus of 8 and so they must all be douns.

Let C.1 and C.2 represent the two tetres, then by L.19 we may suppose $a_{ij} = 1$ ($i = 1, 2$; $j = 1, 2$) where a_{11} and a_{12} are both tripts. As no unos, nodos or notres occur, neither R.1 nor

$R.2$ can contain a nopt so by $L.24$, $T.1/T.2$ in a unun. As none of the planes is a unun, we have a contradiction and so (i) cannot arise.

(ii) If only three treuns occur, then the four other planes must have a surplus of 6 and contain 12 faces. As four D_3-planes have a surplus of 8, we can only have a dodo, two D_3-planes and a D_2-plane. To obtain the surplus of 6 we must therefore have two douns and a unun.

Let $C.1$ and $C.2$ represent the two tetres, then by $L.19$ we may suppose

$$\begin{array}{rr} 1 & 1 \\ 1 & 1 \\ 1 & 0 \\ -1 & 1 \\ -1 & 0 \\ -1 & 0 \\ 0 & -1 \\ 0 & -1 \\ 0 & -1 \end{array}$$

As no unos, nodos or notres occur, the matrix cannot contain any nopts. Let $C.3$, $C.4$ and $C.5$ represent the treuns, three $(+1)$s occurring in each column. By $L.17$ $a_{1j} \neq -1$, $a_{2j} \neq -1$, $a_{4j} \neq -1$ $(j = 3, 4, 5)$. Also by $L.17$ we cannot have $a_{i3} = -1 = a_{i4}$ or an equivalent relation, i.e. the tripts of $C.3$, $C.4$ and $C.5$ must be distributed in different rows. Hence by $L.17$ there must be six dhoats in the 9-con. By $L.17$ rows representing dhoats contain zeros in the columns representing dodos so six zeros occur in the column representing the dodo which is clearly impossible. Thus (ii) cannot arise.

(iii) If only four treuns occur, then the three other planes must have a surplus of 3, and so we can have at most one D_3-plane. Since the three planes must contain 8 faces, we must therefore have a D_4-plane, i.e. a dodo, and either two ununs or a doun and a uno.

Let $C.1$ and $C.2$ represent the tetres, then by $L.19$ we may suppose $a_{j1} = 1 = a_{m2}$ $(j = 1, 2, 3; m = 1, 2, 4)$, $a_{j1} = -1 = a_{m2}$ $(j = 4, 5, 6; m = 7, 8, 9)$ and $a_{j1} = 0 = a_{m2}$ $(j = 7, 8, 9; m = 3, 5, 6)$. In both the above cases at most one nopt occurs in the matrix. Let the $C.l$ $(l = 3, 4, 5, 6)$ represent the treuns, three

$(+1)$s occurring in each column. By $L.17$ $a_{1j} \neq -1$, $a_{2j} \neq -1$, $a_{4j} \neq -1$ ($j = 3, 4, 5, 6$). Also by $L.17$ we cannot have $a_{i3} = -1 = a_{i4}$ or an equivalent relation i.e. the tripts of the $C.l$ ($l = 3, 4, 5, 6$) must be distributed in different rows. Hence by $L.17$ there must be at least six dhoats in the 9-con in both cases. Thus by $L.17$ there are six zeros in the column representing the dodo which is clearly impossible.

Thus (iii) cannot arise.

Hence at least five treuns must occur. However six or seven treuns cannot occur since they have a surplus of at least 18, so suppose we have five treuns. The two remaining planes must have a surplus of zero and so must be unos. But as the seven planes do not contain 24 faces of the 9-con, this is impossible and therefore the case when $l = 7$ cannot arise.

Finally if $l = 6$ then $S_l = 18$. Since the six planes contain 24 faces of the 9-con we must have six D_4-planes and so in order to realise the surplus of 18, we must have six treuns. Let $C.1$ and $C.2$ represent the tetres, then by $L.19$ we may suppose $a_{j1} = 1 = a_{m2}$ ($j = 1, 2, 3$; $m = 1, 2, 4$), $a_{j1} = -1 = a_{m2}$ ($j = 4, 5, 6$; $m = 7, 8, 9$), $a_{j1} = 0 = a_{m2}$ ($j = 7, 8, 9$; $m = 3, 5, 6$). By $L.2$ we may further assume $a_{13} = 1 = -a_{23}$. Clearly there are no nopts in the matrix, so by $L.17$ a_{13} and a_{23} are both sipts. This is impossible however, since $C.3$ must represent a treun.

Hence the case when $l = 6$ cannot arise and so neither can (a).

(b) Now suppose one and only one dotre occurs with two tetres in a 9-con. It is not possible for a dodo to occur by $L.27$ or a treun by $L.28$. Hence all the remaining D_m-planes are D_3-planes, D_2-planes or D_1-planes; let their number be k. Clearly the k planes must contain 19 faces and the surplus of the k planes must be $33 - 3k = S_k$ say. Since the planes contain at most 3 faces, $k \geqslant \frac{19}{3}$ so $k \geqslant 7$. Since $l \leqslant 12$, clearly $k \leqslant 11$.

If $k = 11$ then $S_k = 0$ and so we must have eleven planes with a surplus of zero i.e. eleven unos. But eleven unos do not contain 19 faces, so the case cannot arise.

If $k = 10$ then $S_k = 3$ and so we must have at least seven unos. Thus the other three planes contain 12 faces, which is impossible since a D_4-plane or a dotre cannot occur.

If $k = 9$ then $S_k = 6$ and so we must have at least three unos. Thus the remaining six planes contain 16 faces. Hence we must have at least four D_3-planes. However, four D_3-planes have a surplus of at least 8, so the case cannot occur.

If $k = 8$ then $S_k = 9$. Since the eight planes contain 19 faces we must have at least three D_3-planes; since these give a surplus of at least 6 we must have at least two unos. However, two unos means that six planes contain 17 faces, so five of them must be D_3-planes. But five D_3-planes have a surplus of at least 10 whereas $S_k = 9$. Hence the case cannot occur.

Finally if $k = 7$ then $S_k = 12$. Since the seven planes contain 19 faces we must have at least five D_3-planes. All these five D_3-planes must be douns for if a notre occurred, the surplus for the five D_3-planes would be at least 14. Thus the last two planes contain four faces and have a surplus of 2. Hence, we may have either two ununs or a doun and a uno.

In both cases by $L.26$ we may suppose that the first three columns take one of the forms:

(E₁)			(E₂)			(E₃)		
1	1	0	1	1	0	1	1	0
1	1	0	1	1	0	1	1	0
1	0	0	1	0	0	1	0	
−1	1	1	−1	1	0	−1	1	0
−1	0	−1	−1	0	−1	−1	0	
−1	0	−1	−1	0	1	−1	0	
0	−1	1	0	−1	−1	0	−1	−1
0	−1	1	0	−1	1	0	−1	−1
0	−1	0	0	−1	1	0	−1	

Firstly, consider the case of two tetres, one dotre six douns and a uno. Since there is only one uno, no nodos and no notres by $L.18$, there is only one naik. Thus:

In (E₁) either T.1 and T.2 are both dhoats or T.5 and T.6 are both dhoats.

In (E₂) either T.1 and T.2 are both dhoats or T.5 and T.7 are both dhoats.

In (E₃) either T.1 and T.2 are both dhoats or T.7 and T.8 are both dhoats.

Hence in each case by $L.17$ there are two dhoats such that we must have T.l/T.m in a unun. However, a unun does not occur amongst the planes and so the case cannot occur.

6*

Thus we have only to consider the case of two tetres, one dotre, five douns and two ununs. As there are no unos, nodos or notres by $L.18$ no naiks can occur. Hence, since T.4 in (E_1) is a naik by $L.17$, we may dismiss (E_1) immediately. Consider (E_2) then T.1, T.2, T.4, T.5 and T.7 are all dhoats. Hence by $L.17$ we must have T.1/T.2 in a unun, T.4/T.5 in a unun and T.5/T.7 in a unun. However, only two ununs occur, so we may now dismiss (E_2).

Consider (E_3), then T.1, T.2, T.4, T.7 and T.8 are all dhoats. Hence by $L.17$ we must have T.1/T.2 in a unun and T.7/T.8 in a unun. Thus let $a_{14} = 1 = -a_{24}$, $a_{75} = 1 = -a_{85}$ then the remaining spaces of $C.4$ and $C.5$ are zeros. Hence the $C.l$ ($l = 6, 7, 8, 9, 10$) all represent douns. Let $a_{16} = 1$ then by $L.2$ $a_{36} = -1$ and so $C.6$ has two $(+1)$s. Also by $L.3$ and $L.4$ $a_{26} = 0$. Let $a_{27} = 1$ then by $L.2$ $a_{37} = -1$ and so $C.7$ has two $(+1)$s. Hence by $L.17$ T.3 is a thaik, and we cannot have $a_{33} = 1$. Thus $a_{33} = 0$, $a_{53} = 1 = a_{63} = a_{93}$. Now by $L.3$ $a_{17} = 0 = a_{j6} = a_{j7}$ ($j = 4, 5, 6$). Thus if either a_{96} or a_{97} is a unit, we have a contradiction to $L.6$ when $r_0 = 9$. Hence $a_{96} = 0 = a_{97}$. By symmetry we may therefore assume $a_{76} = 1 = a_{87}$. Let $a_{98} = 1 = a_{99}$ then by $L.6$ with $r_0 = 9$ we may suppose $a_{58} = -1 = a_{69}$. By the symmetry of $R.5$ and $R.6$, by $L.2$ we may further assume $a_{38} = -1$; by $L.3$ the remaining spaces of $C.8$ are zeros. By $L.1$ a_{49} and $a_{4.10}$ must both be units, so by $L.3$ we must have $a_{49} = 1$ and thus $a_{59} = 0$ since $C.9$ represents a doun. Hence let $a_{5.10} = -1$ then by $L.2$ $a_{4.10} = 1 = a_{6.10}$. We therefore have

x	A	y	B	C	D	E	z	F	G
1	1	0	1	0	1	0	0	0	0
1	1	0	-1	0	0	1	0	0	0
1	0	0	0	0	-1	-1	-1	0	0
-1	1	0	0	0	0	0	0	1	1
-1	0	1	0	0	0	0	-1	0	-1
-1	0	1	0	0	0	0	0	-1	1
0	-1	-1	0	1	1	0	0	0	0
0	-1	-1	0	-1	0	1	0	0	0
0	-1	1	0	0	0	0	1	1	0

Choose the coordinate system shown. From boundedness we have: from T.5 $g_1 < 0$; from T.6 $f_1 < 0$; from T.4 $a_1 > 0$. However, T.9 is now unbounded.

Thus the case when $k = 7$ cannot arise and so neither can (b).

Hence if two tetres occur in a 9-con then at least two dotres must occur. However by $L.25$ at most one dotre can occur with two tetres in a 9-con, so we have the following lemma:

LEMMA 30. If a 9-con exists it can contain at most one tetre. $L.16$ and $L.30$ now give:

THEOREM 3. If A is a matrix representation of a 9-con then at most one column of A can contain six units.

CHAPTER FOUR

ON THE EXISTENCE OF A 9-CON CONTAINING ONE TETRE

WE BEGIN the chapter by showing that it is not possible for three or more dotres to occur with a tetre in a 9-con. We then introduce the idea of semi-equivalence to show that if a set of matrices all have a particular type of structure then we need only consider one of them. Finally, the concept of a surplus of a D_m-plane is used to prove the following theorem:

THEOREM 4. If a 9-con containing a tetre exists then it must contain at least nine and at most eleven D_m-planes (m not necessarily being a fixed integer).

We firstly consider the possibility of at least three dotres occurring with the tetre in a 9-con. Let $C.1$ represent the tetre then we may suppose $a_{j1} = 1$ ($j = 1, 2, 3$), $a_{j1} = -1$ ($j = 4, 5, 6$), $a_{j1} = 0$ ($j = 7, 8, 9$). Further, let $C.l$ ($l = 2, 3, 4$) represent dotres assuming that each column contains three $(+1)$s and two (-1)s. Clearly four effective cases arise for $C.l$ for l one of 2, 3 and 4:

(a) Two of the a_{jl} ($j = 1, 2, 3$) are (-1)s or two of the a_{jl} ($j = 4, 5, 6$) are (-1)s.

(b) One of the a_{jl} ($j = 1, 2, 3$) is a (-1) and one of the a_{ml} ($m = 4, 5, 6$) is a (-1).

(c) One of the a_{jl} ($j = 1, 2, 3, 4, 5, 6$) is a (-1) and one of the a_{ml} ($m = 7, 8, 9$) is a (-1).

(d) Two of the a_{jl} ($j = 7, 8, 9$) are (-1)s.

We shall leave consideration of (a) until last.

(b) Clearly we may assume $a_{12} = -1 = a_{42}$. By $L.3$ we must have $a_{j2} = 0$ ($j = 2, 3, 5, 6$) so that $a_{m2} = 1$ ($m = 7, 8, 9$). By $L.17$ none of a_{13}, a_{14}, a_{43} and a_{44} can be (-1)s so two cases now arise: (b$_1$) At least one of a_{13}, a_{14}, a_{43} and a_{44} is a $(+1)$ and (b$_2$) $a_{13} = 0 = a_{14} = a_{43} = a_{44}$.

(b_1) By symmetry we may clearly suppose $a_{13} = 1$; then by $L.3$ we can only have $a_{23} = -1 = a_{33}$, so that $a_{j3} = 0$ ($j = 4, 5, 6$). Hence we may put $a_{73} = 1 = a_{83}$, $a_{93} = 0$. By $L.17$ $a_{14} = 0$. Now if a_{24} is a unit, the unit of opposite sign can only appear in a_{34} and a_{94} and, if this were so, the remaining spaces of $C.4$ would necessarily be zeros by $L.3$ so that $C.4$ would not represent a dotre. Thus $a_{24} = 0$ and by symmetry $a_{34} = 0$. A further two cases now arise, namely: (i) $a_{44} = 1$ and (ii) $a_{44} = 0$.

(i) Suppose $a_{44} = 1$. By $L.3$ $a_{j4} \neq -1$ ($j = 7, 8, 9$) so $a_{54} = -1 = a_{64}$. By $L.4$ $a_{74} = a_{84} = 1$ is impossible so we may further assume $a_{74} = 1 = a_{94}$, $a_{84} = 0$. Let $a_{75} = 1$ then by $L.2$ we must have $a_{85} = -1 = a_{95}$ and by $L.3$ $a_{55} = 0 = a_{65}$. However, we now have a contradiction to $L.6$ when $r_0 = 8$ and so (i) cannot arise.

(ii) Suppose $a_{44} = 0$ then the remaining spaces of $C.4$ must be units. By $L.4$ therefore we may assume $a_{74} = 1$, $a_{84} = -1$. Now if $a_{54} = a_{64} = 1$ we have a contradiction to $L.6$ when $r_0 = 7$ so we may further suppose that $a_{54} = 1 = -a_{64}$. Thus $a_{94} = 1$. Let $a_{75} = 1$ then by $L.2$ we must have $a_{55} = -1 = a_{95}$ and by $L.3$ $a_{25} = 0 = a_{35}$ which contradicts $L.6$ when $r_0 = 9$. Thus (ii) cannot arise and so neither can (b_1).

(b_2) Suppose $a_{13} = 0 = a_{14} = a_{43} = a_{44}$.

(i) Assume $a_{23} = -1$ then by $L.3$ neither a_{53} nor a_{63} is a (± 1) and by $L.5$ not all of a_{73}, a_{83} and a_{93} are $(+1)$s. Hence we must have $a_{33} = 1 = a_{73} = a_{83}$. By $L.3$ $a_{53} = 0 = a_{63}$ so $a_{93} = -1$. Since $a_{14} = 0$, by $L.3$ $a_{24} \neq \pm 1$ so $a_{24} = 0$. Also $a_{34} \neq -1$ by $L.3$. Now if $a_{34} = 1$ by $L.3$ we can only have $a_{74} = -1 = a_{84}$ which is impossible by $L.4$. Hence $a_{34} = 0$. The remaining spaces of $C.4$ must therefore be units and so by $L.4$ a_{74} and a_{84} must be of opposite signs. However by $L.3$ on $R.9$ this means that $a_{94} = 0$ so that $C.4$ does not represent a dotre. Thus $a_{23} \neq -1$.

By symmetry we may therefore assume that none of the a_{j3} and a_{j4} ($j = 2, 3, 5, 6$) are (-1)s. Hence we may suppose $a_{73} = -1 = a_{83}$ and since by $L.4$ we cannot have $a_{74} = a_{84} \neq 0$ we must have $a_{74} = -1 = a_{94}$. By $L.3$ with $R.7$ any row r with $r \leqslant 6$ which has a $(+1)$ in $C.3$ ($C.4$) must have a zero in $C.4$ ($C.3$). Since both of a_{84} and a_{93} cannot be $(+1)$ by $L.3$, it is impossible for both $C.3$ and $C.4$ to represent dotres. Hence (b_2) cannot arise and so neither can (b).

(c) Clearly we may assume $a_{12} = -1 = a_{72}$ then by $L.3$ $a_{42} = 0 = a_{52} = a_{62}$. By $L.21$ on $C.2$ and $C.l$ ($l = 3$ or 4) at least one of the a_{jl} ($j = 4, 5, 6$) must be a unit. Hence if a (-1) occurred amongst the a_{jl} ($j = 1, 2, 3$) by $L.3$ at least one of the a_{ml} ($m = 4, 5, 6$) would have to be a (-1). By interchanging $C.2$ and $C.l$ this becomes case (b) which has been dealt with above. Thus we may assume that none of the a_{j3} and a_{j4} ($j = 1, 2, 3$) are (-1)s.

Suppose $a_{13} = 1$ then by $L.17$ $T.1$ is a naik. Since $a_{23} \neq -1$, $a_{33} \neq -1$ we must have by $L.2$ $a_{22} = 1 = a_{32}$.

We may clearly assume $a_{92} = 1$, $a_{82} = 0$ so that by $L.2$ we must have $a_{73} = -1 = a_{83}$. By $L.3$ $a_{23} = 0 = a_{33} = a_{93}$ so we may put $a_{43} = 1 = a_{53}$, $a_{63} = 0$. By $L.17$ $a_{14} = 0$. Since neither a_{24} nor a_{34} is a (-1), by $L.4$ at least one of a_{24} and a_{34} is a zero. Thus suppose $a_{24} = 0$. Now if $a_{44} = 1 = -a_{54}$ by $L.3$ we would have $a_{34} = 0 = a_{74} = a_{84}$ and so $C.4$ would not represent a dotre. Hence by $L.4$ at least one of a_{44} and a_{54} is a zero. Thus suppose $a_{54} = 0$. By $L.17$ $a_{74} \neq -1$ and if $a_{74} = 1$ we can only have $a_{64} = -1 = a_{84}$ so that by $L.3$ $a_{34} = 0 = a_{44}$ and thus $C.4$ would not represent a dotre. Thus $a_{74} = 0$ and the remaining spaces of $C.4$ are units. By $L.3$ $a_{64} = a_{34} = a_{44} = a_{84}$ which is clearly impossible.

Hence we may suppose $a_{13} = 0 = a_{14}$. By $L.21$ we must have at least one of a_{23}, a_{33}, a_{24} and a_{34} non-zero. Hence from the above we may assume that $a_{23} = 1$ with the result that two of the a_{j3} ($j = 7, 8, 9$) must be (-1)s. Two cases now arise: (c_1) $a_{73} = -1 = a_{83}$ or a_{93} and (c_2) $a_{83} = -1 = a_{93}$.

(c_1) By symmetry we may assume $a_{73} = -1 = a_{83}$ then by $L.3$ $a_{22} = 0$ so $a_{32} = 1 = a_{82} = a_{92}$. Thus by $L.3$ $a_{33} = 0 = a_{93}$ so we may suppose $a_{43} = 1 = a_{53}$, $a_{63} = 0$. Since $a_{14} = 0$ by $L.3$ we must have $a_{74} = 0$. Now if $a_{44} = 1 = -a_{54}$ then by $L.3$ $a_{24} = 0 = a_{34} = a_{84}$ so that $C.4$ does not represent a dotre. Thus since $a_{44} = a_{54} \neq 0$ is impossible by $L.4$, we may suppose that $a_{54} = 0$. Hence at least one of a_{24} and a_{34} is a unit; as neither can be a (-1) from the above it follows from $L.3$ that neither a_{44} nor a_{64} can be a (-1). Thus $a_{84} = -1 = a_{94}$; then by $L.3$ $a_{24} = 0 = a_{44}$ and $C.4$ does not represent a dotre. Hence (c_1) cannot occur.

(c_2) Assume $a_{83} = -1 = a_{93}$. Since at least one of a_{82} and a_{92} must be a $(+1)$ suppose $a_{82} = 1$ so that $a_{73} = 0$ by $L.3$. Now none of the a_{j4} ($j = 1, 2, 3$) are units for if one was, it follows as before that the two (-1)s would occur amongst a_{74}, a_{84} and

a_{94}. The case when $a_{74} = -1$ has been dealt with under (c_1) so we would be able to suppose that $a_{84} = -1 = a_{94}$; but then there are at least five zeros in $C.4$ by $L.3$ which is impossible. Hence $a_{14} = 0 = a_{24} = a_{34}$.

Now if $a_{92} = 0$ then we must have $a_{22} = a_{32} = 1$. Thus by $L.4$ $a_{33} = 0$ so we may suppose $a_{43} = 1 = a_{53}$, $a_{63} = 0$. Now $a_{44} = 1 = -a_{54}$ is impossible because there would then be five zeros in $C.4$ by $L.3$. Hence by $L.4$ we may assume $a_{44} = 0$ and so the remaining spaces of $C.4$ are units. But by $L.3$ $a_{94} = a_{54} = a_{84} = a_{74}$ which is impossible. Thus $a_{92} \neq 0$.

Hence $a_{92} = 1$, then by $L.4$ we cannot have $a_{84} = a_{94} = \pm 1$. Further $a_{84} = 1 = -a_{94}$ is impossible because there would then be five zeros in $C.4$ by $L.3$. Thus we may suppose $a_{94} = 0$. Consequently, the remaining spaces of $C.4$ are units. By $L.3$ we must have $a_{74} = a_{84}$ so that, since we cannot have $a_{44} = a_{54} = a_{64}$ by $L.5$, the two (-1)s of $C.4$ must occur amongst the a_{j4} ($j = 4, 5, 6$). By symmetry we may clearly suppose $a_{44} = 1 = a_{74} = a_{84}$ and $a_{54} = -1 = a_{64}$. Hence by $L.3$ $a_{53} = 0 = a_{63}$ so that $a_{33} = 1 = a_{43}$. By symmetry we may now suppose $a_{22} = 1$, $a_{32} = 0$. Let $a_{95} = -1 = a_{96}$ then by $L.6$ with $r_0 = 9$ we may suppose $a_{55} = 1 = a_{66}$. By the symmetry of $R.5$ and $R.6$ by $L.2$ we may further assume $a_{85} = 1$. By $L.3$ the remaining spaces of $C.5$ and $C.6$ are zeros except possibly a_{56}. Let $a_{47} = 1$ then by $L.2$ $a_{77} = -1$ and by $L.3$ $a_{j7} = 0$ ($j = 2, 5, 6, 8, 9$). Let $a_{28} = 1$ then by $L.2$ $a_{38} = -1$ and by $L.3$ $a_{j8} = 0$ ($j = 4, 5, 6, 8, 9$).

We now consider the possibilities for the spaces left in the matrix and we find that they divide into three cases:

(i) Suppose that $a_{37} = 1$. By $L.3$ $a_{17} \neq -1$ so by $L.2$ we must have $a_{18} = 1$. Thus

A	B	x	C	D	E	y	z
1	−1	0	0	0	0		1
1	1	1	0	0	0	0	1
1	0	1	0	0	0	1	−1
−1	0	1	1	0	0	1	0
−1	0	0	−1	1		0	0
−1	0	0	−1	0	1	0	0
0	−1	0	1	0	0	−1	
0	1	−1	1	1	0	0	0
0	1	−1	0	−1	−1	0	0

Choose the coordinate system shown. From boundedness we have: from T.3 $a_2 < 0$, $a_3 > 0$; from T.4 $c_2 < 0$, $c_3 > 0$; from T.2 $b_2 > 0$, $b_3 < 0$.

Thus if $a_{17} = 1$ T.1 is unbounded in the z-direction. Hence $a_{17} = 0$. Let $a_{19} = 1$; since $a_{78} \neq -1$ by L.3, we must have $a_{79} = -1$ by L.2. Let the equation of the D_m-plane represented by C.9 be $F = 0$, then from T.1 $f_2 > 0$. However we now see that T.7 is unbounded in the y-direction.

Hence (i) does not arise and so $a_{37} \neq 1$. Further, by L.3 $a_{37} \neq -1$ so we must have $a_{37} = 0$.

(ii) We now suppose that $a_{78} = 1$. By L.3 $a_{18} \neq -1$ so by L.2 on R.1 and R.7 we must have $a_{17} = 1$. Hence we have

x	A	y	B	C	D	E	z
1	-1	0	0	0	0	1	
1	1	1	0	0	0	0	1
1	0	1	0	0	0	0	-1
-1	0	1	1	0	0	1	0
-1	0	0	-1	1		0	0
-1	0	0	-1	0	1	0	0
0	-1	0	1	0	0	-1	1
0	1	-1	1	1	0	0	0
0	1	-1	0	-1	-1	0	0

Choose the coordinate system shown. From boundedness we have: from T.2 $a_3 < 0$; from T.4 $b_3 e_3 < 0$; from T.7 at least one of $b_3 < 0$ and $e_3 > 0$ must hold. Thus we must have both $b_3 < 0$ and $e_3 > 0$. Hence if $a_{18} = 1$, T.1 is unbounded in the z-direction so $a_{18} = 0$. Let $a_{19} = 1$ then by L.2 we must have $a_{39} = -1$. Let the equation of the D_m-plane represented by C.9 be $F = 0$, then from T.2 $a_1 < 0$; from T.3 $f_1 > 0$; from T.1 $e_1 < 0$; from T.4 $b_1 > 0$. However, T.7 is now unbounded in the x-direction.

Thus (ii) cannot arise and so $a_{78} \neq 1$. By L.3 $a_{78} \neq -1$ so $a_{78} = 0$.

Since $a_{37} = 0$ let $a_{39} = 1$ then by L.2 on R.3 and R.7 we must have $a_{79} = -1$. By L.3 the remaining spaces of C.9 are zeros except possibly for a_{19}. Hence we have

x	A	y	B	C	D	E	F	z
1	−1	0	0	0	0			
1	1	1	0	0	0	0	1	0
1	0	1	0	0	0	0	−1	1
−1	0	1	1	0	0	1	0	0
−1	0	0	−1	1		0	0	0
−1	0	0	−1	0	1	0	0	0
0	−1	0	1	0	0	−1	0	−1
0	1	−1	1	1	0	0	0	0
0	1	−1	0	−1	−1	0	0	0

Choose the coordinate system shown. From boundedness we have: from T.3 $f_1 > 0$; from T.2 $a_1 < 0$. Thus if $a_{19} = 1$ then by $L.2$ on $R.1$ and $R.3$ we must have $a_{18} = 1$. However this is impossible since T.1 would be unbounded. Thus $a_{19} \neq 1$. Hence by $L.2$ on $R.1$ and $R.7$ we must have $a_{17} = 1$. By $L.2$ on $R.1$ and $R.3$ we must have one of $a_{18} = 1$ and $a_{19} = 0$ and $a_{18} = 0$, $a_{19} = -1$. In either case we must have: from T.1 $e_1 < 0$ and then from T.4 $b_1 > 0$. However T.7 is now unbounded.

Thus (c_2) cannot arise and so neither can (c).

Consider (d). Suppose that this case occurs in $C.2$, $C.3$ and $C.4$, then the (−1)s of these columns lie in $R.7$, $R.8$ and $R.9$. By $L.17$ we cannot have $a_{j2} = a_{j3} = a_{j4} = -1$ for j one of 7, 8 and 9 so each row r ($r = 7, 8, 9$) must contain two (−1)s. Thus we may suppose $a_{72} = -1 = a_{73} = a_{82}$, $a_{74} \neq -1$. Hence we must have $a_{84} = -1 = a_{94}$. Thus $a_{83} \neq -1$ so $a_{93} = -1$. By $L.3$ there can be at most one (+1) amongst a_{92}, a_{83} and a_{74} so by symmetry we can clearly suppose that $a_{92} = 0$. By $L.5$ we cannot have $a_{12} = a_{22} = a_{32} = 1$ so by symmetry we may further assume $a_{12} = a_{22} = a_{42} = 1$. By $L.3$ therefore we have $a_{j3} = 0 = a_{j4}$ ($j = 1, 2, 4$). However, this is impossible by $L.21$.

Hence as (b) and (c) have been eliminated at least one case (a) must occur. Thus we may suppose $a_{12} = -1 = a_{22}$ so by $L.3$ $a_{42} = 0 = a_{52} = a_{62}$. Now if a_{13} is a unit by $L.17$ it can only be a (+1); further since $C.2$ contains three (+1)s, by $L.3$ one of the (−1)s of $C.3$ would have to be $a_{23} = -1$; then by $L.3$, $C.3$ must contain five zeros which is impossible. Hence $a_{13} = 0$ and by symmetry $a_{14} = 0 = a_{23} = a_{24}$.

Suppose $C.3$ and $C.4$ are both of type (d) then at least one row of $R.7$ and $R.8$ and $R.9$ contains two (-1)s. We may clearly suppose $a_{73} = -1 = a_{74} = a_{83}$. Whether $a_{84} = -1$ or $a_{94} = -1$ by $L.3$ there can only be one $(+1)$ amongst a_{93}, a_{84} and a_{94}. Since by $L.3$ on $R.7$ we cannot have $a_{j3} = 1 = a_{j4}$, there can be at most five $(+1)$s in $C.3$ and $C.4$. Hence one of $C.3$ and $C.4$ does not represent a dotre and so the case cannot arise.

Thus we may suppose that $C.3$ is of type (a) also and we may clearly assume $a_{43} = -1 = a_{53}$ so by $L.3$ $a_{33} = 0$. By the same argument that makes $a_{13} = 0$ we must have $a_{44} = 0 = a_{54}$. Thus the remaining spaces of $C.4$ must be units. By $L.3$ we must have $a_{34} = a_{64}$. If they were (-1)s case (b), which has already been dealt with, occurs. Therefore $a_{34} = 1 = a_{64}$. Hence we may assume $a_{74} = -1 = a_{84}$, $a_{94} = 1$. Two cases now arise: (i) $a_{92} = 1 = a_{93}$ and (ii) at least one of a_{92} and a_{93} is a zero.

(i) Suppose $a_{92} = 1 = a_{93}$. Let $a_{95} = 1$ then by $L.2$ we must have $a_{35} = -1 = a_{65}$. By $L.3$ the remaining spaces of $C.5$ are zeros. Now if $a_{32} = 0$ we have a contradiction to $L.6$ with $r_0 = 3$ so $a_{32} = 1$. Similarly, $a_{63} \neq 0$ and so $a_{63} = 1$. Thus we have

x	A	y	z	B
1	-1	0	0	0
1	-1	0	0	0
1	1	0	1	-1
-1	0	-1	0	0
-1	0	-1	0	0
-1	0	1	1	-1
0		-1		0
0		-1		0
0	1	1	1	1

Choose the coordinate system shown. From boundedness we have: from T.6 $b_1 < 0$; from T.9 $a_1 > 0$.

However, T.3 is now unbounded so (i) cannot occur.

(ii) We may clearly suppose that $a_{92} = 0$ so that $a_{32} = 1 = a_{72} = a_{82}$. Now by $L.4$ $a_{73} = 1 = a_{83}$ is impossible, so we may suppose that $a_{63} = a_{73} = a_{93} = 1$, $a_{83} = 0$. Let $a_{95} = 1 = a_{96}$ then by $L.6$ with $r_0 = 9$ we may suppose $a_{15} = -1 = a_{26}$.

By the symmetry of $R.1$ and $R.2$, by $L.2$ we may further assume $a_{65} = -1$. By $L.3$ the remaining spaces of $C.5$ and $C.6$

must be zeros except possibly for a_{35}, a_{16} and a_{36}. We now consider the two cases: (iii) $a_{35} = -1$ and (iv) $a_{35} \neq -1$.

(iii) If $a_{35} = -1$ by $L.1$ $a_{36} = 0$ and we have

A	B	x	y	z	C
1	−1	0	0	−1	
1	−1	0	0	0	−1
1	1	0	1	−1	0
−1	0	−1	0	0	0
−1	0	−1	0	0	0
−1	0	1	1	−1	0
0	1	1	−1	0	0
0	1	0	−1	0	0
0	0	1	1	1	1

Choose the coordinate system shown. From boundedness we have: from T.6 $a_2 > 0$, $a_3 < 0$; from T.3 $b_2 < 0$, $b_3 > 0$; from T.9 $c_2 < 0$, $c_3 < 0$.

Now if $a_{16} = 1$ then T.1 is unbounded in the z-direction. Thus $a_{16} \neq 1$. By $L.4$ $a_{16} \neq -1$ so $a_{16} = 0$. Let $a_{17} = 1$ then by $L.2$ $a_{27} = -1$. Let the equation of the D_m-plane represented by $C.7$ be $D = 0$ then from T.1 $d_2 < 0$. However, this makes T.2 unbounded in the y-direction and so (iii) cannot arise.

(iv) If $a_{35} \neq -1$ then by $L.3$ $a_{35} \neq 1$ so $a_{35} = 0$. By $L.2$ on $R.9$ we must have $a_{36} = -1$. By $L.3$ $a_{16} \neq 1$ and by $L.4$ $a_{16} \neq -1$ so $a_{16} = 0$. Hence let $a_{17} = 1$ so by $L.2$ $a_{27} = -1$. Thus we have

x	A	B	y	C	z	D
1	−1	0	0	−1	0	1
1	−1	0	0	0	−1	−1
1	1	0	1	0	−1	
−1	0	−1	0	0	0	
−1	0	−1	0	0	0	
−1	0	1	1	−1	0	
0	1	1	−1	0	0	
0	1	0	−1	0	0	
0	0	1	1	1	1	

Choose the coordinate system shown. From boundedness we have: from T.3 $a_1 < 0$; from T.2 $d_1 > 0$; from T.1 $c_1 > 0$; from T.6 $b_1 > 0$. However, this makes T.9 unbounded.

Hence (iv) cannot occur and so we have proved the following lemma:

LEMMA 31. It is not possible for three or more dotres to occur with a tetre in a 9-con.

DEFINITION. Let A be a matrix that may possibly be a matrix representation of a 9-con; i.e. A satisfies the conditions that a matrix representation must. (Except that we only require $L.9$ to be satisfied instead of the stronger $L.9A$.) Suppose also that each column of A contains at least one unit, then A is called a permatrix.

Since it may be a representation of a 9-con, a permatrix must contain nine rows. Suppose we have a permatrix A containing l columns of which r are tem-columns. By elementary transformations we can arrange that the first r columns of the matrix are tem-columns. Let B be the matrix defined by these first r columns then we have the following definition.

DEFINITION. A permatrix G is semi-equivalent to A if G contains a submatrix M that is equivalent to B.

LEMMA 32. The columns of G other than those in M can only contain nopts.

Proof. Since the columns of A, other than those in B, only contain nopts, given two distinct rows of A, $R.p$ and $R.q$ say, by $L.2$ there exists a column, j say, in B such that a_{pj} and a_{qj} have opposite units. Hence since M is equivalent to B given any two distinct rows $R.u$ and $R.v$ of G, there exists a column, k say, in M such that a_{uk} and a_{vk} have opposite units. Thus by $L.3$ we cannot have a column, h say, in G but not in M such that a_{ch} and a_{dh} have opposite signs. The lemma now follows. From $L.32$ it follows that if G is semi-equivalent to A then A is semi-equivalent to G. Clearly semi-equivalence is also transitive.

LEMMA 33. Suppose A is a permatrix that has a column $C.l$ that contains one or two nopts and another column $C.m$ that contains one and only one nopt, say a_{pm}. Let B be the matrix obtained from A by neglecting $C.m$ and making a_{pl} a nopt (if it is not already a nopt), then B is a permatrix which is semi-equivalent to A.

Proof. Clearly if B is a permatrix it is semi-equivalent to A. Also by $L.17$ $R.p$ cannot contain two nopts, so in A a_{pl} is not a nopt and so $a_{pl} = 0$. Thus B satisfies $L.1$ and the only lemmas it may not satisfy are $L.4$, $L.5$, and $L.6$. Clearly B satisfies $L.9$ since A does and this is the reason we require $L.9$ rather than $L.9A$. By elementary transformations we can arrange that $a_{1m} = 1$, $a_{qm} = 0$ $(q > 1)$, $a_{1l} = 0 = a_{rl}$ $(r > 3)$, $a_{2l} = 1$ in A. When $C.l$ contains two nopts we have $a_{3l} = 1$ and when $C.l$ contains only one nopt $a_{3l} = 0$.

(a) Suppose B contradicts $L.4$, in both the above cases we may assume that the offending rows are $R.1$ and $R.2$ for if they are $R.2$ and $R.3$ A also contradicts $L.4$.

Thus in A there must exist two columns which by elementary transformations we may assume to be $C.1$ and $C.2$ such that $a_{11} = a_{21}$ $(= 1$ say$)$, $a_{12} = a_{22}$ $(= 1$ say$)$. Further by elementary transformations we can arrange by $L.16$ that neither a_{91} nor a_{92} is (-1). Let the remaining unit of $R.1$ be a_{1g}, then by $L.2$ we must have $a_{2g} = a_{9g} = -a_{1g}$. However by $L.3$, $R.2$ and $R.9$ cannot obey $L.2$. As A is a permatrix this is impossible and so B must obey $L.4$.

(b) Suppose B contradicts $L.5$. The case when $a_{3l} = 0$ is immediately eliminated since in that case A would also contradict $L.5$. Hence we have to consider the case when $a_{3l} = 1$; for convenience we shall suppose $l > 4$. Since B contradicts $L.5$ there must exist a column in A which we may assume to be $C.1$ such that $a_{11} = a_{21} = a_{31}$ $(= 1$ say$)$. By elementary transformations we may suppose $a_{12} = 1 = a_{13}$. By $L.4$ we cannot have $a_{22} = a_{32} \neq 0$ or $a_{23} = a_{33} \neq 0$, so by $L.2$ we may suppose that $a_{22} = -1 = a_{33}$. Now we cannot have either $a_{23} = 1$ or $a_{32} = 1$ for then $L.4$ would be infringed in B which is impossible by (a). Thus $a_{23} = 0 = a_{32}$. Hence we may suppose $a_{24} = 1$ then by $L.2$ we must have $a_{34} = -1$. As $R.1$ contains a nopt by $L.17$, $T.1$ is a naik and so by $L.17$ at least one of $C.2$ and $C.3$ contains three (-1)s; clearly we may suppose $C.2$ contains three (-1)s so that $a_{22} = -1 = a_{g2} = a_{h2}$. Now by $L.3$ $a_{g1} \neq -1$, $a_{h1} \neq -1$ so by $L.2$ on $R.2$ we must have $a_{g4} = -1 = a_{h4}$. Further by $L.2$ on $R.3$ we must now have $a_{g3} = 1 = a_{h3}$ which is impossible by $L.4$. Thus B must also obey $L.5$.

If B contradicts $L.6$ we may suppose that $R.1$ and $R.2$ are the rows that correspond to $R.i$ and $R.j$ of $L.6$ for otherwise, A

also contradicts $L.6$. By (a) there is at most one column $C.h$ of A such that $a_{1h} = a_{2h} \neq 0$. Hence by $L.2$ on the rows of A if $a_{r_0 h} \neq -a_{1h}$ then there must exist an f such that $a_{r_0 f} = -a_{1f} \neq 0$ and, since $a_{2f} \neq a_{1f}$, also $a g \neq f$ such that $a_{r_0 g} = -a_{2g}$. Clearly $C.f$ and $C.g$ are carried over to B, so B does not contradict $L.6$ and the Lemma is proved.

COROLLARY. Suppose A is a permatrix that has three columns in each of which there is one and only one nopt; let the columns be l, m and p and the nopts a_{fl}, a_{gm} and a_{hp}. Let C be the matrix obtained from A by neglecting $C.m$ and $C.p$ and making a_{gl} and a_{hl} nopts. Then C is a permatrix which is semi-equivalent to A.

Proof. Let B be the matrix obtained from A by neglecting $C.p$ and making a_{hl} a nopt; then from $L.33$ B is a permatrix which is semi-equivalent to A. Hence applying $L.33$ again we have the required result.

The converses to $L.33$ and its Corollary are trivial but we state them for completeness.

LEMMA 34. Suppose B is a permatrix that has a column $C.l$ that contains at least two nopts, one of which is a_{pl} say. Let A be the matrix obtained from B by putting $a_{pl} = 0$ and adding an extra column $C.m$ to B where a_{pm} is a unit and $a_{qm} = 0$ $(q \neq p)$, then A is a permatrix which is semi-equivalent to B.

COROLLARY. Suppose C is a permatrix that has a column $C.l$ that contains three nopts two of which are a_{fl} and a_{gl}. Let A be the matrix obtained from B by putting $a_{fl} = 0 = a_{gl}$ and adding two extra columns $C.m$ and $C.p$ to B where a_{fm} and a_{gp} are both units and $a_{qm} = 0$ $(q \neq f)$, $a_{rp} = 0$ $(r \neq g)$, then A is a permatrix which is semi-equivalent to C.

Let S be a set of l planes that could possibly contain all the faces of a 9-con which contains n naiks, each of the l planes containing at least one face of the 9-con. Further let V be the set of planes of S that are tem-planes. Contruct all the permatrices, S_i say, whose columns represent the set S; if no such permatrices exist then clearly S cannot contain all the faces of a 9-con. For each S_i let W_i be the matrix composed of the columns representing the tem-planes. By $L.18$ if S contains s_1 unos, s_2 nodos and s_3 notres, then $s_1 + 2s_2 + 3s_3 = n$. Let B be the set of planes consisting of the set V and n unos. By $L.34$ and its

Corollary we see that for each permatrix S_i, a permatrix B_i exists where B_i is semi-equivalent to S_i and the columns of B_i represent the set B. By $L.33$ and its Corollary for each permatrix B_j of B a permatrix S_k existsw here S_k is semi-equivalent to B_j and the columns of S_k represent the set S.

Consider a permatrix S_i of S: by elementary transformations we can arrange that the first $l - s_1 - s_2 - s_3$ columns are the matrix W_i and that for $n \geqslant 1$, $R.10 - n$, $R.11 - n$, ... $R.9$ represent the n naiks. Now, if we can choose a coordinate system such that arguments involving only $T.1$, ... $T.9 - n$ lead to an impossibility, then, as each of $R.1$, ... $R.9 - n$ have their four units in W_i because none of them represent naiks, it follows that S_i, and all permatrices semi-equivalent to S_i, cannot lead to a 9-con.

If this can be done for each S_i, then as each permatrix B_j of B is semi-equivalent to some permatrix S_k it follows that neither S nor B can lead to a 9-con. In fact no set of planes similar to S (i.e. differing from S only in the values of $s_1 \geqslant 0$, $s_2 \geqslant 0$ and $s_3 \geqslant 0$ such that $s_1 + 2s_2 + 3s_3 = n$) can lead to a 9-con; for let U be such a set, then as for S for each of its permatrices U_i, a permatrix B_j of B exists, where B_j is semi-equivalent to U_i. As B_j is semi-equivalent to some S_k, U_i is semi-equivalent to S_k and so cannot lead to a 9-con.

As this argument does not depend on the 9-con containing a tetre we shall use it when applicable whether the 9-con contains a tetre or not.

To analyse the possibilities of the existence of a 9-con containing one tetre we use the concept of a surplus which was developed in Chapter 3. Supposing such a 9-con exists, let the faces of the 9-con be contained in l planes where each of the l planes contains at least one face of the 9-con. The sum of the surpluses is therefore $36 - 3l$. As we have one and only one tetre, the sum of the surpluses of the remaining $(l - 1)$ planes must be $39 - 3l$. Clearly this is $\geqslant 0$ so $3l \leqslant 39$, $l \leqslant 13$. Now the l planes must contain 36 faces; as we have one tetre and at most two dotres the remaining planes must be D_m-planes with $m \leqslant 4$. Hence we certainly have $6 + 10 + 4(l - 3) \geqslant 36$, i.e. $l \geqslant 8$.

Suppose $l = 13$ then $39 - 3l = 0$ and so twelve planes must have a surplus of zero, i.e. they must be either dotres or unos. From $L.31$ at most two can be dotres, so at least ten are unos.

However the planes do not now contain 36 faces, so the case cannot arise.

Suppose $l = 12$ then $39 - 3l = 3$; so eight planes must be either dotres or unos. Thus by $L.31$ we must have at least six unos. Six unos and one tetre means that the other five planes must contain 24 faces, and so we must have at least four dotres which is impossible by $L.31$.

Suppose $l = 8$ then seven planes contain 30 faces, so we must have at least two dotres. Hence by $L.31$ we have two dotres and five D_4-planes. Since the surplus is $39 - 24 = 15$ the five D_4-planes must all be treuns. If these eight planes give rise to a per-matrix, then clearly no nopts will occur in the permatrix. Also only two of its columns will contain dopts so by $L.17$ none of the rows represent naiks or chardhos. Let $C.1$ and $C.2$ represent the two dotres so we may suppose $a_{j1} = 1$ $(j = 1, 2, 3)$, $a_{j1} = -1$ $(j = 4, 5)$, $a_{j1} = 0$ $(j = 6, 7, 8, 9)$. By $L.17$ $R.l$ $(l = 1, 2, 3)$ must contain another dopt so we must have $a_{12} = a_{22} = a_{32} \neq 0$ which is impossible by $L.5$.

We have therefore proved the following theorem:

THEOREM 4. If a 9-con containing a tetre exists, then it must contain at least nine and at most eleven D_m-planes (m not necessarily being a fixed integer).

Suppose $l = 11$ then $39 - 3l = 6$, so at least four planes are dotres or unos. Hence by $L.31$ we have at least two unos, so from the above we may consider the possibilities of permatrices occurring in this case under the case $l = 10$. In fact we shall prove without using any arguments concerning rows that represent naiks, that all the permatrices that arise for the cases $l = 9$ and $l = 10$ do not lead to a 9-con. It therefore follows that the case when $l = 11$ will not lead to a 9-con either.

CHAPTER FIVE

ON THE NON-EXISTENCE OF A 9-CON CONTAINING NINE D_m-PLANES, ONE OF WHICH IS A TETRE

WE BEGIN the chapter by enumerating the equivalence classes of the three-rowed matrices which have a column that contains three units of the same sign. By means of these equivalence classes, we show that a 9-con containing nine D_m-planes, one of which is a tetre, cannot exist.

Firstly we enumerate the equivalence classes of the threes rowed matrices which have a column that contains three units of the same sign. Thus we may suppose $a_{j1} = 1$ $(j = 1, 2, 3)$. By $L.2$ we may further assume $a_{12} = 1 = -a_{22}$. Since the case $a_{32} = 1$ is equivalent to the case $a_{32} = -1$ two cases now arise: (i) $a_{32} = -1$ and (ii) $a_{32} = 0$.

(i) Suppose $a_{32} = -1$, then by $L.2$ we may assume $a_{23} = 1 = -a_{33}$. Thus by $L.3$ $a_{13} = 0$. Let $a_{24} = 1$ then by $L.3$ and $L.4$ $a_{34} = 0$ so suppose $a_{35} = 1$. Now if $a_{14} = 1 = a_{15}$ we have

x	y	A	z	B
1	1	0	1	1
1	−1	1	1	0
1	−1	−1	0	1

Choose the coordinate system shown. From boundedness we have: from T.1 $b_2 < 0$; from T.2 $a_2 > 0$. However, T.3 is now unbounded.

Hence by the symmetry of $R.2$ and $R.3$ only two effective cases arise from (i) namely:

(a) $a_{14} = 1 = a_{16}$, $a_{15} = 0$ and (b) $a_{14} = 0 = a_{15}$, $a_{16} = 1 = a_{17}$.

(ii) Suppose $a_{32} = 0$, then by $L.2$ we may assume $a_{13} = 1 = -a_{33}$. Now the case $a_{23} = 1$ is equivalent to (i) so by $L.3$ $a_{23} = 0$. Thus by $L.2$ we may suppose $a_{24} = 1 = -a_{34}$. By $L.3$ $a_{14} = 0$.

7*

Let $a_{15} = 1$ then by $L.5$ we cannot have $a_{25} = 1 = a_{35}$ so by symmetry (ii) gives rise to two cases, namely:

(c) $a_{25} = 1 = a_{36}$, $a_{35} = 0$ and (d) $a_{25} = 0 = a_{35}$, $a_{26} = 1 = a_{37}$.
(The case when $a_{26} = 1 = a_{36}$ is equivalent to (c).)

Thus to summarise, there are four possibilities:

(a)						(b)						
1	1	0	1	0	1	1	1	0	0	0	1	1
1	−1	1	1	0	0	1	−1	1	1	0	0	0
1	−1	−1	0	1	0	1	−1	−1	0	1	0	0

(c)						(d)						
1	1	1	0	1	0	1	1	1	0	1	0	0
1	−1	0	1	1	0	1	−1	0	1	0	1	0
1	0	−1	−1	0	1	1	0	−1	−1	0	0	1

If a 9-con containing nine D_m-planes, one of which is a tetre, exists, then it can be represented by a (9×9) matrix whose first column is $a_{j1} = 1$ $(j = 1, 2, 3)$, $a_{j1} = -1$ $(j = 4, 5, 6)$, $a_{j1} = 0$ $(j = 7, 8, 9)$. Hence the (3×9) matrix consisting of the first three rows must contain a minor equivalent to one of the above forms and so must the (3×9) matrix consisting of the rows 4, 5 and 6. We denote these (3×9) matrices by H_1 and H_2 respectively.

Notation. By (a — c) we shall mean that H_1 contains a minor equivalent to (a) and H_2 contains a minor equivalent to (c).

By symmetry it is clear that if (a — c) is impossible, then so is (c — a).

DEFINITION. We shall say that a column $C.l$ is a tem-column w. r. t. H_i if $C.l$ contains at least one $(+1)$ and at least one (-1) in H_i.

By $L.3$ if $C.l$ is a tem-column w. r. t. H_i then $a_{jl} = 0$ $(j = 1, 2, 3$ when $i = 2$ and $j = 4, 5, 6$ when $i = 1)$.

Notation. If $C.l$ is not a tem-column w. r. t. H_i but it does contain units of H_i, then we shall assume the unit (or units) concerned are $(+1)$s.

If $C.l$ contains units in both H_1 and H_2 then by $L.3$ they must be of the same sign, so the notation is perfectly valid.

Hence, since the units of both (b) and (d) fall in seven distinct columns and both (c) and (d) contain three tem-columns, we clearly cannot have (b — c), (b — d), (d — c) and (d — d). Thus six possibilities occur:

$$\text{I (c — c);} \quad \text{II (a — d);} \quad \text{III (c — a);}$$
$$\text{IV (b — b);} \quad \text{V (a — b);} \quad \text{VI (a — a).}$$

I. Suppose (c — c).
Clearly we may assume that

$$
\begin{array}{rrrrrrrrr}
1 & 1 & 1 & 0 & 1 & 0 & 0 & 0 & 0 \\
1 & -1 & 0 & 1 & 1 & 0 & 0 & 0 & 0 \\
1 & 0 & -1 & -1 & 0 & 1 & 0 & 0 & 0 \\
-1 & 0 & 0 & 0 & & & 1 & 1 & 0 \\
-1 & 0 & 0 & 0 & & & -1 & 0 & 1 \\
-1 & 0 & 0 & 0 & & & 0 & -1 & -1 \\
\end{array}
$$

By $L.16$ $a_{45} = a_{55} = 1$ is impossible so we may suppose $a_{46} = 1 = a_{56}$ and $a_{65} = 1$. Consider the possibilities for the last three rows. Clearly in order that each of them should obey $L.2$ with respect to $R.i$ ($i = 1, \ldots 6$) each of them must have a (-1) in either $C.5$ or $C.6$; they cannot have a (-1) in both columns for then by $L.3$ there would be no places for the remaining two units of the row. Also by $L.30$ we cannot have three (-1)s in either $C.5$ or $C.6$. Hence we may assume by symmetry that $a_{76} = -1 = a_{85} = a_{95}$, then by $L.16$ $a_{75} = 0 = a_{86} = a_{96}$ and by $L.3$ $a_{82} = 0$, $a_{92} = 0 = a_{77}$. Now $T.8/T.9$ in $C.l$ and by inspection we see by $L.3$ that l can only be 7. Hence we may suppose $a_{87} = 1 = -a_{97}$ so that by $L.2$ $a_{88} = -1 = a_{99}$. By $L.3$ $a_{89} = 0 = a_{98}$. Now by $L.2$ on $R.6$ and $R.7$ one of a_{78} and a_{79} is a $(+1)$ and by symmetry we may suppose $a_{78} = 1$ so by $L.3$ $a_{79} = 0$. Also by $L.2$ on $R.7$ with $R.1$ and $R.2$ at least one of a_{73} and a_{74} is a (-1) and again we may assume by symmetry that $a_{73} = -1$; then by $L.3$ $a_{83} = 0$ so by $L.2$ $a_{84} = 1$. Thus $a_{74} \neq -1$ by $L.3$ so by $L.2$ on $R.7$ and $R.2$ $a_{72} = 1$. By $L.1$ $a_{74} = 0$. By $L.2$ on $R.7$ and $R.9$ we have $a_{93} = 1$ so $a_{94} = 0$. Thus we have

$$
\begin{array}{ccccccccc}
x & A & y & B & z & C & D & E & F \\
1 & 1 & 1 & 0 & 1 & 0 & 0 & 0 & 0 \\
1 & -1 & 0 & 1 & 1 & 0 & 0 & 0 & 0 \\
1 & 0 & -1 & -1 & 0 & 1 & 0 & 0 & 0 \\
-1 & 0 & 0 & 0 & 0 & 1 & 1 & 1 & 0 \\
-1 & 0 & 0 & 0 & 0 & 1 & -1 & 0 & 1 \\
-1 & 0 & 0 & 0 & 1 & 0 & 0 & -1 & -1 \\
0 & 1 & -1 & 0 & 0 & -1 & 0 & 1 & 0 \\
0 & 0 & 0 & 1 & -1 & 0 & 1 & -1 & 0 \\
0 & 0 & 1 & 0 & -1 & 0 & -1 & 0 & -1 \\
\end{array}
$$

Choose the coordinate system shown. From boundedness we have: from T.1 $a_1 < 0$; from T.2 $b_1 < 0$; from T.3 $c_1 < 0$; from T.4 at least one of $d_1 > 0$ and $e_1 > 0$ holds; from T.8 at least one of $d_1 > 0$ and $e_1 < 0$ holds. Hence $d_1 > 0$. Thus from T.5 $f_1 > 0$. However, T.9 is now unbounded. Hence (I) cannot arise.

II. Suppose (a — d).

Due to the symmetry of the rows in (d) we may suppose that the first six rows are

$$
\begin{array}{rrrrrrrrr}
1 & 1 & 0 & 1 & 1 & 0 & 0 & 0 & 0 \\
1 & -1 & 1 & 1 & 0 & 0 & 0 & 0 & 0 \\
1 & -1 & -1 & 0 & 0 & 1 & 0 & 0 & 0 \\
-1 & 0 & 0 & 1 & 0 & 0 & 1 & 1 & 0 \\
-1 & 0 & 0 & 0 & 1 & 0 & -1 & 0 & 1 \\
-1 & 0 & 0 & 0 & 0 & 1 & 0 & -1 & -1
\end{array}
$$

Now if $a_{72} = -1$ then by $L.2$ on $R.2$ we must have one of $a_{73} = -1$ and $a_{74} = -1$. However, $a_{74} \neq -1$ by $L.3$, so $a_{73} = -1$. Hence by $L.2$ on $R.3$ we must have $a_{76} = -1$; then clearly $L.2$ is contradicted by $R.7$ with one of $R.4$ and $R.5$. Thus $a_{72} \neq -1$ and so we may suppose $a_{j2} \neq -1$ ($j = 7, 8, 9$).

(i) Suppose $a_{72} = 0$ and $a_{74} \neq -1$ then by $L.2$ on $R.1$ $a_{75} = -1$, on $R.2$ $a_{73} = -1$ and on $R.3$ $a_{76} = -1$. Similarly, if $a_{82} \neq 1$ and $a_{84} \neq -1$ then $a_{85} = -1 = a_{83} = a_{86}$ which is impossible, by $L.2$ on $R.7$ and $R.8$. Hence either $a_{82} = 1$ or $a_{84} = -1$; by $L.3$ on $R.2$ we cannot have both. Similarly either $a_{92} = 1$ or $a_{94} = -1$.

(i$_1$) Suppose $a_{82} = 1$ then by $L.2$ on $R.1$ $a_{85} = -1$. By $L.3$ $a_{83} = 0$ and also by $L.16$ $a_{84} = 0$. Considering $R.8$ we must have by $L.2$: on $R.4$ one of $a_{87} = -1$ and $a_{88} = -1$; on $R.6$ one of $a_{88} = 1$ and $a_{89} = 1$ since $a_{86} \neq -1$ by $L.3$. Also by $L.2$ on $R.4$ we must have one of $a_{77} = -1$ and $a_{78} = -1$. By $L.2$ on $R.7$ and $R.8$ we therefore conclude that the only possibility is $a_{78} = -1$, $a_{88} = 1$, $a_{87} = -1$.

By exactly similar reasoning if $a_{92} = 1$ then we must have $a_{95} = -1 = a_{97}$, $a_{98} = 1$ which is impossible by $L.4$ on $R.8$ and $R.9$. Thus $a_{92} \neq 1$ and so $a_{94} = -1$. By $L.2$ on $R.3$ we must have one of $a_{93} = 1$ and $a_{96} = -1$. Thus we have

x	A	B	y	z	C	D	E	F
1	1	0	1	1	0	0	0	0
1	-1	1	1	0	0	0	0	0
1	-1	-1	0	0	1	0	0	0
-1	0	0	1	0	0	1	1	0
-1	0	0	0	1	0	-1	0	1
-1	0	0	0	0	1	0	-1	-1
0	0	-1	0	-1	-1	0	-1	0
0	1	0	0	-1	0	-1	1	0
0			-1					

Choose the coordinate system shown. From boundedness we have: from T.1 $a_1 < 0$; from T.2 $b_1 < 0$; from T.3 $c_1 < 0$; from T.7 $e_1 > 0$; from T.6 $f_1 < 0$; from T.5 $d_1 < 0$.

If $a_{93} = 1$ then by L.3 $a_{95} = 0 = a_{96} = a_{98}$ so by L.2 on R.6 and then on R.5 we have $a_{99} = 1 = a_{97}$. However from the above T.9 is then unbounded in the x-direction.

Hence $a_{96} = -1$ then by L.3 $a_{93} = 0 = a_{98}$. Hence by L.2 on R.7 $a_{95} = 1$. Thus by L.3 $a_{97} = 0$ and by L.2 $a_{99} = -1$. Once more, however, T.9 is unbounded in the x-direction.

Thus (i$_1$) cannot arise.

Hence (i$_2$). We may suppose $a_{82} = 0 = a_{92}$, $a_{84} = -1 = a_{94}$. If $a_{86} = 1$ then by L.3 on R.7 $a_{83} \neq 1$ so R.8 and R.3 contradict L.2. Thus we have $a_{86} \neq 1$ and $a_{96} \neq 1$ by symmetry. By L.3 therefore the only possible l for which T.8/T.9 in C.l is $l = 9$. Thus, suppose $a_{89} = 1 = -a_{99}$. By L.3 $a_{88} = 0$, $a_{85} \neq -1$, $a_{86} \neq -1$. Thus by L.2 on R.3 and R.5 we must have $a_{83} = 1 = a_{87}$. By L.3 $a_{77} \neq -1$ so by L.2 on R.4 $a_{78} = -1$. Thus we have

x	A	B	y	z	C	D	E	F
1	1	0	1	1	0	0	0	0
1	-1	1	1	0	0	0	0	0
1	-1	-1	0	0	1	0	0	0
-1	0	0	1	0	0	1	1	0
-1	0	0	0	1	0	-1	0	1
-1	0	0	0	0	1	0	-1	-1
0	0	-1	0	-1	-1	0	-1	0
0	0	1	-1	0	0	1	0	1
0	0		-1					-1

Choose the coordinate system shown. From boundedness we have: from T.1 $a_1 < 0$; from T.2 $b_1 < 0$; from T.3 $c_1 < 0$; from T.7 $e_1 > 0$; from T.6 $f_1 < 0$; from T.5 $d_1 < 0$.

However, T.8 is now unbounded in the x-direction. Thus (i_2) cannot occur and so neither can (i). Hence (ii) either $a_{j2} = 1$ or $a_{j4} = -1$ for each of $j = 7, 8, 9$; we cannot have both by L.3 on R.2. As C.2 cannot contain four $(+1)$s and C.4 is not a tetre we may clearly suppose $a_{72} = 1$ and $a_{94} = -1$. Then $a_{73} = 0 = a_{74} = a_{92}$ by L.3. Thus by L.2 on R.1 $a_{75} = -1$.

(ii_1) Suppose $a_{82} = 1$, then as above $a_{83} = 0 = a_{84}$, $a_{85} = -1$. By L.3 the only possible l for which T.7/T.8 in C.l is $l = 8$. Thus let $a_{78} = 1 = -a_{88}$. By L.3 $a_{86} \neq -1$ so by L.2 on R.6 $a_{89} = 1$ and by L.2 on R.4 $a_{77} = -1$. Thus we have

x	A	B	y	z	C	D	E	F
1	1	0	1	1	0	0	0	0
1	−1	1	1	0	0	0	0	0
1	−1	−1	0	0	1	0	0	0
−1	0	0	1	0	0	1	1	0
−1	0	0	0	1	0	−1	0	1
−1	0	0	0	0	1	0	−1	−1
0	1	0	0	−1	0	−1	1	0
0	1	0	0	−1	0	0	−1	1
0			−1					

By L.17 we see that only T.3, T.6 and T.9 can possibly be naiks. Hence in order to eliminate all permatrices semi-equivalent to this one, we need to ignore R.3, R.6 and R.9 when determining the signs of the coefficients.

Choose the coordinate system shown. From boundedness we have: from T.1 $a_3 < 0$; from T.4 $d_3 e_3 < 0$; from T.7 at least one of $d_3 < 0$ and $e_3 > 0$ holds. Hence both $d_3 < 0$ and $e_3 > 0$ hold. From T.5 $f_3 < 0$. However, T.8 is now unbounded in the z-direction and so (ii_1) cannot arise.

Hence (ii_2) $a_{84} = -1$. Then $a_{82} = 0$ by L.3. If $a_{86} = 1$ then by L.2 on R.3 $a_{83} = 1$ so that R.8 with one of R.5 and R.6 contradicts L.2. Thus $a_{86} \neq 1$ and also $a_{96} \neq 1$. Hence by L.3 the only possible l for which T.8/T.9 in C.l is $l = 9$. Thus suppose $a_{89} = 1 = -a_{99}$. By L.3 $a_{85} \neq -1$, $a_{86} \neq -1$ so by L.2 on R.5 and R.3 we must have $a_{87} = 1 = a_{83}$. By L.3 $a_{79} \neq -1$ so by L.2

on $R.8$ $a_{77} = -1$. Also by $L.3$ $a_{97} = 0$. By $L.3$ $a_{76} \neq -1$ so by $L.2$ on $R.6$ we must have one of $a_{78} = 1$ and $a_{79} = 1$. Thus we must have $a_{76} = 0$. Hence we have

x	A	B	y	z	C	D	E	F
1	1	0	1	1	0	0	0	0
1	-1	1	1	0	0	0	0	0
1	-1	-1	0	0	1	0	0	0
-1	0	0	1	0	0	1	1	0
-1	0	0	0	1	0	-1	0	1
-1	0	0	0	0	1	0	-1	-1
0	1	0	0	-1	0	-1		
0	0	1	-1	0	0	1	0	1
0	0		-1			0		-1

As $a_{96} \neq 1$ we see by $L.17$ that only $T.3$ and $T.6$ can possibly be naiks. Hence as before, we neglect them in our analysis.

Choose the coordinate system shown. From boundedness we have: from $T.1$ $a_2 < 0$; from $T.2$ $b_2 < 0$; from $T.5$ $d_2 f_2 > 0$; from $T.8$ at least one of $d_2 > 0$ and $f_2 > 0$ holds. Hence both $d_2 > 0$ and $f_2 > 0$ hold. From $T.4$ $e_2 < 0$. Now if $a_{78} = 1$, $T.7$ is unbounded in the y-direction. Hence $a_{79} = 1$ and so by $L.3$ $a_{95} = 0$. Now if $a_{96} = -1$ then by $L.3$ $a_{93} = 0 = a_{98}$ and so $R.9$ contradicts $L.1$. Thus $a_{96} = 0$ so by $L.2$ $a_{93} = 1 = a_{98}$. However from the above we see that $T.9$ is unbounded in the y-direction. Thus (ii$_2$) cannot arise and so neither can (ii). Hence II does not occur.

III. Suppose $(c - a)$.

Clearly we may assume that

1	1	1	0	1	0	0	0	0
1	-1	0	1	1	0	0	0	0
1	0	-1	-1	0	1	0	0	0
-1	0	0	0			1	0	
-1	0	0	0			-1	1	
-1	0	0	0			-1	-1	

We assume that the remaining unit of $R.5$. a_{5l} say, is such that $a_{5l} = a_{4l} = 1$.

By the structure of (a) $C.5$, $C.6$ and $C.9$ must each contain at least one unit in rows 4, 5 and 6. Further by $L.16$ we cannot have $a_{45} = a_{55} = 1$ so $a_{55} = 0$. Hence by $L.16$ also $a_{j5} \neq 1$ ($j = 7, 8, 9$).

If $a_{72} = a_{82} = -1$ then by $L.3$ $a_{75} \neq -1$, $a_{85} \neq -1$ so by $L.2$ on $R.2$ $a_{74} = -1 = a_{84}$. By $L.6$ with $r_0 = 3$ we may therefore suppose $a_{73} = 1$ and $a_{86} = -1$. However, it is now clear that $R.7$ with one of $R.4$, $R.5$ and $R.6$ contradicts $L.2$. Thus $a_{72} = a_{82} = -1$ is impossible.

By the symmetry of $R.1$ and $R.2$ clearly $a_{72} = a_{82} = 1$ is also impossible.

If $a_{73} = a_{83} = -1$ then we cannot have $a_{74} = a_{84} = -1$, by $L.6$ with $r_0 = 3$. From the above therefore by $L.2$ on $R.2$ we may suppose that $a_{72} = 1$, $a_{84} = -1$ since $a_{75} \neq -1$, $a_{85} \neq -1$ by $L.3$. Now $a_{74} \neq 1$ for if so, $R.7$ with one of $R.4$, $R.5$ and $R.6$ contradicts $L.2$. Hence $a_{74} = 0$. Thus by $L.2$ on $R.3$ we must have $a_{76} = -1 = a_{86}$. Since $a_{46} = a_{56} = a_{66} = 1$ is impossible by $L.5$ the remaining unit of $R.7$ must, by $L.2$, be of opposite sign to a unit in $R.l$ where l is one of 4, 5, 6. As, for the same l, this is also true for the remaining unit of $R.8$, $R.7$ and $R.8$ cannot obey $L.2$. Hence $a_{73} = a_{83} = -1$ is impossible.

Again by symmetry $a_{74} = a_{84} = -1$ is also impossible.

Hence by $L.2$ on $R.1$ only two effective cases can arise: (i) $a_{72} = -1 = a_{83} = a_{95}$ and (ii) $a_{75} = -1 = a_{85}$.

(i) Suppose $a_{72} = -1 = a_{83} = a_{95}$. By $L.3$ $a_{92} = 0$, $a_{75} \neq -1$, $a_{85} \neq -1$ so $a_{75} = 0 = a_{85}$. By $L.2$ on $R.2$ $a_{74} = -1$. Now $a_{84} \neq 1$ for if $a_{84} = 1$, by $L.2$ on $R.2$, $a_{82} = 1$ and then $R.8$ with one of $R.4$, $R.5$ and $R.6$ contradicts $L.2$. From the above $a_{84} \neq -1$ so $a_{84} = 0$. Also $a_{73} \neq 1$ for if $a_{73} = 1$ $R.7$ with one of $R.4$, $R.5$ and $R.6$ contradicts $L.2$. By $L.3$ $a_{73} \neq -1$ so $a_{73} = 0$. Thus by $L.2$ on $R.2$ $a_{82} = 1$ and on $R.3$ $a_{76} = -1 = a_{86}$. Now $a_{96} \neq 1$ for if $a_{96} = 1$, by $L.3$ $a_{93} \neq 1$, $a_{94} \neq 1$ so that $R.9$ and $R.3$ contradict $L.2$. Thus two cases now arise: (i$_1$) $a_{96} = -1$ and (i$_2$) $a_{96} = 0$.

(i$_1$) Suppose $a_{96} = -1$ then since $C.6$ is not a tetre we cannot have $a_{46} = a_{56} = 1$ so we must have $a_{49} = a_{59} = 1$ so by $L.1$ $a_{56} = 0$. Further by $L.3$ $a_{93} = 0 = a_{94}$. Hence since we must have either $a_{45} = 1 = a_{66}$ or $a_{46} = 1 = a_{65}$, by $L.3$ $a_{97} = 0$ and $a_{99} \neq -1$. However, as a_{98} and a_{99} must both be units $a_{99} = 1$, so by $L.2$ on $R.5$ $a_{98} = -1$. Now if $a_{78} = 1$ (or $a_{88} = 1$) then $R.7$ (or $R.8$) with $R.5$ contradicts $L.2$. Thus by $L.2$ on $R.9$

$a_{79} = -1 = a_{89}$ so by $L.2$ on $R.6$ $a_{66} = 1$ and thus $a_{45} = 1$. However, rows 3, 4, 5, 8 and 9 now contradict $L.9$.

Hence (i_1) cannot arise.

(i_2) Suppose $a_{96} = 0$. Then by $L.2$ on $R.3$ we must have one of $a_{93} = 1$ and $a_{94} = 1$. By symmetry we may suppose $a_{93} = 1$ then by $L.3$ $a_{94} = 0$. Let the remaining unit of $R.7$ be a_{7l} then by $L.2$ $a_{9l} = -a_{7l}$. Thus by $L.3$ $a_{8l} = 0$. Thus $a_{46} = 1 = a_{56}$, $a_{66} = 0$ otherwise $L.2$ on $R.7$ and $R.8$ would mean that $L.4$ is contradicted by two of the rows of $R.4$, $R.5$ and $R.6$. Hence by $L.3$ $a_{77} = 0 = a_{87}$. Now we know that $a_{78} = a_{88} = 1$ is impossible so for $R.6$ to obey $L.2$ with $R.7$ and $R.8$ we must have $a_{69} = 1$ and one of $a_{79} = -1$ and $a_{89} = -1$. By $L.1$ $a_{65} = 0$ so $a_{45} = 1$. Thus we have

x	A	y	B	z	C	D	E	F
1	1	1	0	1	0	0	0	0
1	−1	0	1	1	0	0	0	0
1	0	−1	−1	0	1	0	0	0
−1	0	0	0	1	1	1	0	0
−1	0	0	0	0	1	−1	1	0
−1	0	0	0	0	0	−1	−1	1
0	−1	0	−1	0	−1	0		
0	1	−1	0	0	−1	0		
0	0	1	0	−1	0			

Choose the coordinate system shown. As one of a_{79} and a_{89} is a (-1) by $L.17$ none of the tetrahedra are naiks.

From boundedness we have: from $T.1$ $a_1 < 0$; from $T.2$ $b_1 < 0$; from $T.3$ $c_1 < 0$; from $T.4$ $d_1 > 0$; from $T.5$ $e_1 > 0$; from $T.6$ $f_1 > 0$.

If $a_{78} = 1$ then $T.7$ is unbounded, so by $L.2$ on $R.6$ $a_{79} = -1$. Thus $a_{89} \neq -1$ so by $L.2$ on $R.6$ $a_{88} = 1$. Hence $a_{98} = -1$ so by $L.3$ $a_{97} = 0$. Thus by $L.2$ $a_{99} = -1$ and $T.9$ is unbounded in the x-direction.

Thus (i_2) cannot occur and so neither can (i).

(ii) Suppose $a_{75} = -1 = a_{85}$. By $L.3$ $a_{72} = 0 = a_{82}$.

If $a_{78} = 1 = -a_{88}$ then by $L.3$ $a_{65} = 0$ so $a_{45} = 1$. Thus by $L.3$ $a_{77} = 0 = a_{87}$. However, if a_{5l} is the remaining unit of $R.5$ then $a_{4l} = a_{5l}$ by the structure of (a). But by $L.3$ on $R.4$

this means $a_{7l} \neq -1$ and so $R.5$ and $R.7$ contradict $L.2$. Hence $a_{78} = 1 = -a_{88}$ is impossible.

Since one of a_{45} and a_{65} is a $(+1)$, by $L.3$ the only possible values of l for which $T.7/T.8$ in $C.l$ are (ii_1) $l = 6$ and (ii_2) $l = 9$.

(ii_1) Suppose $T.7/T.8$ in $C.6$ then we may assume $a_{76} = 1 = -a_{86}$. By $L.2$ on $R.3$ we must have either $a_{73} = 1$ or $a_{74} = 1$ and by symmetry we may suppose it is $a_{73} = 1$; then by $L.3$ $a_{74} = 0 = a_{83} = a_{84}$. Thus at least one of a_{87} and a_{88} is a unit. By the structure of (a) and since $C.6$ contains at most three $(+1)$s there can only be one unit among a_{45} and a_{65} and only one amongst a_{j6} ($j = 4, 5, 6,$). Thus $a_{49} = a_{59} = 1$ and $a_{56} = 0$. Since either $a_{45} = 1 = a_{66}$ or $a_{65} = 1 = a_{46}$ by $L.3$ $a_{87} = 0$ and $a_{88} = -1$ so $a_{89} = 1$. Further by $L.3$ on $R.8$ $a_{79} \neq -1$ so in order that $R.7$ should obey $L.2$ we must have $a_{77} = 1$. Thus by $L.3$ $a_{45} = 1 = a_{66}$ and we have

x	A	y	B	z	C	D	E	F
1	1	1	0	1	0	0	0	0
1	−1	0	1	1	0	0	0	0
1	0	−1	−1	0	1	0	0	0
−1	0	0	0	1	0	1	0	1
−1	0	0	0	0	0	−1	1	1
−1	0	0	0	0	1	−1	−1	0
0	0	1	0	−1	1	1	0	0
0	0	0	0	−1	−1	0	−1	1
0								

Since $C.5$ is not a tetre $a_{95} = 0$. Hence if $a_{99} \neq -1$ then by $L.2$ on $R.4$ $a_{97} = -1$ so by $L.2$ on $R.5$ $a_{98} = -1$. Thus by $L.2$ on $R.6$ $a_{96} = -1$ and $R.9$ with one of $R.1$ and $R.2$ contradicts $L.4$. Thus $a_{99} = -1$ and so by $L.17$ none of the tetrahedra are naiks.

Choose the coordinate system shown. From boundedness we have: from $T.1$ $a_1 < 0$; from $T.2$ $b_1 < 0$; from $T.3$ $c_1 < 0$; from $T.7$ $d_1 > 0$; from $T.6$ $e_1 < 0$; from $T.5$ $f_1 > 0$. However, this makes $L.8$ unbounded. Thus (ii_1) cannot arise.

(ii_2) Suppose $T.7/T.8$ in $C.9$ then we may assume $a_{79} = 1 = -a_{89}$. Two further cases now arise: (ii_2^1) $a_{49} = 1 = a_{59}$ and (ii_2^{11}) $a_{46} = 1 = a_{56}$.

(ii$_2^1$) Suppose $a_{49} = 1 = a_{59}$, $a_{69} = 0$, then by $L.3$ $a_{45} = 0$ so $a_{65} = 1 = a_{46}$ and $a_{66} = 0 = a_{56}$. Thus by $L.3$ $a_{87} = 0 = a_{88}$. Hence one of a_{83} and a_{84} is a $(+1)$ and by symmetry we may assume $a_{83} = 1$ then by $L.3$ $a_{84} = 0$ so by $L.3$ $a_{86} = 1$. Also by $L.3$ $a_{77} \neq 1$ so by $L.2$ on $R.5$ $a_{78} = -1$. By $L.3$ $a_{76} \neq -1$ so by $L.2$ on $R.4$ $a_{77} = -1$. However, $R.7$ and $R.3$ now contradict $L.4$. Thus (ii$_2^1$) cannot arise.

(ii$_2^{11}$) Suppose $a_{46} = 1 = a_{56}$, $a_{66} = 0$. Since either $a_{45} = 1 = a_{69}$ or $a_{49} = 1 = a_{65}$, by $L.3$ $a_{87} = 0$, $a_{86} \neq -1$ so by $L.2$ on $R.5$ $a_{88} = -1$ and on $R.3$ one of a_{83} and a_{84} is a $(+1)$. By symmetry we may suppose $a_{83} = 1$. Now if $a_{76} = -1$ then by $L.3$ $a_{45} = 0$ so $a_{65} = 1$. Hence by $L.3$ $a_{73} = 0 = a_{74} = a_{77} = a_{78}$ and $R.7$ would contradict $L.1$. Thus $a_{76} = 0$. Hence by $L.2$ on $R.3$ one of a_{73} and a_{74} is a $(+1)$ so if $R.7$ is to obey $L.2$ with $R.4$, $R.5$ and $R.6$ we must have $a_{77} = 1$. Hence by $L.3$ $a_{65} = 0$ so $a_{45} = 1$ and $a_{69} = 1$. Since $C.5$ is not a tetre $a_{95} = 0$. Thus if $a_{96} \neq -1$, by $L.2$ on $R.4$ $a_{97} = -1$, then on $R.5$ $a_{98} = -1$ and finally on $R.6$ $a_{99} = -1$; clearly $R.9$ with one of $R.1$ and $R.2$ now contradicts $L.2$. Hence $a_{96} = -1$. Thus we have

x	A	y	B	z	C	D	E	F
1	1	1	0	1	0	0	0	0
1	−1	0	1	1	0	0	0	0
1	0	−1	−1	0	1	0	0	0
−1	0	0	0	1	1	1	0	0
−1	0	0	0	0	1	−1	1	0
−1	0	0	0	0	0	−1	−1	1
0	0			−1	0	1		1
0	0	1	0	−1	0	0	−1	−1
0				−1				

Choose the coordinate system shown. From boundedness we have: from $T.1$ $a_1 < 0$; from $T.2$ $b_1 < 0$; from $T.3$ $c_1 < 0$; from $T.4$ $d_1 > 0$; from $T.5$ $e_1 > 0$; from $T.6$ $f_1 > 0$. However, $T.8$ is now unbounded in the x-direction.

Thus (ii$_2^{11}$) cannot arise and so neither can (ii).

Hence III cannot occur.

IV. Suppose (b — b).

Clearly we may assume that

$$
\begin{array}{ccccccccc}
1 & 1 & 0 & 1 & 1 & 0 & 0 & 0 & 0 \\
1 & -1 & 1 & 0 & 0 & 1 & 0 & 0 & 0 \\
1 & -1 & -1 & 0 & 0 & 0 & 1 & 0 & 0 \\
-1 & 0 & 0 & & & & & 1 & 0 \\
-1 & 0 & 0 & & & & & -1 & 1 \\
-1 & 0 & 0 & & & & & -1 & -1 \\
\end{array}
$$

By $L.16$ $C.2$ cannot contain four (-1)s so $L.2$ on $R.1$ gives only two effective cases: (A) $a_{74} = -1 = a_{84}$ and (B) $a_{72} = -1 = a_{84} = a_{95}$.

Clearly the case $a_{75} = -1 = a_{85}$ is equivalent to (A).

(A) Suppose $a_{74} = -1 = a_{84}$. Since, by the structure of (b) $C.4$ must contain a $(+1)$ in one of the $R.l$ $(l = 4, 5, 6)$, by $L.3$ the only possible values of l for which $T.7/T.8$ in $C.l$ are: (A_1) $l = 3$; (A_2) $l = 6$; (A_3) $l = 9$.

By the symmetry of $R.2$ and $R.3$ the case $l = 7$ is equivalent to (A_2).

(A_1) Suppose $T.7/T.8$ in $C.3$ then we may assume $a_{73} = 1 = -a_{83}$ so by $L.3$ $a_{72} = 0 = a_{82}$. By $L.2$ on $R.2$ and $R.3$ we must have $a_{76} = -1 = a_{87}$. By the structure of (b) each column $C.l$ $(l = 4, 5, 6, 7)$ contains one and only one $(+1)$ in rows 4, 5 and 6. Hence by $L.2$ and $L.3$ the last unit in both $R.7$ and $R.8$ has one and only one unit of opposite sign in the same column in the first six rows; thus, since $a_{78} = -1 = a_{88}$ is impossible by $L.16$ either (i) one is in $C.8$ and the other in $C.9$ or (ii) both are in $C.9$.

(i) By symmetry we may clearly suppose $a_{79} = -1$, $a_{88} \neq 0$; from the above $a_{88} \neq 1$ so $a_{88} = -1$. Thus by $L.3$ $a_{44} = 0 = a_{54}$ so $a_{64} = 1$. Hence by $L.2$ $a_{46} = 1 = a_{57}$. Hence $a_{45} = 1$. However rows 2, 4, 5, 6 and 8 now contradict $L.9$. Thus (i) cannot arise.

(ii) By $L.3$ $a_{79} = -a_{89} \neq 0$ is impossible so by symmetry we may suppose that $a_{79} = a_{89} = -1$. Then by $L.1$ $a_{75} = 0 = a_{85} = a_{78} = a_{88} = a_{77} = a_{86}$ and by $L.3$ $a_{54} = 0 = a_{56} = a_{57}$ so $a_{55} = 1$, $a_{45} = 0 = a_{65}$. By $L.1$ $a_{66} = 1 = a_{67}$ is impossible so by $L.2$ we have $a_{64} = 1 = a_{46} = a_{47}$.

If $a_{95} \neq -1$ then, since $a_{99} \neq -1$ by $L.16$, by $L.2$ on $R.5$ $a_{98} = 1$. Thus by $L.3$ $a_{99} = 0$, $a_{94} \neq -1$ so by $L.2$ on $R.1$ $a_{92} = -1$. By $L.2$ on $R.2$ and $R.3$ at least one of a_{96} and a_{97} is a (-1).

However, by $L.3$ on $R.4$ both cannot be (-1)s so a_{93} must be a unit. Hence $R.9$ with one of $R.7$ and $R.8$ contradicts $L.2$.

Hence $a_{95} = -1$ and we have

x	y	A	B	C	z	D	E	F
1	1	0	1	1	0	0	0	0
1	-1	1	0	0	1	0	0	0
1	-1	-1	0	0	0	1	0	0
-1	0	0	0	0	1	1	1	0
-1	0	0	0	1	0	0	-1	1
-1	0	0	1	0	0	0	-1	-1
0	0	1	-1	0	-1	0	0	-1
0	0	-1	-1	0	0	-1	0	-1
0				-1				

Choose the coordinate system shown. From boundedness we have: from T.2 $a_1 < 0$; from T.3 $d_1 < 0$; from T.4 $e_1 > 0$; from T.7 at least one of $b_1 < 0$ and $f_1 < 0$ holds; from T.8 at least one of $b_1 > 0$ and $f_1 > 0$ holds. Thus $b_1 f_1 < 0$ so for T.6 to be bounded we must have $b_1 > 0$, $f_1 < 0$. From T.5 $c_1 > 0$. However, T.1 is now unbounded.

Thus (ii) cannot arise and so neither can (A_1).

(A_3) Suppose T.7/T.8 in $C.9$ then we may assume $a_{79} = 1 = -a_{89}$. By $L.3$ $a_{54} = 0 = a_{64}$ so $a_{44} = 1$ and the case is equivalent to (A_1).

(A_2) Suppose T.7/T.8 in $C.6$ then we may assume $a_{76} = 1 = -a_{86}$. By $L.3$ $a_{82} = 0$. Now $a_{73} \neq -1$ for if $a_{73} = -1$, by $L.2$ on $R.3$ $a_{77} = -1$ so that $R.7$ with one of $R.4$, $R.5$ and $R.6$ contradicts $L.2$. Thus by $L.2$ on $R.2$ $a_{72} = 1$ so by $L.3$ $a_{73} = 0$. Hence in order that $R.7$ should obey $L.2$ we must have by the structure of (b) $a_{78} = 1$. Thus by $L.3$ $a_{54} = 0 = a_{64}$ so $a_{44} = 1$. By $L.3$ $a_{46} = 0$ so by the symmetry of $R.5$ and $R.6$ we may suppose $a_{56} = 1$, $a_{66} = 0$ so by $L.3$ $a_{88} = 0$.

If $a_{94} = -1$, by $L.3$ $a_{92} \neq -1$, $a_{98} \neq -1$, so by $L.2$ on $R.7$ $a_{96} = -1$. Since (A_1) and (A_3) cannot arise from the above, we must have T.9/T.8 in $C.7$, so we may suppose $a_{87} = 1 = -a_{97}$ by the symmetry of $R.8$ and $R.9$. Thus by $L.2$ on $R.3$ $a_{83} = 1$ and so $R.8$ with $R.6$ contradicts $L.2$.

Thus $a_{94} \neq -1$ so by $L.2$ on $R.1$ either (i) $a_{92} = -1$ or (ii) $a_{95} = -1$.

(i) Suppose $a_{92} = -1$ then by $L.3$ $a_{96} \neq -1$. Thus by $L.2$ on $R.2$ $a_{93} = -1$ and then on $R.3$ $a_{97} = -1$. Hence in order that $R.9$ should obey $L.2$ we must have $a_{98} = 1$. Thus by $L.2$ on $R.9$ $a_{47} = 1$ so $a_{65} = 1$.

Hence we have

x	y	A	B	C	z	D	E	F
1	1	0	1	1	0	0	0	0
1	-1	1	0	0	1	0	0	0
1	-1	-1	0	0	0	1	0	0
-1	0	0	1	0	0	1	1	0
-1	0	0	0	0	1	0	-1	1
-1	0	0	0	1	0	0	-1	-1
0	1	0	-1	0	1	0	1	0
0	0	-1			-1		0	
0	-1	-1	0	0	0	-1	1	0

By $L.17$ only $T.1$ and $T.5$ can possibly be naiks so we neglect them in our analysis.

Choose the coordinate system shown. From boundedness we have: from $T.2$ $a_1 < 0$; from $T.3$ $d_1 < 0$; from $T.9$ $e_1 < 0$; from $T.4$ $b_1 > 0$. However, this makes $T.7$ unbounded and so (i) cannot arise.

(ii) Suppose $a_{95} = -1$. By the symmetry of the configuration $a_{98} = -1$ has been dealt with under (i).

(ii$_1$) Suppose $a_{87} = -1$ then by $L.3$ $a_{47} = 0 = a_{57} = a_{83}$ so $a_{67} = 1$ and $a_{45} = 1$. By $L.3$ $a_{89} = 0$ so $a_{85} = 1$. Thus we have

x	y	A	B	C	z	D	E	F
1	1	0	1	1	0	0	0	0
1	-1	1	0	0	1	0	0	0
1	-1	-1	0	0	0	1	0	0
-1	0	0	1	1	0	0	1	0
-1	0	0	0	0	1	0	-1	1
-1	0	0	0	0	0	1	-1	-1
0	1	0	-1	0	1	0	1	0
0	0	0	-1	1	-1	-1	0	0
0			-1					

Choose the coordinate system shown. From boundedness we have: from $T.2$ $a_2 > 0$; from $T.3$ $d_2 > 0$; from $T.5$ $e_2 f_2 > 0$;

thus from **T**.6 $e_2 > 0$ and $f_2 > 0$; from **T**.7 $b_2 > 0$; from **T**.1 $c_2 < 0$.

However, **T**.8 is now unbounded so (ii$_1$) cannot arise.

Thus (ii$_2$) $a_{87} \neq -1$. Hence by L.2 on R.3 $a_{83} = 1$. By L.3 $a_{85} \neq -1$ so by L.2 on R.6 $a_{89} = 1$. Now $a_{96} \neq -1$ for if $a_{96} = -1$ then by L.3 $a_{93} \neq -1$, $a_{94} \neq 1$, $a_{99} \neq -1$, so R.9 and R.8 would contradict L.2. From the above we may assume $a_{98} \neq -1$; also by L.3 $a_{92} \neq -1$ so by L.2 on R.7 $a_{94} = 1$. Thus by L.3 $a_{96} = 0$, $a_{93} \neq -1$ so by L.2 on R.2 $a_{92} = 1$. In order that R.9 should conform to L.2 we must clearly have $a_{98} = 1$ so by L.3 $a_{55} = 0 = a_{65}$. Thus $a_{45} = 1$ and $a_{67} = 1$ and we have

A	x	B	y	z	C	D	E	F
1	1	0	1	1	0	0	0	0
1	−1	1	0	0	1	0	0	0
1	−1	−1	0	0	0	1	0	0
−1	0	0	1	1	0	0	1	0
−1	0	0	0	0	1	0	−1	1
−1	0	0	0	0	0	1	−1	−1
0	1	0	−1	0	1	0	1	0
0	0	1	−1	0	−1	0	0	1
0	1	0	1	−1	0	0	1	0

By L.17 both **T**.3 and **T**.6 are naiks so we neglect them in our analysis.

Choose the coordinate system shown. From boundedness we have: from **T**.1 $a_3 < 0$; from **T**.4 $e_3 < 0$. However, **T**.9 is now unbounded in the z-direction. Thus (ii$_2$) cannot arise and so neither can (ii).

Hence (A$_2$) cannot occur and so neither can (A).

(B) Suppose $a_{72} = -1 = a_{84} = a_{95}$.

If a_{73} is a unit, we may suppose by symmetry that $a_{73} = -1$. Then by L.2 on R.3 $a_{77} = -1$. For R.7 to conform to L.2 clearly we must have $a_{78} = 1$, so by L.3 $a_{57} = 0 = a_{67}$. Thus $a_{47} = 1$. Now one of a_{88} and a_{98} is a (-1), otherwise by L.2 on R.4 we must have a case equivalent to (A). Clearly we may suppose $a_{88} = -1$. However, by L.3 $a_{82} \neq 1$, $a_{83} \neq 1$ and $a_{87} \neq -1$ so R.8 and R.3 contradict L.2.

Hence $a_{73} = 0$ so by L.2 on R.2 and R.3 $a_{76} = -1 = a_{77}$. By L.3 $a_{46} = a_{47} = 1$ is impossible, so by symmetry we may suppose $a_{44} = 1$.

If $a_{79} = -1$ then by $L.2$ on $R.4$ one of a_{46} and a_{47} is a $(+1)$. By symmetry we may suppose $a_{46} = 1$ so by $L.2$ on $R.6$ $a_{67} = 1$. Hence $a_{55} = 1$. The cases when $a_{94} = -1$ and when $a_{96} = -1$ are both equivalent to (A) so we may suppose $a_{94} \neq -1, a_{96} \neq -1$ and then by $L.2$ on $R.4$ $a_{98} = -1$. Now the case when a_{99} is a unit is equivalent to the case when a_{73} is a unit, so we may assume $a_{99} = 0$. Thus by $L.2$ on $R.6$ $a_{97} = -1$ and on $R.2$ $a_{93} = 1$ since $a_{92} \neq 1$ by $L.3$. However $R.9$ and $R.7$ now contradict $L.2$.

Thus $a_{79} \neq -1$ and by symmetry $a_{79} \neq 1$ so $a_{79} = 0$. Now by $L.2$ and the structure of (b), the remaining unit of $R.7$ must have one and only one unit of opposite sign in rows 4, 5 and 6 in the same column. Hence as $a_{74} \neq -1$, $a_{75} \neq -1$ we must have $a_{78} = -1$. By $L.3$ $a_{46} = 0 = a_{47}$ so $a_{45} = 1$ and by symmetry we may suppose $a_{56} = 1 = a_{67}$. However, rows 1, 4, 5, 6 and 7 now contradict $L.9$.

Hence (B) cannot occur and so neither can IV.

V. Suppose $(a - b)$.

Clearly we may assume that

$$
\begin{array}{ccccccccc}
1 & 1 & 0 & 1 & 1 & 0 & 0 & 0 & 0 \\
1 & -1 & 1 & 1 & 0 & 0 & 0 & 0 & 0 \\
1 & -1 & -1 & 0 & 0 & 1 & 0 & 0 & 0 \\
-1 & 0 & 0 & & & & 1 & 0 \\
-1 & 0 & 0 & & & & -1 & 1 \\
-1 & 0 & 0 & & & & -1 & -1 \\
\end{array}
$$

By the structure of (b) we note that each column $C.l$ ($l = 4, 5, 6, 7$) must have one and only one unit amongst rows 4, 5, and 6. Hence by $L.16$ $a_{j4} \neq 1$ for $j = 7, 8, 9$.

(i) Suppose $a_{72} = 1 = a_{82}$. By $L.3$ $a_{74} \neq -1$, $a_{84} \neq -1$, so by $L.2$ on $R.1$ $a_{75} = -1 = a_{85}$. By $L.3$ $a_{73} = 0 = a_{83} = a_{74} = a_{84}$. As one of the a_{j5} ($j = 4, 5, 6$) is a $(+1)$ by $L.3$, the only possible values of l for which $T.7/T.8$ in $C.l$ are $l = 9$ and $l = 7$.

If $T.7/T.8$ in $C.9$ we may clearly suppose $a_{79} = 1 = -a_{89}$ so by $L.3$ $a_{55} = 0 = a_{65}$. Hence $a_{45} = 1$. Thus by $L.3$ $a_{78} = 0 = a_{88}$, $a_{76} \neq -1$, $a_{86} \neq -1$. Hence by the structure of (b) either $R.7$ with $R.5$ or $R.8$ with $R.6$ must contradict $L.2$.

Hence $T.7/T.8$ in $C.7$ so we may suppose $a_{77} = 1 = -a_{87}$. Thus the remaining unit of $R.7$ must have two units of opposite sign in rows 4, 5 and 6 in the same column. Hence $a_{78} = 1$. By

$L.3$ $a_{55} = 0 = a_{65}$ so $a_{45} = 1$. Also by $L.3$ $a_{47} = 0$ so by symmetry we may suppose $a_{57} = 1$, $a_{67} = 0$. By $L.3$ $a_{88} = 0$, $a_{86} \neq -1$ so by $L.2$ on $R.6$ $a_{89} = 1$. Since $C.2$ does not represent a tetre $a_{92} = 0$. If $a_{93} = -1$ then by $L.3$ $a_{94} \neq -1$ so by $L.2$ on $R.1$ and $R.3$ $a_{95} = -1 = a_{96}$ and $R.9$ with one of $R.7$ and $R.8$ must contradict $L.2$. Hence $a_{93} \neq -1$ so by $L.2$ on $R.2$ $a_{94} = -1$. Thus we have

x	A	B	y	z	C	D	E	F
1	1	0	1	1	0	0	0	0
1	-1	1	1	0	0	0	0	0
1	-1	-1	0	0	1	0	0	0
-1	0	0		1		0	1	0
-1	0	0	0	0	0	1	-1	1
-1	0	0		0		0	-1	-1
0	1	0	0	-1	0	1	1	0
0	1	0	0	-1	0	-1	0	1
0			-1					

In our analysis we neglect the rows that represent naiks.

Choose the coordinate system shown. From boundedness we have: from $T.1$ $a_3 < 0$; from $T.7$ at least one of $d_3 > 0$ and $e_3 > 0$ holds; from $T.8$ at least one of $d_3 < 0$ and $f_3 > 0$ holds. Now if $d_3 < 0$, then $e_3 > 0$ so from $T.5$ $f_3 > 0$, whilst if $d_3 \geqslant 0$ then $f_3 > 0$ and from $T.5$ $e_3 > 0$.

Hence we must have $e_3 > 0$ and $f_3 > 0$.

Now if $a_{44} = 1$ then $T.4$ is not a naik and is unbounded. Thus $a_{44} \neq 1$ so $a_{64} = 1$. However, $T.6$ is now unbounded and is also not a naik. Hence (i) cannot occur.

(ii) Suppose $a_{73} = -1 = a_{83}$, then by $L.3$ $a_{72} \neq 1$, $a_{82} \neq 1$, so by $L.2$ on $R.3$ $a_{76} = -1 = a_{86}$. By $L.3$ $a_{74} \neq -1$, $a_{84} \neq -1$ so $a_{74} = 0 = a_{84}$. By $L.6$ with $r_0 = 1$ we may therefore suppose $a_{75} = -1 = a_{82}$. By $L.3$ $a_{72} = 0$. By $L.2$ the remaining unit of $R.8$ must have two units of the opposite sign amongst rows 4, 5 and 6 in the same column. Thus $a_{88} = 1$, so by $L.3$ $a_{56} = 0 = a_{66}$ and hence $a_{46} = 1$. However, by $L.3$ $a_{78} \neq -1$ so that $R.7$ and $R.8$ contradict $L.2$. Thus (ii) cannot arise.

(iii) Suppose $a_{74} = -1 = a_{84}$ then by $L.3$ $a_{72} = 0 = a_{82}$. Since one of the a_{j4} ($j = 4, 5, 6$) is a ($+1$), by $L.3$ the only possible values of l for which $T.7/T.8$ in $C.l$ are $l = 6, 7$ and 9. In each case $a_{94} = 0$ since $C.4$ does not represent a tetre.

8*

(A) Suppose $T.7/T.8$ in $C.6$ then we may clearly assume $a_{76} = 1 = -a_{86}$. By $L.2$ on $R.3$ $a_{73} = 1$. By $L.2$ the remaining unit of $C.7$ must have two units of the opposite sign amongst rows 4, 5 and 6 in the same column. Hence we must have $a_{78} = 1$. By $L.3$ $a_{54} = 0 = a_{64}$ so $a_{44} = 1$. By $L.3$ $a_{46} = 0$ so by symmetry we may assume $a_{56} = 1$, $a_{66} = 0$. By $L.3$ $a_{83} = 0 = a_{88}$. If $a_{93} = -1$ then by $L.3$ $a_{92} \neq 1$ so by $L.2$ on $R.3$ $a_{96} = -1$ which is impossible by $L.3$. Thus $a_{93} \neq -1$. Hence by $L.2$ on $R.2$ $a_{92} = 1$ and on $R.1$ $a_{95} = -1$. By $L.3$ $a_{93} = 0$, $a_{96} \neq -1$ so by $L.2$ on $R.7$ $a_{98} = -1$. By $L.3$ $a_{45} = 0$ so $a_{65} = 1$ and therefore $a_{47} = 1$. As $a_{96} \neq -1$ by $L.2$ on $R.5$ $a_{99} = -1$. By $L.3$ $a_{85} \neq -1$ so by $L.2$ on $R.6$ $a_{89} = 1$. Thus by $L.3$ $a_{85} = 0$ so $a_{87} = 1$.

Hence we have

x	y	A	z	B	C	D	E	F
1	1	0	1	1	0	0	0	0
1	−1	1	1	0	0	0	0	0
1	−1	−1	0	0	1	0	0	0
−1	0	0	1	0	0	1	1	0
−1	0	0	0	0	1	0	−1	1
−1	0	0	0	1	0	0	−1	−1
0	0	1	−1	0	1	0	1	0
0	0	0	−1	0	−1	1	0	1
0	1	0	0	−1	0	0	−1	−1

By $L.17$, $T.4$ and $T.8$ are naiks so we neglect them in our analysis.

Choose the coordinate system shown. From boundedness we have: from $T.1$ $b_2 < 0$; from $T.2$ $a_2 > 0$; from $T.3$ $c_2 > 0$; from $T.7$ $e_2 < 0$; from $T.9$ $f_2 > 0$. However, $T.5$ is now unbounded, so (A) cannot occur.

(B) Suppose $T.7/T.8$ in $C.9$, then we may clearly assume $a_{79} = 1 = -a_{89}$. By $L.3$ $a_{54} = 0 = a_{64}$ so $a_{44} = 1$. Thus by $L.3$ $a_{78} = 0 = a_{88}$, $a_{75} \neq -1$, $a_{85} \neq -1$. Hence by $L.2$ on $R.5$ with $R.7$ $a_{55} = 0$ and on $R.6$ with $R.8$ $a_{65} = 0$, so $a_{45} = 1$. Thus by symmetry we may suppose $a_{56} = 1 = a_{67}$. By $L.2$ on $R.5$ and $R.6$ $a_{76} = -1 = a_{87}$. By $L.3$ $a_{73} = 0 = a_{77}$ so $a_{75} = 1$. Also by $L.3$ $a_{86} \neq -1$ so by $L.2$ on $R.3$ $a_{83} = 1$. If $a_{92} = -1$ then by $L.2$ on $R.2$ $a_{93} = -1$ and on $R.3$ $a_{96} = -1$ so that $R.9$ with one of $R.4$ and

$R.6$ contradicts $L.2$. Hence $a_{92} \neq -1$ so by $L.2$ on $R.1$ $a_{95} = -1$. Thus we have

x	y	A	z	B	C	D	E	F
1	1	0	1	1	0	0	0	0
1	−1	1	1	0	0	0	0	0
1	−1	−1	0	0	1	0	0	0
−1	0	0	1	1	0	0	1	0
−1	0	0	0	0	1	0	−1	1
−1	0	0	0	0	0	1	−1	−1
0	0	0	−1	1	−1	0	0	1
0	0	1	−1	0	0	−1	0	−1
0			−1					

Choose the coordinate system shown. From boundedness we have: from $T.1$ $b_1 < 0$; from $T.2$ $a_1 < 0$; from $T.3$ $c_1 < 0$; from $T.4$ $e_1 > 0$; from $T.5$ $f_1 > 0$; from $T.6$ $d_1 > 0$. However, $T.8$ is now unbounded so (B) cannot occur.

Hence we must have (C) $T.7/T.8$ in $C.7$. We may clearly suppose $a_{77} = 1 = -a_{87}$.

(C_1) Suppose $a_{47} = 1$, then by $L.3$ $a_{44} = 0$, so by symmetry we may assume $a_{54} = 1$, $a_{64} = 0$. Now $a_{73} \neq 1$ for if so, $R.7$ with one of $R.4$ and $R.6$ contradicts $L.2$. Hence by $L.2$ on $R.3$ $a_{76} = -1$. By $L.3$ $a_{73} = 0 = a_{88}$, $a_{75} \neq -1$. Thus by the structure of (b) by $L.2$ we must have one of $a_{78} = -1$ and $a_{79} = 1$ so $a_{75} = 0$.

Now if $a_{92} = -1$ then by $L.2$ on $R.2$ $a_{93} = -1$ and on $R.3$ $a_{96} = -1$. Thus for $R.9$ to obey $L.2$ we must have $a_{98} = 1$ so by $L.2$ on $R.4$ $a_{46} = 1$. By $L.3$ $a_{78} \neq -1$ so that $R.9$ and $R.7$ contradict $L.2$.

Thus $a_{92} \neq -1$ so by $L.2$ on $R.1$ $a_{95} = -1$. Hence we have

x	y	A	z	B	C	D	E	F
1	1	0	1	1	0	0	0	0
1	−1	1	1	0	0	0	0	0
1	−1	−1	0	0	1	0	0	0
−1	0	0	0			1	1	0
−1	0	0	1	0	0	0	−1	1
−1	0	0	0			0	−1	−1
0	0	0	−1	0	−1	1		
0	0		−1			−1	0	
0				0	−1			

Choose the coordinate system shown. From boundedness we have: from T.1 $b_1 < 0$; from T.2 $a_1 < 0$; from T.3 $c_1 < 0$; from L.5 at least one of $e_1 < 0$ and $f_1 > 0$ holds; from T.6 at least one of $e_1 < 0$ and $f_1 < 0$ holds whether $a_{65} = 1$ or $a_{66} = 1$. Thus $e_1 < 0$. Hence from T.4 $d_1 > 0$.

Now $a_{78} \neq -1$ otherwise T.7 is unbounded, so $a_{79} = 1$. Hence by L.2 on R.4 $a_{46} = 1$ so $a_{65} = 1$. By L.3 $a_{85} \neq -1$ so by L.2 on R.6 $a_{89} = 1$ and on R.3 $a_{83} = 1$ since $a_{86} \neq -1$ by L.3. From T.7 $f_1 < 0$.

However, T.8 is now unbounded so (C_1) cannot arise.

Thus $a_{47} \neq 1$ so $a_{47} = 0$ and by symmetry we may suppose $a_{57} = 1$, $a_{67} = 0$.

(C_2) Suppose $a_{92} = -1$, then by L.2 on R.2 and R.3 $a_{93} = -1 = a_{96}$. Hence for R.9 to obey L.2 we must have $a_{98} = 1$ so by L.2 on R.9 $a_{46} = 1$. Thus we have

x	y	A	z	B	C	D	E	F
1	1	0	1	1	0	0	0	0
1	-1	1	1	0	0	0	0	0
1	-1	-1	0	0	1	0	0	0
-1	0	0		1	0	1	0	
-1	0	0	0	0	0	1	-1	1
-1	0	0			0	0	-1	-1
0	0	-1		1				
0	0	-1			-1			
0	-1	-1	0	0	-1	0	1	0

In our analysis we neglect the rows that represent naiks. Choose the coordinate system shown. From boundedness we have: from T.2 $a_1 < 0$; from T.3 $c_1 < 0$; from T.9 $e_1 < 0$.

Now $a_{44} \neq 1$ otherwise T.4 is unbounded, so $a_{64} = 1$. By L.3 $a_{78} \neq 1$ so by L.2 on R.5 $a_{79} = -1$. Thus by L.2 on R.7 we must have $a_{76} = -1$. However, R.7 and R.9 now contradict L.2 so (C_2) does not arise.

Thus $a_{92} \neq -1$ so by L.2 on R.1 $a_{95} = -1$. Now either (C_3) C.6 contains a (-1) or (C_4) C.6 does not contain a (-1).

(C_3) Suppose C.6 contains a (-1) then none of the tetrahedra can be naiks and we have

x	y	A	z	B	C	D	E	F
1	1	0	1	1	0	0	0	0
1	−1	1	1	0	0	0	0	0
1	−1	−1	0	0	1	0	0	0
−1	0	0				0	1	0
−1	0	0	0	0	0	1	−1	1
−1	0	0				0	−1	−1
0	0	−1				1		
0	0	−1				−1		
0			0	−1				

Choose the coordinate system shown. From boundedness we have: from T.1 $b_1 < 0$; from T.2 $a_1 < 0$; from T.3 $c_1 < 0$. Hence from T.4 $e_1 > 0$ and from T.6 $f_1 < 0$ so from T.5 $d_1 > 0$.

If $a_{76} = -1$ then by L.3 either $a_{44} = 1 = a_{66}$ or $a_{46} = 1 = a_{64}$; in either case by L.3 $a_{78} \neq 1$ so by L.2 on R.5 $a_{79} = -1$; but from the above T.7 is then unbounded.

Thus $a_{76} \neq -1$ so by L.2 on R.3 $a_{73} = 1$ and for R.7 to obey L.2 we must have $a_{78} = 1$. Hence by L.2 on R.7 $a_{44} = 1$. By L.3 $a_{88} = 0$.

If $a_{93} = -1$ then by L.3 $a_{92} = 0$ so by L.2 on R.3 $a_{96} = -1$. By L.3 either $a_{45} = 1 = a_{66}$ or $a_{46} = 1 = a_{65}$ but in either case by L.3 $a_{98} = 0$ and $a_{97} \neq -1$ so by L.2 on R.5 $a_{99} = -1$. From the above T.9 is unbounded.

Thus $a_{93} \neq -1$ so by L.2 on R.2 $a_{92} = 1$ and by L.3 $a_{93} = 0$, $a_{96} \neq -1$. Hence, by the assumption $a_{86} = -1$, so by L.3 $a_{83} = 0 = a_{46}$. Thus $a_{45} = 1 = a_{66}$. By L.3 $a_{89} = 0$ so $a_{85} = 1$. By L.3 $a_{98} \neq -1$ so by L.2 on R.7 $a_{97} = -1$ and on R.6 $a_{99} = 1$ since by L.3 $a_{96} \neq -1$, $a_{98} \neq 1$. Hence we have

x	y	A	z	B	C	D	E	F
1	1	0	1	1	0	0	0	0
1	−1	1	1	0	0	0	0	0
1	−1	−1	0	0	1	0	0	0
−1	0	0	1	1	0	0	1	0
−1	0	0	0	0	0	1	−1	1
−1	0	0	0	0	1	0	−1	−1
0	0	1	−1	0	0	1	1	0
0	0	0	−1	1	−1	−1	0	0
0	1	0	0	−1	0	−1	0	1

From boundedness we have: from T.1 $b_2 < 0$; from T.2 $a_2 > 0$; from T.3 $c_2 > 0$; from T.4 $e_2 > 0$; from T.7 $d_2 < 0$; from T.5 $f_2 > 0$. However, T.9 is now unbounded so (C_3) cannot arise.

Hence (C_4) $C.6$ does not contain a (-1). Thus by $L.2$ on $R.3$ $a_{73} = 1 = a_{83}$. For $R.7$ to obey $L.2$ we must have $a_{78} = 1$ and then $a_{44} = 1$. Thus by $L.3$ $a_{88} = 0$, $a_{85} \neq -1$, $a_{86} \neq -1$ so by $L.2$ on $R.6$ $a_{89} = 1$. Now by $L.16$ $a_{93} \neq 1$ so by $L.2$ on $R.3$ $a_{92} = 1$. By $L.3$ $a_{93} = 0$. Now $a_{97} \neq -1$ for if so, by $L.3$ $a_{99} \neq -1$ so that $R.9$ and $R.8$ contradict $L.2$. Hence by $L.2$ on $R.7$ $a_{98} = -1$, so by $L.3$ $a_{45} = 0$. Thus $a_{65} = 1 = a_{46}$. By $L.2$ on $R.5$ $a_{99} = -1$ so we have

x	A	B	y	z	C	D	E	F
1	1	0	1	1	0	0	0	0
1	-1	1	1	0	0	0	0	0
1	-1	-1	0	0	1	0	0	0
-1	0	0	1	0	1	0	1	0
-1	0	0	0	0	0	1	-1	1
-1	0	0	0	1	0	0	-1	-1
0	0	1	-1	0	0	1	1	0
0	0	1	-1	0	0	-1	0	1
0	1	0	0	-1	0	0	-1	-1

By T.17 $L.3$ and $T.4$ are naiks, so we neglect them in our analysis.

Choose the coordinate system shown. From boundedness we have: from T.1 $a_2 < 0$; from T.2 $b_2 < 0$; from T.6 $e_2 f_2 < 0$; from T.5 $d_2 e_2 > 0$. Hence from T.7 $d_2 > 0$ and $e_2 > 0$ so $f_2 < 0$. However, T.8 is now unbounded.

Hence (C_4) cannot occur and so neither can (C). Thus (iii) cannot arise.

(iv) From the above by $L.2$ on $R.2$ we must therefore have $a_{72} = 1$, $a_{83} = -1 = a_{94}$ or its equivalent. By $L.3$ $a_{73} = 0 = a_{92}$, $a_{82} \neq 1$, $a_{74} \neq -1$. Thus by $L.2$ on $R.1$ $a_{75} = -1$ and on $R.3$ $a_{86} = -1$. By $L.3$ $a_{74} \neq -1$, $a_{84} \neq -1$, so by $L.16$ $a_{74} = 0 = a_{84}$.

Thus we have

x	y	A	z	B	C	D	E	F
1	1	0	1	1	0	0	0	0
1	−1	1	1	0	0	0	0	0
1	−1	−1	0	0	1	0	0	0
−1	0	0					1	0
−1	0	0					−1	1
−1	0	0					−1	−1
0	1	0	0	−1				
0		−1	0	−1				
0	0		−1					

In our analysis we neglect the rows that represent naiks.

Choose the coordinate system shown. From boundedness we have: from **T**.1 $b_1 < 0$, $b_2 < 0$; from **T**.2 $a_1 < 0$, $a_2 > 0$; from **T**.3 $c_1 < 0$, $c_2 > 0$.

If $a_{82} = -1$ then in order that R.8 should obey L.2 we must have $a_{88} = 1$, so by L.2 $a_{46} = 1$. From **T**.8 $e_1 < 0$, $e_2 > 0$. Hence from R.4 $a_{47} = 1$ for if either $a_{44} = 1$ or $a_{45} = 1$ **T**.4 is unbounded in the x-direction. By the symmetry of R.5 and R.6 we may assume $a_{54} = 1 = a_{65}$. Thus from **T**.6 $f_2 < 0$ and so **T**.5 is unbounded in the y-direction.

Thus $a_{82} \neq -1$ so $a_{82} = 0$ and by L.2 on R.1 $a_{85} = -1$.

If $a_{76} = 1$, in order that R.7 should obey L.2 we must have $a_{78} = 1$ and $a_{45} = 1$. By L.3 $a_{46} = 0$, so by symmetry we may suppose $a_{56} = 1$. From **T**.7 $e_2 < 0$ so that if $a_{44} = 1$ **T**.4 is unbounded in the y-direction. Hence $a_{64} = 1 = a_{47}$. From **T**.6 $f_2 > 0$ and so **T**.5 is unbounded in the y-direction.

Thus $a_{76} \neq 1$ so $a_{76} = 0$. Thus the only possible values of l for which **T**.7/**T**.8 in $C.l$ are $l = 9$ and $l = 7$.

Suppose **T**.7/**T**.8 in C.9. By the symmetry of R.5 and R.6 we may suppose $a_{79} = 1 = -a_{89}$, so by L.3 $a_{55} = 0 = a_{65}$. Thus $a_{45} = 1$ so by L.2 on R.8 $a_{66} = 1$. By L.3 $a_{78} = 0$ so by L.2 we must have $a_{57} = 1 = -a_{77}$. Hence $a_{44} = 1$. From **T**.8 $f_1 > 0$; from **T**.6 $e_1 < 0$ and so **T**.4 is unbounded in the x-direction.

Thus $T.7/T.8$ in $C.7$. By the structure of (b) the remaining unit of $R.8$ must have a unit of the opposite sign in the same column amongst rows 4, 5, 6. Thus we must have $a_{77} = 1 = -a_{87}$. Hence for $R.7$ to obey $L.2$ we must have $a_{78} = 1$ and $a_{45} = 1$. By $L.3$ $a_{46} \neq 1$, $a_{47} \neq 1$ so $a_{44} = 1$. From $T.8$ $d_1 > 0$; from $T.7$ $e_1 < 0$. However, $T.4$ is now unbounded.

Hence (iv) cannot occur and so neither can V.

VI. Finally suppose (a — a).

Clearly we may assume that

1	1	0	1	1	0	0	0	0
1	−1	1	1	0	0	0	0	0
1	−1	−1	0	0	1	0	0	0
−1	0	0				1	0	
−1	0	0				−1	1	
−1	0	0				−1	−1	

We assume that the remaining unit of $R.5$, a_{5l} say, is such that $a_{5l} = a_{4l} = 1$. Thus by $L.16$ $a_{54} = 0$.

(i) Suppose $a_{72} = -1$ then by $L.3$ $a_{74} \neq -1$, so by $L.2$ on $R.2$ $a_{73} = -1$ and on $R.3$ $a_{76} = -1$. By $L.2$ the remaining unit of $R.7$ must have at least one unit of the opposite sign amongst rows 4, 5 and 6 in the same column. By $L.3$ $a_{74} \neq -1$, $a_{75} \neq -1$ so $a_{74} = 0 = a_{75}$.

(A) Suppose $a_{85} = -1 = a_{95}$. Since $C.2$ does not represent a tetre $a_{82} = a_{92} = 1$ is impossible; further $a_{83} = -1 = a_{93}$ is impossible by $L.16$. Since by $L.3$ $a_{84} \neq -1$, $a_{94} \neq -1$, by $L.2$ on $R.2$ we may suppose $a_{82} = 1$, $a_{93} = -1$. Thus by $L.3$ $a_{92} = 0 = a_{83} = a_{86}$. By $L.2$ on $R.3$ $a_{96} = -1$. Hence if a_{9l} is the remaining unit of $R.9$ then by $L.2$ $a_{7l} = -a_{9l} = a_{8l}$. Since $C.8$ does not represent a tetre $a_{98} = 0$ so that $a_{78} = 0$ also. Further since $a_{74} = 0$, $a_{94} = 0$. Now if $T.7/T.9$ in $C.9$, by $L.3$ on $R.7$ and $R.9$ $a_{56} = 0 = a_{66}$ so that $R.7$ with one of $R.5$ and $R.6$ contradicts $L.2$. Hence $T.7/T.9$ in $C.7$ and so by $L.2$ on $R.7$ and the above, we must have $a_{77} = -1 = a_{87}$, $a_{97} = 1$ and at least one $(+1)$ amongst rows 4, 5 and 6, $a_{j7} = 1$ say. Thus by $L.3$ $a_{j6} = 0 = a_{j5}$ so $R.j$ and $R.9$ contradict $L.2$. Hence (A) cannot arise.

Now $a_{85} = -1 = a_{95}$ is impossible and by $L.16$ $a_{82} \neq -1$, $a_{92} \neq -1$. Thus by $L.2$ on $R.1$ we may suppose $a_{94} = -1$ so by $L.3$ $a_{92} = 0$. Hence we have

x	y	A	z	B	C	D	E	F
1	1	0	1	1	0	0	0	0
1	−1	1	1	0	0	0	0	0
1	−1	−1	0	0	1	0	0	0
−1	0	0					1	0
−1	0	0					−1	1
−1	0	0					−1	−1
0	−1	−1	0	0	−1			
0								
0	0		−1					

Choose the coordinate system shown. From boundedness we have: from **T**.2 $a_1 < 0$, $a_2 > 0$, $a_3 < 0$; from **T**.3 $c_1 < 0$, $c_2 > 0$, $c_3 < 0$.

Providing **T**.1 is not a naik, i.e. providing $a_{85} = −1$ since $a_{95} \neq −1$, by $L.3$ we may also use from $L.1$ $b_1 < 0$, $b_2 < 0$, $b_3 < 0$.

(B) Suppose $a_{56} = 1 = a_{46}$, so by $L.3$ $a_{78} = 0$. By $L.1$ $a_{54} = a_{55} = a_{57} = 0$.

If $a_{96} = −1$ then by $L.3$ $a_{93} = 0 = a_{98}$, so by $L.3$ the only possible l for which **T**.7/**T**.9 in $C.l$ is $l = 7$; hence by $L.2$ on $R.7$ $a_{77} = −1$, $a_{67} = 1 = a_{97}$. Thus by $L.2$ on $R.6$ $a_{99} = 1$. Then from **T**.7 $d_2 < 0$; from **T**.9 $f_2 > 0$; from **T**.6 $e_2 < 0$. However, this makes **T**.5 unbounded in the y-direction.

Thus $a_{96} \neq −1$ so by $L.2$ on $R.3$ $a_{93} = 1$ and by $L.3$ $a_{96} = 0$. If $a_{84} = −1$ then $a_{82} = 0$ by $L.3$ and as above $a_{86} \neq −1$. Thus by $L.2$ $a_{83} = 1$ so by $L.3$ $a_{86} = 0$. By $L.6$ with $r_0 = 5$ we may therefore suppose $a_{88} = +1 = −a_{99}$. By $L.3$ $a_{64} = 0 = a_{89} = a_{79}$, $a_{98} \neq 1$ so by $L.2$ on $R.6$ $a_{67} = 1$, $a_{77} = −1 = a_{97}$. By $L.3$ $a_{87} = 0$ so $R.8$ and $R.9$ contradict $L.2$.

Hence $a_{84} \neq −1$, so by $L.2$ on $R.1$ $a_{85} = −1$. If $a_{83} = −1$ then by $L.3$ $a_{82} = 0$, so by $L.2$ on $R.3$ $a_{86} = −1$; by $L.3$ the only possible l for which **T**.7/**T**.8 in $C.l$ is $l = 7$ and then $R.6$ with one of $R.7$ and $R.8$ contradicts $L.2$. Thus $a_{83} \neq −1$ and since $a_{84} \neq −1$, by $L.2$ on $R.2$ $a_{82} = 1$. By $L.3$ $a_{83} = 0 = a_{86}$.

If $a_{79} = 1$, by $L.3$ $a_{89} \neq −1$, $a_{99} \neq −1$ so by $L.2$ on $R.5$ $a_{88} = 1 = a_{98}$; by $L.3$ $a_{64} = 0 = a_{65}$ so $a_{67} = 1$ with the result that $R.4$ with one of $R.8$ and $R.9$ contradicts $L.2$ since only one of a_{44} and a_{45} is a $(+1)$ and $a_{84} \neq −1$, $a_{95} \neq −1$ by $L.3$.

Thus $a_{79} \neq 1$ so by $L.2$ on $R.7$ we must have $a_{67} = 1 = −a_{77}$. By $L.3$ $a_{84} \neq −1$, $a_{95} \neq −1$ so by $L.2$ on $R.4$ we have one of

a_{88} and a_{98} is a (-1), say $a_{l8} = -1$; then $R.l$ with one of $R.5$ and $R.6$ contradicts $L.2$. Thus (B) cannot arise.

Hence $a_{56} = 1 = a_{46}$ is impossible so $a_{56} = 0$.

(C) Suppose $a_{78} = 1$ then by $L.3$ $a_{66} = 0$, so by $L.2$ on $R.7$ $a_{46} = 1$. Now $a_{96} \neq -1$ for if so, by $L.3$ $a_{93} \neq 1$, $a_{98} \neq -1$ so that $R.7$ and $R.9$ contradict $L.2$. Hence by $L.2$ on $R.3$ $a_{93} = 1$. By $L.3$ $a_{96} = 0$, $a_{98} \neq -1$, $a_{95} \neq -1$ so by the structure of (a) by $L.2$ on $R.4$ we must have $a_{47} = 1 = a_{57}$, $a_{97} = -1$. Thus we have

x	y	A	z	B	C	D	E	F
1	1	0	1	1	0	0	0	0
1	−1	1	1	0	0	0	0	0
1	−1	−1	0	0	1	0	0	0
−1	0	0	0	0	1	1	1	0
−1	0	0	0	0	0	1	−1	1
−1	0	0			0	0	−1	−1
0	−1	−1	0	0	−1	0	1	
0								
0	0	1	−1			0	−1	

As above, $a_2 > 0$ and $c_2 > 0$. From **T.**7 $e_2 > 0$; from **T.**4 $d_2 < 0$; from **T.**5 $f_2 \not> 0$. If $a_{64} = 1$, **T.**6 is unbounded so $a_{65} = 1$. By $L.3$ $a_{95} \neq -1$, $a_{98} \neq 1$ so by $L.2$ on $R.6$ $a_{99} = 1$.

However, **T.**9 is now unbounded so (C) cannot arise.

Now, since $a_{56} = 0$, in order that $R.7$ should obey $L.2$ with rows 4, 5 and 6 the remaining unit of $R.7$ must have two units of opposite sign in rows 4, 5 and 6 in the same column. Thus as $a_{78} \neq 1$ we can only have $a_{47} = 1 = a_{57}$, $a_{77} = -1$. By $L.2$ on $R.7$ $a_{66} = 1$ so by $L.1$ we have

x	y	A	z	B	C	D	E	F
1	1	0	1	1	0	0	0	0
1	−1	1	1	0	0	0	0	0
1	−1	−1	0	0	1	0	0	0
−1	0	0			0	1	1	0
−1	0	0	0	0	0	1	−1	1
−1	0	0	0	0	1	0	−1	−1
0	−1	−1	0	0	−1	−1	0	0
0								
0	0		−1					

As above, we have $a_2 > 0$, $a_3 < 0$ and $c_2 > 0$, $c_3 < 0$. From **T.**7 $d_2 < 0$, $d_3 > 0$; from **T.**6 at least one of $e_2 > 0$ and $f_2 > 0$

holds; from T.5 at least one of $e_2 < 0$ and $f_2 > 0$ holds. Hence we must have $f_2 > 0$.

Now if $a_{96} = -1$, by L.3 $a_{93} = 0$ so by L.2 on R.7 $a_{97} = 1$. By L.3 $a_{98} \neq 1$ so by L.2 on R.5 $a_{99} = -1$. From the above however T.9 is unbounded in the y-direction.

Hence $a_{96} \neq -1$ so by L.2 on R.3 $a_{93} = 1$ and by L.3 $a_{96} = 0$. Further if $a_{99} = 1$ then by L.3 $a_{98} \neq 1$ so by L.2 on R.5 $a_{97} = -1$ and T.9 is unbounded in the y-direction. Thus $a_{99} \neq 1$. Hence by L.2 on R.6 $a_{98} = 1$ so by L.3 $a_{97} = 0 = a_{99}$. By L.1 and L.3 $a_{95} = 1$ so by L.2 on R.4 $a_{44} = 1$.

Now $a_{84} \neq -1$, for if so, as above, we would have to have $a_{83} = 1 = a_{85}$ which is impossible by L.4. Hence by L.2 on R.1 $a_{85} = -1$. Thus we have from above $b_3 < 0$ and from T.4 $e_3 < 0$. However, T.9 is now unbounded in the z-direction.

Hence (i) cannot occur.

Thus we may assume now $a_{j2} \neq -1$ and by symmetry $a_{j8} \neq -1$ ($j = 7, 8, 9$). Thus T.l/T.k in $C.2$ (or $C.8$) is impossible for $l \neq k$ ($l, k = 7, 8, 9$).

(ii) Suppose T.7/T.8 in $C.3$, then we may clearly assume $a_{73} = 1 = -a_{83}$ so by L.3 $a_{72} = 0 = a_{82}$, $a_{84} \neq -1$. Hence by L.2 on R.2 $a_{74} = -1$, on R.1 $a_{85} = -1$ and on R.3 $a_{86} = -1$. Thus by L.3 $a_{84} = 0 = a_{75} = a_{76}$.

(A) Suppose $a_{78} = 1$ then by L.3 $a_{79} = 0$ and a_{77} is a unit. Now if $a_{47} = a_{57} = 1$, by L.3 $a_{77} = 1$ and so $a_{87} \neq -1$. Since $a_{88} \neq -1$ also by L.3, R.4 with one of R.7 and R.8 contradicts L.2. Hence $a_{57} = 0$ and either $a_{46} = 1 = a_{56}$ or $a_{45} = 1 = a_{55}$ so that by L.3 $a_{88} = 0$ in either case and $a_{44} = 1$ or $a_{47} = 1$. Thus we have

x	y	A	z	B	C	D	E	F
1	1	0	1	1	0	0	0	0
1	−1	1	1	0	0	0	0	0
1	−1	−1	0	0	1	0	0	0
−1	0	0					1	0
−1	0	0	0			0	−1	1
−1	0	0					−1	−1
0	0	1	−1	0	0		1	0
0	0	−1	0	−1	−1		0	
0								

As above, $a_1 < 0$, $b_1 < 0$ and $c_1 < 0$.

If $a_{44} = 1$ then from T.4 $e_1 > 0$ and from T.5 $f_1 > 0$. Hence from boundedness we have $a_{89} \neq 1$ and $a_{65} \neq 1$, $a_{66} \neq 1$ so by L.2 on R.6 $a_{67} = 1 = -a_{87}$. However by L.3 $a_{77} = 0$ which is impossible.

Thus $a_{44} = 0$ so $a_{47} = 1$ and by L.2 on R.7 $a_{77} = -1$. By L.3 $a_{64} = 0 = a_{87}$. Hence either $a_{45} = a_{55} = a_{66} = 1$ or $a_{46} = a_{56} = a_{65} = 1$, but in either case $a_{89} = 0$ by L.3, so that R.8 contradicts L.1. Thus (A) cannot arise.

Hence $a_{78} \neq 1$ so $a_{78} = 0$. By L.1 therefore a_{77} and a_{79} are both units.

If $a_{79} = 1$, then by L.2 on R.5 we must have $a_{47} = a_{57} = 1$, $a_{77} = -1$. Thus by L.3 $a_{44} = 0 = a_{64}$ so either $a_{45} = 1 = a_{66}$ or $a_{46} = 1 = a_{65}$. However, in either case by L.3 $a_{87} \neq -1$, $a_{88} = 0$ and $a_{89} \neq -1$ (from R.7). Thus R.8 and R.5 contradict L.2.

Hence $a_{79} \neq 1$ so $a_{79} = -1$. By the structure of (a) and L.2 $a_{77} = -1$. By L.3 $a_{57} = 0$ so either $a_{45} = 1 = a_{55}$ or $a_{46} = 1 = a_{56}$. Thus by L.3 $a_{88} = 0$, $a_{89} \neq 1$, so by L.2 on R.6 we must have $a_{67} = 1 = -a_{87}$. Thus we have

x	y	A	z	B	C	D	E	F
1	1	0	1	1	0	0	0	0
1	-1	1	1	0	0	0	0	0
1	-1	-1	0	0	1	0	0	0
-1	0	0					1	0
-1	0	0	0			0	-1	1
-1	0	0	0	0	0	1	-1	-1
0	0	1	-1	0	0	-1	0	-1
0	0	-1	0	-1	-1	-1	0	0

As above $a_3 < 0$, $b_3 < 0$, $c_3 < 0$. From T.8 $d_3 > 0$; from T.7 $f_3 < 0$; from T.6 $e_3 > 0$. However T.5 is now unbounded in the z-direction.

Hence (ii) cannot occur. Thus T.l/T.k in C.3 (or by symmetry C.9) is impossible for $l \neq k$ ($l, k = 7, 8, 9$).

(iii) Suppose T.7/T.8 in C.4 then we may clearly assume $a_{74} = 1 = -a_{84}$. By L.16 we must have $a_{44} = 0 = a_{54} = a_{64}$. By L.2 on R.1 $a_{75} = -1$. If $a_{73} = -1$, by L.3 $a_{72} = 0$ so by L.2 on R.3 $a_{76} = -1$; with the above coordinate system we have $a_1 < 0$, $b_1 < 0$, $c_1 < 0$ so that T.7 is unbounded in the x-direction. Thus $a_{73} \neq -1$ so by L.2 on R.2 $a_{72} = 1$ and by L.3 $a_{73} = 0$, $a_{76} \neq -1$. As the remaining unit of R.7 must have at least one unit of the opposite sign amongst rows 4, 5 and 6 in the same column $a_{76} = 0$. By $L.3$ $a_{82} = 0 = a_{85}$.

(A) Suppose $a_{94} \neq -1$ then by $L.16$ $a_{94} = 0$ and by $L.2$ on $R.1$ $a_{95} = -1$. Thus by (i), (ii) and the symmetry of the configuration we must have $T.7/T.9$ in $C.7$. By $L.2$ on $R.7$ we must have $a_{77} = -1$, $a_{97} = 1$.

Now if $a_{47} = a_{57} = 1$ then by $L.3$ $a_{45} = 0 = a_{55}$. By $L.2$ on $R.2$ one of $a_{92} = 1$ and $a_{93} = -1$ holds, so it is clear that $R.9$ with one of $R.4$ and $R.5$ contradicts $L.2$.

Thus we have $a_{57} = 0$. Hence if $R.7$ is to obey $L.2$ with rows 4, 5 and 6 we must have $a_{45} = 1 = a_{55}$ and $a_{67} = 1$. Thus $a_{46} = 1$. From (i) $a_{88} \neq -1$ so by $L.2$ on $R.4$ $a_{86} = -1$ and so by $L.3$ $a_{98} = 0 = a_{83}$. Also $a_{88} = 0$ for, if $a_{88} = 1$, by $L.3$ $a_{89} = 0 = a_{87}$ which is impossible by $L.1$. Thus by $L.2$ on $R.5$ and $R.6$ $a_{89} = -1 = a_{87}$. However, by $L.3$ $a_{99} \neq 1$ so $R.9$ and $R.6$ now contradict $L.2$. Thus (A) cannot arise.

Hence $a_{94} = -1$ so by $L.3$ $a_{92} = 0 = a_{95}$. Now if $a_{86} = 1 = -a_{96}$ by $L.2$ on $R.3$ $a_{83} = 1$ and $R.8$ with one of $R.4$, $R.5$ and $R.6$ contradicts $L.2$. Thus from the above we must have $T.8/T.9$ in $C.7$; we may clearly suppose $a_{87} = 1 = -a_{97}$. By $L.3$ $a_{77} = 0$ so by $L.2$ on $R.4$ and (i) $a_{45} = 1$. Further by (i), by $L.2$ on $R.4$ we must have $a_{46} = 1$, $a_{86} = -1 = a_{96}$ so $a_{67} = 1$. By $L.3$ $a_{83} = 0 = a_{93} = a_{98}$, $a_{99} \neq 1$ so $a_{99} = -1$. By $L.3$ $a_{56} = 0$ so $a_{55} = 1$. By $L.3$ $a_{78} = 0$, $a_{79} \neq 1$ so $R.7$ and $R.6$ contradict $L.2$. Hence (iii) cannot occur.

(iv) Suppose $T.7/T.8$ in $C.5$, then we may clearly assume $a_{75} = 1 = -a_{85}$ so by $L.2$ on $R.1$ $a_{74} = -1$. By $L.3$ $a_{72} = 0 = a_{84}$. By $L.16$ $a_{55} = 0$.

(A) Suppose $a_{95} = -1$ then by $L.3$ $a_{94} = 0$. Now we cannot have $a_{86} = 1 = -a_{96}$ for if so, by $L.3$ $a_{76} = 0 = a_{92}$, so by $L.2$ on $R.2$ $a_{93} = -1$; by $L.3$ $a_{73} = 0$ so $R.7$ and $R.3$ contradict $L.2$. Thus by the above and symmetry we can only have $T.8/T.9$ in $C.7$; we may clearly suppose $a_{87} = 1 = -a_{97}$. Thus from (iii) we cannot have $a_{47} = 1 = a_{57}$ so $a_{46} = 1 = a_{56}$. Also from $L.3$ $a_{77} = 0$. Now $a_{86} = -1 = a_{96}$ is impossible for if so by $L.3$ $a_{82} = 0 = a_{92}$ and we have a contradiction to $L.6$ with $r_0 = 2$. Hence by $L.2$ on $R.4$ with $R.8$ and $R.9$ and (i) we must have either $a_{45} = 1$ or $a_{47} = 1$. Hence by $L.2$ on $R.4$ and (i) $a_{76} = -1$. By $L.3$ $a_{73} = 0 = a_{78}$, $a_{79} \neq -1$ so we must have $a_{79} = 1$. Thus by $L.3$ $a_{44} = 0 = a_{64}$. Hence either $a_{45} = 1 = a_{67}$ or $a_{47} = 1 = a_{65}$

but in both cases by $L.3$ $a_{98} = 0$, $a_{96} \neq -1$ and $a_{99} \neq -1$ (from $R.7$). Thus $R.9$ and $R.5$ contradict $L.2$ and so (A) cannot arise. Hence $a_{95} \neq -1$ so by $L.2$ on $R.1$ $a_{94} = -1$; by $L.3$ $a_{92} = 0$.

(B) Suppose $T.7/T.9$ in $C.6$. Now if $a_{76} = 1$, by $L.2$ on $R.3$ $a_{73} = 1$, so that $R.7$ and $R.5$ contradict $L.2$. Hence we have $a_{76} = -1$, $a_{96} = 1$. Hence by $L.2$ on $R.3$ $a_{93} = 1$. By (ii) $a_{83} \neq -1$ so by $L.2$ on $R.2$ $a_{82} = 1$. By $L.3$ $a_{86} = 0$. By $L.16$ $a_{56} = 0$ so we must have $a_{47} = 1 = a_{57}$. So by (iii) the only possible value of l for which $T.8/T.9$ in $C.l$ is $l = 5$. However, $l = 5$ is impossible for then $R.9$ and $R.5$ contradict $L.2$. Thus (B) cannot arise.

Hence from the above we can only have $T.7/T.9$ in $C.7$, i.e. $a_{77} = -a_{97} \neq 0$. By (iii) we cannot have $a_{47} = a_{57} = 1$ so $a_{57} = 0$ and $a_{46} = 1 = a_{56}$. Hence if $a_{73} = 1$, $R.7$ with $R.5$ contradicts $L.2$. Thus $a_{73} \neq 1$ so by $L.4$ on $R.3$ $a_{76} = -1$. By $L.3$ $a_{44} = 0$. Now $a_{86} = 0$ for if $a_{86} = -1$ by $L.2$ on $R.2$ $a_{83} = -1$ since $a_{82} = 0$ by $L.3$; by (ii) therefore $a_{93} \neq 1$ so by $L.2$ on $R.3$ $a_{96} = -1$ and $C.6$ represents a tetre which is impossible. Further, $a_{83} \neq 1$ for if so $a_{82} = 0$ by $L.3$, so that $R.2$ and $R.8$ contradict $L.2$. Hence by $L.2$ on $R.3$ $a_{82} = 1$. By (i) and $L.2$ on $R.8$ we must have either $a_{45} = 1$ or $a_{47} = 1 = -a_{87}$; if the latter, then $a_{97} = -a_{77} \neq a_{87}$ by $L.3$, so that, in either case by $L.2$ on $R.4$ $a_{96} = -1$. By $L.3$ $a_{93} = 0 = a_{98} = a_{47}$ so $a_{45} = 1$. Thus by $L.16$ $a_{95} \neq 1$ so $a_{95} = 0$. Thus a_{99} is a unit and by $L.3$ $a_{99} = 1$ so $a_{64} = 0$, $a_{67} = 1 = a_{97}$, $a_{77} = -1$. By $L.2$ on $R.8$ and $R.9$ and (ii) we must have $a_{87} = -1$. Thus by $L.3$ $a_{88} = 0$ and $a_{89} \neq -1$ (on $R.9$). Hence $R.8$ and $R.5$ contradict $L.2$.

Thus (iv) cannot occur.

Hence the only possible values of l for which $T.u/T.v$ in $C.l$ where $u \neq v$ ($u,v = 7$, 8, 9) are $l = 6$ and $l = 7$. Thus considering the three tetrahedra both $l = 6$ and $l = 7$ must be used. Hence from (iii) and (iv) $a_{46} \neq 1$, $a_{47} \neq 1$, so by $L.16$ we must have $a_{44} = 1 = a_{45} = a_{55}$. Thus

x	y	A	z	B	C	D	E	F
1	1	0	1	1	0	0	0	0
1	-1	1	1	0	0	0	0	0
1	-1	-1	0	0	1	0	0	0
-1	0	0	1	1	0	0	1	0
-1	0	0	0	1	0	0	-1	1
-1	0	0	0	0			-1	-1

As $a_{j2} \neq -1$ ($j = 7, 8, 9$) and neither $C.4$ nor $C.5$ represents tetres, by $L.2$ on $R.1$ (-1)s occur in both $C.4$ and $C.5$. Hence none of the tetrahedra are naiks.

Choose the coordinate system shown. From boundedness we have: from T.1 $b_1 < 0$, $b_2 < 0$; from T.2 $a_1 < 0$, $a_2 > 0$; from T.3 $c_1 < 0$, $c_2 > 0$; from T.4 $e_1 > 0$, $e_2 > 0$; from T.5 $f_1 > 0$, $f_2 > 0$. Thus for T.6 to be bounded in the x-direction $a_{66} \neq 1$, i.e. $a_{67} = 1$. Hence from T.6 $d_1 > 0$, $d_2 > 0$. By the symmetry of the first six rows, we may therefore suppose without loss of generality that $a_{74} = -1 = a_{84} = a_{95}$ (from $L.2$ on $R.7$, $R.8$ and $R.9$ with $R.1$). By $L.3$ $a_{72} = 0 = a_{82} = a_{98}$.

If T.7/T.8 in $C.7$ we may clearly suppose $a_{77} = 1 = -a_{87}$. Hence by $L.2$ on $R.3$ we see that either $a_{73} = 1$ or $a_{76} = -1$. Thus for $R.7$ to obey $L.2$ we must have $a_{78} = 1$. However, if $a_{73} = 1$, T.7 is unbounded in the y-direction whilst if $a_{76} = -1$ T.7 is unbounded in the x-direction.

Hence T.7/T.8 in $C.6$ and we may suppose $a_{76} = 1 = -a_{86}$ so by $L.2$ on $R.3$ $a_{73} = 1$. Thus for $R.7$ to obey $L.2$ we must have $a_{78} = 1$. However, T.7 is now unbounded in the y-direction.

Hence VI cannot occur.

We have thus shown that a 9-con containing nine D_m-planes, one of which is a tetre, cannot exist. Hence Theorem 4 now becomes:

THEOREM 5. If a 9-con containing a tetre exists, then it must contain at least ten and at most eleven D_m-planes (m not necessarily being a fixed integer).

CHAPTER SIX

ON THE NON-EXISTENCE OF A 9-CON CONTAINING ELEVEN D_m-PLANES, ONE OF WHICH IS A TETRE

WE BEGIN the chapter by showing that if a 9-con containing a tetre exists, then it can contain at most two naiks. The rest of the chapter is devoted to proving that a certain set of D_m-planes cannot be contained in a 9-con. From these two facts we deduce that if a 9-con containing a tetre exists, then it must contain exactly ten D_m-planes and also it can contain at most one naik.

LEMMA 35. If a 9-con containing ten D_m-planes, one of which is a tetre exists, at most two of the tetrahedra of the 9-con can be naiks. Further, if two naiks do occur in the 9-con, the D_m-planes must be one tetre, one nodo, two dotres, three dodos and three ununs.

Proof. Suppose a 9-con containing ten D_m-planes, one of which is a tetre, exists.

Clearly at most one of the D_m-planes can be a uno for, if there are more, by the remarks of Chapter Four the case has been dealt with in the previous chapter.

Now suppose one of the D_m-planes is a notre. Since a notre has a surplus of 6 the eight D_m-planes other than the notre and tetre have a total surplus of $36 - 30 + 3 - 6 = 3$. Thus at least five D_m-planes have a surplus of zero. Hence as we can have at most one uno at least four dotres must occur and this is impossible by $L.31$.

Thus suppose a nodo occurs amongst the D_m-planes. Since a nodo has a surplus of 3 the eight D_m-planes other than the nodo and tetre have a total surplus of $36 - 30 + 3 - 3 = 6$.

Thus at least two D_m-planes have a surplus of zero so we must have two dotres for, if a uno occurs, by the remarks of Chapter Four the case has been dealt with in the previous chapter. By $L.31$ another dotre cannot occur, so we need only consider the case when the six remaining D_m-planes all have a surplus of 1. As the only D_m-planes which have a surplus of 1 are ununs and dodos and since the six planes must contain eighteen faces of the 9-con we can only have three dodos and three ununs.

As a naik must have a face contained in a uno, or a nodo or a notre, the lemma is proved.

We shall use the following lemma.

LEMMA 36. If a dotre and two dodos occur in a 9-con then their units in the matrix representation fall in at least seven distinct rows.

Proof. Suppose the units fall in only six distinct rows. Let $C.1$ represent the dotre and $C.2$ and $C.3$ the dodos. We may clearly assume $a_{j1} = 1$ $(j = 1, 2, 3)$, $a_{j1} = -1$ $(j = 4, 5)$, $a_{j1} = 0$ $(j > 5)$. By $L.23$ on $C.1$ and $C.2$ and then on $C.1$ and $C.3$ we must have $a_{j2} = 0 = a_{j3}$ $(j = 4, 5)$. Thus the units of $C.2$ and $C.3$ can fall in at most four distinct rows and this is impossible by $L.22$.

We now consider the case when one tetre, two dotres and two dodos occur in a 9-con containing ten D_m-planes. Let $C.1$ represent the tetre, $C.2$ and $C.3$ which we assume contain only two (-1)s, the dotres and $C.4$ and $C.5$ the dodos.

For $C.l$ $(l = 2$ or $3)$ four effective cases arise:

(a) Two (-1)s in $R.1$, $R.2$ and $R.3$ or two in $R.4$, $R.5$ and $R.6$.

(b) One (-1) in $R.1$, $R.2$ and $R.3$ and one in $R.4$, $R.5$ and $R.6$.

(c) One (-1) in $R.j$ $(j = 1, \ldots 6)$ and one in $R.7$, $R.8$ and $R.9$.

(d) No (-1)s in $R.j$ $(j = 1, \ldots 6)$.

Suppose (a) occurs; by symmetry we may assume $a_{12} = -1 = a_{22}$, then by $L.3$ $a_{42} = 0 = a_{62}$ so three of the a_{j2} $(j = 3, 7, 8, 9)$ are $(+1)$s. By $L.24$ $a_{1l} = 0 = a_{2l}$ $(l = 3, 4, 5)$.

9*

If $a_{33} = -1$ then by $L.3$ $a_{j3} \neq 1$ $(j = 4, 5, 6)$ so we have $a_{l3} = 1$ $(l = 7, 8, 9)$. Thus we may suppose $a_{43} = -1$. By $L.5$ $a_{l2} = 1$ $(l = 7, 8, 9)$ is impossible so we may assume $a_{32} = 1 = a_{72} = a_{82}$. By $L.17$ $T.3$ is a naik and $a_{34} = 0 = a_{35}$. Further, we may assume $a_{44} = 0 = a_{45}$ for, if a_{44} say is a unit, $T.4$ is also a naik, so by $L.35$ we may suppose $C.6$ is a dodo. By $L.17$ $a_{45} = 0 = a_{46}$ so by interchanging $C.4$ and $C.6$ we have the above assumption. However, $C.4$ and $C.5$ now contradict $L.22$.

Thus $a_{33} \neq -1$ and two cases therefore arise: (i) $a_{33} = 1$ and (ii) $a_{33} = 0$.

(i) Suppose $a_{33} = 1$ then by $L.3$ $a_{j3} \neq -1$ $(j = 4, 5, 6)$ so we may assume $a_{73} = -1 = a_{83}$. Thus we may also put $a_{43} = 1$ and by $L.5$ $a_{63} = 0$. Further, as three of the a_{j2} $(j = 3, 7, 8, 9)$ are $(+1)$s we may suppose $a_{72} = 1$. By $L.3$ we must have $a_{34} = 0 = a_{35}$ for if a_{34} say is a unit the only possible value of l for which $a_{l4} = -a_{34}$ is $l = 9$. Hence by $L.22$ we may assume $a_{44} = 1$ so by $L.17$ $a_{45} = 0$. By $L.3$ $a_{74} \neq -1$ so either (A) $a_{74} = 1$ or (B) $a_{74} = 0$.

(A) Suppose $a_{74} = 1$, then by $L.3$ $a_{84} \neq -1$, so $a_{84} = 0$ and by $L.17$ $a_{75} = 0$. By $L.22$ a_{85} must be a unit so we assume $a_{85} = 1$. Since $a_{j3} = 1$ for j one of 5 and 9, by $L.3$ $a_{j4} \neq -1$, $a_{j5} \neq -1$, so clearly $a_{64} = -1 = a_{65}$. Now if $a_{93} = 1$, a_{94} and $a_{95} \neq -1$ so we must have $a_{54} = -1 = a_{55}$ which is impossible by $L.4$ on $R.5$ and $R.6$. Thus $a_{93} \neq 1$ so $a_{93} = 0$, $a_{53} = 1$. Hence $a_{94} = -1 = a_{95}$, $a_{55} = 1$ since $a_{54} \neq -1$, $a_{55} \neq -1$; also $a_{54} = 0$. Let $a_{16} = 1$ then by $L.2$ we may suppose $a_{26} = -1$, so by $L.3$ $a_{j6} = 0$ $(j = 4, 5, 6, 7)$. Let $a_{47} = 1$ then by $L.2$ $a_{57} = -1$ and by $L.3$ the remaining spaces of $C.7$ are zeros. Let $a_{68} = 1$ then by $L.2$ $a_{98} = -1$ and by $L.3$ $a_{j8} = 0$ $(j = 4, 5, 7, 8)$.

Suppose $a_{38} = 0$. Now $R.3$ and $R.9$ clearly cannot obey $L.2$ in $C.2$ nor in fact can they in $C.6$ for if $a_{36} = -a_{96} \neq 0$ then by $L.3$ $a_{32} = 0 = a_{92}$ which is impossible by definition of $C.2$. Thus by $L.2$ we may suppose $a_{39} = 1 = -a_{99}$. By $L.1$ $a_{92} = 0 = a_{96}$. By $L.6$ with $r_0 = 9$ we may therefore suppose $a_{18} = 1 = a_{29}$. By $L.1$ $a_{19} = 0 = a_{28}$ and we have a contradiction to $L.15B$ in rows 1, 2, 4, 5, 6 and 9.

Hence $a_{38} \neq 0$; by $L.3$ $a_{38} \neq -1$ so $a_{38} = 1$. By $L.3$ $a_{18} \neq -1$, $a_{28} \neq -1$ so by $L.6$ with $r_0 = 3$ we must have $a_{32} = 1$. By $L.3$

$a_{36} = 0$ and we have

x	A	y	z	B	C	D	E
1	−1	0	0	0	1	0	
1	−1	0	0	0	−1	0	
1	1	1	0	0	0	0	1
−1	0	1	1	0	0	1	0
−1	0	1	0	1	0	−1	0
−1	0	0	−1	−1	0	0	1
0	1	−1	1	0	0	0	0
0		−1	0	1		0	0
0			0	−1	−1	0	−1

Choose the coordinate system shown. From boundedness we have: from T.4 $d_1 > 0$; from T.5 $b_1 > 0$; from T.6 $e_1 > 0$; from T.3 $a_1 < 0$.

Now if $a_{92} = 1$, T.9 is unbounded in the x-direction so $a_{92} = 0$, $a_{82} = 1$. By L.3 $a_{86} = 0$. Now by symmetry we may clearly suppose $c_1 \geqslant 0$. Thus $a_{18} \neq 1$ if T.1 is to be bounded and $a_{96} \neq -1$ if T.9 is to be bounded. Hence by L.2 we may suppose $a_{19} = 1 = -a_{99}$. By L.1 $a_{96} = 0 = a_{18}$. By L.4 $a_{29} \neq 1$ so by L.2 on R.9 $a_{28} = 1$. Thus by L.3 the remaining spaces of C.9 are zeros. Let $a_{7.10} = 1$ then by L.2 $a_{8.10} = -1$ and by L.3 the remaining spaces of C.10 are zeros. Hence we have

x	A	B	y	z	C	D	E	F	G
1	−1	0	0	0	1	0	0	1	0
1	−1	0	0	0	−1	0	1	0	0
1	1	1	0	0	0	0	1	0	0
−1	0	1	1	0	0	1	0	0	0
−1	0	1	0	1	0	−1	0	0	0
−1	0	0	−1	−1	0	0	1	0	0
0	1	−1	1	0	0	0	0	0	1
0	1	−1	0	1	0	0	0	0	−1
0	0	0	−1	−1	0	0	−1	−1	0

Choose the coordinate system shown. From boundedness we have: from T.6 $e_1 > 0$; from T.3 at least one of $a_1 < 0$ and $b_1 < 0$ holds.

Now if $a_1 b_1 \leqslant 0$ then clearly one of T.7 and T.8 would be unbounded. Thus $a_1 b_1 > 0$ so that both $a_1 < 0$ and $b_1 < 0$.

However, since $b_1 < 0$ one of T.4 and T.5 must be unbounded. Hence (A) cannot occur.

(B) Suppose $a_{74} = 0$ then by $L.22$ we may assume $a_{75} = 1$.

(B_1) Suppose $a_{53} = 1$ then $a_{93} = 0$. By $L.3$ $a_{55} \neq -1$ whilst if $a_{55} = 1$ by interchanging $R.4$ and $R.5$ and $C.4$ and $C.5$ we have case (A). Thus $a_{55} = 0$. By $L.22$ a_{54} is a unit and by $L.4$ $a_{54} \neq 1$ so $a_{54} = -1$. By $L.3$ $a_{84} = 0$ so we may suppose by symmetry $a_{64} = -1$, $a_{94} = 1$. Now both a_{65} and a_{95} are units so by $L.3$ we must have $a_{65} = -1 = a_{95}$, $a_{85} = 1$. Hence by $L.4$ $a_{82} \neq 1$ so $a_{82} = 0$, $a_{32} = 1 = a_{92}$. Let $a_{96} = -1$ then by $L.2$ $a_{36} = 1 = a_{46}$ and by $L.3$ the remaining spaces of $C.6$ are zeros. Let $a_{57} = 1$ then by $L.2$ $a_{67} = -1$ and by $L.3$ the remaining spaces of $C.7$ are zeros. Thus we have

A	x	y	B	C	z	E
1	-1	0	0	0	0	0
1	-1	0	0	0	0	0
1	1	1	0	0	1	0
-1	0	1	1	0	1	0
-1	0	1	-1	0	0	1
-1	0	0	-1	-1	0	-1
0	1	-1	0	1	0	0
0	0	-1	0	1	0	0
0	1	0	1	-1	-1	0

Choose the coordinate system shown. From boundedness we have: from T.3 $a_2 < 0$; from T.4 $b_2 < 0$; from T.5 $e_2 < 0$; from T.6 $c_2 > 0$. However T.9 is now unbounded. Hence (B_1) cannot arise so $a_{53} \neq 1$; thus $a_{53} = 0$, $a_{93} = 1$. Two cases now arise: (B_2) $a_{82} = 1$ and (B_3) $a_{82} = 0$.

(B_2) Suppose $a_{82} = 1$ then by symmetry and (A) we may clearly suppose $a_{84} = 0$, so by $L.22$ a_{85} is a unit. By $L.4$ $a_{85} \neq 1$ so $a_{85} = -1$. By $L.3$ $a_{95} = 0$ so we may suppose $a_{55} = 1 = -a_{65}$. As a_{54} and a_{64} are both units by $L.3$ we must have $a_{54} = a_{64} = -1$, $a_{94} = 1$. By $L.2$ we may suppose $a_{16} = 1 = -a_{26}$, then by $L.3$ $a_{j6} = 0$ $(j = 4, 5, 6, 7, 8)$. Let $a_{57} = 1$ then by $L.2$ $a_{77} = -1$ and by $L.3$ the remaining spaces of $C.7$ are zeros. Let $a_{68} = 1$ then by $L.2$ $a_{88} = -1$ and by $L.3$ the remaining spaces of $C.8$ are zeros. Let $a_{49} = 1$ then by $L.2$ $a_{99} = -1$ and by $L.3$ $a_{j9} = 0$ $(j = 5, 6, 7, 8)$. If $a_{92} = 1$ then $a_{32} = 0$ and by $L.2$ on $R.9$ $a_{39} = 1$;

thus by $L.3$ $a_{19} = 0 = a_{29}$ and we have a contradiction to $L.6$ with $r_0 = 3$. Hence $a_{92} \neq 1$ so $a_{92} = 0$, $a_{32} = 1$. By $L.3$ $a_{36} = 0$. Now if $a_{19} = 0 = a_{29}$ we have a contradiction to $L.6$ with $r_0 = 9$, so we may suppose a_{19} is a unit. By $L.3$ $a_{19} \neq -1$ so $a_{19} = 1$. Clearly by $L.3$ and $L.4$ $a_{29} = 0$. By $L.3$ $a_{39} \neq -1$ so two cases now arise: (B_{21}) $a_{39} = 1$ and (B_{22}) $a_{39} = 0$.

(B_{21}) Suppose $a_{39} = 1$ then we have

A	x	y	B	C	D	E	F	z
1	-1	0	0	0	1	0	0	1
1	-1	0	0	0	-1	0	0	0
1	1	1	0	0	0	0	0	1
-1	0	1	1	0	0	0	0	1
-1	0	0	-1	1	0	1	0	0
-1	0	0	-1	-1	0	0	1	0
0	1	-1	0	1	0	-1	0	0
0	1	-1	0	-1	0	0	-1	0
0	0	1	1	0		0	0	-1

Choose the coordinate system shown. From boundedness we have: from T.3 $a_3 < 0$; from T.4 $b_3 < 0$; from T.7 $c_3 e_3 > 0$; from T.8 $c_3 f_3 < 0$.

Hence if $c_3 \geqslant 0$ T.5 is unbounded whilst if $c_3 \leqslant 0$ T.6 is unbounded.

Thus (B_{21}) cannot arise.

(B_{22}) If $a_{39} = 0$ let $a_{3.10} = 1$ then by $L.2$ $a_{9.10} = -1$ so $a_{96} = 0$. Thus by $L.2$ $a_{2.10} = 1$. By $L.3$ the remaining spaces of $C.10$ are zeros. Thus we have

x	A	y	B	C	D	E	F	G	z
1	-1	0	0	0	1	0	0	1	0
1	-1	0	0	0	-1	0	0	0	1
1	1	1	0	0	0	0	0	0	1
-1	0	1	1	0	0	0	0	1	0
-1	0	0	-1	1	0	1	0	0	0
-1	0	0	-1	-1	0	0	1	0	0
0	1	-1	0	1	0	-1	0	0	0
0	1	-1	0	-1	0	0	-1	0	0
0	0	1	1	0	0	0	0	-1	-1

Choose the coordinate system shown. From boundedness we have: from T.3 $a_1 < 0$; from T.2 $d_1 > 0$; from T.1 $g_1 < 0$; from T.4 $b_1 > 0$. However, T.9 is now unbounded so (B_{22}) cannot arise.

Hence (B_2) cannot occur.

(B_3) Suppose $a_{82} = 0$ then $a_{32} = 1 = a_{92}$. Now a_{94} and a_{95} cannot both be units for if they were $R.9$ and $R.3$ would contradict $L.2$. Furthermore, a_{84} and a_{85} cannot both be units for if they are, we have a contradiction to $L.6$ with $r_0 = 8$. Hence we must have either a_{84} and a_{95} are both units or a_{85} and a_{94} are both units. If the former then by $L.3$ $a_{84} = 1 = a_{95}$ so that we would have $a_{54} = a_{64} = -1$, $a_{55} = a_{65} = -1$ which is impossible by $L.4$. Thus $a_{84} = 0 = a_{95}$ and a_{85} and a_{94} are both units. Let $a_{36} = 1$, by $L.2$ $a_{96} = -1$ and by $L.3$ $a_{j6} = 0$ $(j = 1, 2, 7, 8)$. Hence we have

x	y	z	A	B	C
1	-1	0	0	0	0
1	-1	0	0	0	0
1	1	1	0	0	1
-1	0	1	1	0	
-1	0	0			
-1	0	0			
0	1	-1	0	1	0
0	0	-1	0		0
0	1	1		0	-1

Choose the coordinate system shown. From boundedness we have: from $T.3$ $c_1 < 0$, $c_2 < 0$. Now if $a_{94} = 1$ then by $L.2$ $a_{46} = 1$; from $T.9$ $a_1 < 0$ and $T.4$ is then unbounded in the x-direction. Thus since a_{94} must be a unit, we have $a_{94} = -1$ and so we may suppose $a_{54} = 1 = -a_{64}$. Hence by $L.3$ $a_{55} = a_{65} = -1$, $a_{85} = 1$. By $L.2$ $a_{66} = 1$ so by $L.3$ $a_{46} = 0 = a_{56}$. Let $a_{47} = 1$ then by $L.2$ $a_{57} = -1$ and by $L.3$ the remaining spaces of $C.7$ are zeros. Thus we have

x	y	z	A	B	C	D
1	-1	0	0	0	0	0
1	-1	0	0	0	0	0
1	1	1	0	0	1	0
-1	0	1	1	0	0	1
-1	0	0	1	-1	0	-1
-1	0	0	-1	-1	1	0
0	1	-1	0	1	0	0
0	0	-1	0	1	0	0
0	1	1	-1	0	-1	0

From T.9 $a_2 > 0$; from T.6 $b_2 < 0$; from T.4 $d_2 < 0$. However, T.5 is now unbounded so (B$_3$) cannot arise.

Hence (B) cannot occur and so neither can (i).

(ii) We have $a_{33} = 0$. By $L.3$ a_{34} and a_{35} cannot both be units, so we may assume $a_{34} = 0$. By $L.2$ we may suppose $a_{16} = 1 = -a_{26}$ then by $L.3$ $a_{j6} = 0$ $(j = 4, 5, 6)$. Further from $L.36$ on $C.3$, $C.4$ and $C.5$ we may suppose $a_{35} = 1$.

(A) Suppose $a_{43} = -1$ then neither $a_{53} = -1$ nor $a_{63} = -1$, for, if say $a_{53} = -1$, by $L.24$ $a_{44} = 0 = a_{45} = a_{54} = a_{55}$ and $C.4$ and $C.5$ contradict $L.22$. Thus we may suppose $a_{73} = -1$. By $L.23$ $a_{44} = 0 = a_{74}$. Clearly we may assume $a_{53} = 1 = a_{83}$. Two cases now arise: (A$_1$) $a_{45} = 1$; (A$_2$) $a_{45} \neq 1$.

(A$_1$) Suppose $a_{45} = 1$ then by $L.3$ $a_{j5} \neq -1$ $(j = 5, 6, 8)$ so we must have $a_{75} = -1 = a_{95}$ and $a_{j5} = 0$ $(j = 5, 6, 8)$. Thus by $L.3$ $a_{93} \neq 1$ so $a_{63} = 1$. By $L.4$ $a_{54} = a_{64} = \pm 1$ is impossible so we may suppose $a_{54} = 1 = -a_{64}$ and $a_{84} = 1 = -a_{94}$.

Now T.4 is a naik. Hence if either T.1 or T.2 is a naik by $L.35$ we may suppose $C.7$ is a dodo, as $C.6$ is not a dodo by $L.24$. By $L.24$ $a_{17} = 0 = a_{27}$ so by $L.3$ a_{37} cannot be a unit either. However, $C.3$, $C.4$ and $C.7$ now contradict $L.26$.

Thus both T.1 and T.2 are dhoats and so we must have $a_{j6} = 0$ $(j \geqslant 3)$. Let $a_{57} = 1$, then by $L.2$ $a_{87} = -1$ so by $L.3$ $a_{j7} = 0$ $(j = 4, 6, 7, 9)$. Let $a_{68} = 1$ then by $L.2$ $a_{98} = -1$ so by $L.3$ $a_{j8} = 0$ $(j = 3, 4, 5, 8)$. If $a_{82} = 0$ we may assume $a_{89} = -1$, then by $L.6$ with $r_0 = 8$ we may further suppose $a_{17} = 1 = a_{29}$. However, rows 1, 2, 4, 5, 6 and 8 now contradict $L.15$B.

Thus $a_{82} \neq 0$ so $a_{82} = 1$. By $L.2$ on $R.8$ $a_{37} = 1$ and by $L.3$ $a_{17} = 0 = a_{27}$. Hence by $L.6$ with $r_0 = 3$ we must have $a_{32} = 1$. Thus we have

x	A	y	B	C	D	E	z
1	−1	0	0	0	1	0	
1	−1	0	0	0	−1	0	
1	1	0	0	1	0	1	0
−1	0	−1	0	1	0	0	0
−1	0	1	1	0	0	1	0
−1	0	1	−1	0	0	0	1
0		−1	0	−1	0	0	
0	1	1	1	0	0	−1	0
0		0	−1	−1	0	0	−1

Choose the coordinate system shown. From boundedness we have: from T.6 $b_2 > 0$; from T.5 $e_2 < 0$; from T.8 $a_2 < 0$; from T.3 $c_2 > 0$.

Hence if $a_{92} = 1$, T.9 is unbounded. Thus $a_{92} = 0$, $a_{72} = 1$. Hence if $a_{78} \neq 0$, T.7 is unbounded, so $a_{78} = 0$. Thus let $a_{79} = 1$, then by L.2 $a_{99} = -1$. Let $F = 0$ be the equation of the plane represented by $C.9$. From T.7 $f_2 > 0$. However, T.9 is now unbounded, so (A_1) cannot occur.

(A_2) We have $a_{45} \neq 1$; by L.3 $a_{45} \neq -1$ so $a_{45} = 0$. Thus by L.22 a_{75} is a unit. Now if $a_{75} = 1$ by L.3 $a_{j5} \neq -1$ $(j = 5, 6, 8)$ so only one (-1) can occur in $C.5$ which is impossible. Hence $a_{75} = -1$ so by L.3 $a_{55} = 0$. By L.22 we may suppose $a_{54} = 1$.

If $a_{63} = 1$ then by L.3 $a_{65} = 0$ and by L.4 $a_{64} \neq 1$ so $a_{64} = -1$. Thus we may suppose $a_{84} = 1 = -a_{94}$. By L.3 $a_{85} \neq 1$ so $a_{85} = -1$. But now $a_{95} \neq 1$ by L.3, so $C.5$ does not represent a dodo.

Thus $a_{63} \neq 1$ so $a_{63} = 0$, $a_{93} = 1$. Hence by L.3 $a_{85} \neq 1$, $a_{95} \neq 1$ so $a_{65} = 1$ and we may suppose $a_{85} = -1$, $a_{95} = 0$ by symmetry. Thus by L.3 $a_{64} = a_{84} = -1$, $a_{94} = 1$. By L.6 with $r_0 = 8$ we must have $a_{82} = 1$. Let $a_{57} = 1$ then by L.2 $a_{97} = -1$ and by L.3 $a_{j7} = 0$ $(j = 4, 6, 7, 8)$. Let $a_{68} = -1$ then by L.2 $a_{48} = 1$ and by L.3 $a_{j8} = 0$ $(j = 1, 2, 3, 5, 8, 9)$.

Suppose $a_{92} = 1$ then by L.2 on R.9 $a_{37} = 1$ and by L.3 $a_{17} = 0 = a_{27}$. By L.6 with $r_0 = 3$ we must have $a_{32} = 1$. However, rows 3, 4, 8 and 9 now contradict L.9. Thus $a_{92} \neq 1$ so $a_{92} = 0$, $a_{32} = 1 = a_{72}$. By L.3 $a_{36} = 0 = a_{76} = a_{86}$. If $a_{17} \neq 1$, $a_{27} \neq 1$ we have a contradiction to L.6 with $r_0 = 9$ so we may suppose $a_{17} = 1$. By L.3 and L.4 $a_{27} = 0$. Let $a_{29} = 1$. Now if $a_{99} = -1$ we have a contradiction to L.15B in rows 1, 2, 4, 5, 6, and 9. Thus $a_{99} \neq -1$ so by L.2 on R.2 $a_{96} = 1$. Thus by L.2 on R.9 $a_{37} = 1$ and we have

x	A	y	z	B	C	D	E
1	−1	0	0	0	1	1	0
1	−1	0	0	0	−1	0	0
1	1	0	0	1	0	1	0
−1	0	−1	0	0	0	0	1
−1	0	1	1	0	0	1	0
−1	0	0	−1	1	0	0	−1
0	1	−1	0	−1	0	0	
0	1	1	−1	−1	0	0	0
0	0	1	1	0	1	−1	0

Choose the coordinate system shown. From boundedness we have: from T.5 $d_1 > 0$; from T.9 $c_1 > 0$; from T.1 $a_1 > 0$; from T.8 $b_1 > 0$. However, T.3 is now unbounded.

Hence (A_2) cannot arise and so neither can (A).

Thus $a_{43} \neq -1$ and by symmetry $a_{53} \neq -1$, $a_{63} \neq -1$ so we may suppose $a_{73} = -1 = a_{83}$. Hence by $L.5$ we may further assume $a_{43} = a_{53} = 1 = a_{93}$, $a_{63} = 0$. By $L.23$ we have $a_{74} = 0 = a_{84}$ so the remaining spaces of $C.4$ are units. By $L.4$ $a_{44} = a_{54} \neq 0$ is impossible, so we may suppose $a_{44} = 1$, $a_{54} = -1 = a_{64}$, $a_{94} = 1$. By $L.17$ $a_{45} = 0 = a_{55}$. Now $a_{95} = 0$, for if it was a unit, by $L.3$ there could be at most one unit of the opposite sign in $C.5$. Hence a_{65} is a unit, and by $L.3$ $a_{65} \neq -1$ so $a_{65} = 1$, $a_{75} = -1 = a_{85}$. By $L.4$ $a_{72} = a_{82} = 1$ is impossible so we may suppose $a_{82} = 0$, $a_{32} = a_{72} = a_{92} = 1$. By $L.3$ $a_{36} = 0 = a_{76} = a_{96}$. Let $a_{57} = 1$, then by $L.2$ $a_{67} = -1$ and the remaining spaces of $C.7$ are zeros. Let $a_{98} = 1$ then by $L.2$ $a_{38} = -1 = a_{48}$ and the remaining spaces of $C.8$ are zeros by $L.3$. Thus we have

A	x	y	z	B	C	D	E
1	−1	0	0	0	1	0	0
1	−1	0	0	0	−1	0	0
1	1	0	0	1	0	0	−1
−1	0	1	1	0	0	0	−1
−1	0	1	−1	0	0	1	0
−1	0	0	−1	1	0	−1	0
0	1	−1	0	−1	0	0	0
0	0	−1	0	−1	0	0	0
0	1	1	1	0	0	0	1

Choose the coordinate system shown. From boundedness we have: from T.9 $e_1 < 0$; from T.4 $a_1 > 0$; from T.3 $b_1 < 0$; from T.5 $d_1 > 0$. However T.6 is now unbounded. Hence (ii) cannot occur and so neither can (a).

Consider (b). Let $a_{12} = -1 = a_{42}$, then by $L.3$ $a_{j2} = 0$ $(j = 2, 3, 5, 6)$ so $a_{l2} = 1$ $(l = 7, 8, 9)$. As $a_{53} = a_{63} = -1$ is equivalent to (a) two cases now arise: (A) $a_{53} = -1$ or $a_{63} = -1$ and (B) $a_{53} \neq -1$ and $a_{63} \neq -1$.

(A) We may clearly suppose $a_{53} = -1$. Now $a_{j3} \neq -1$ $(j = 1, 2, 3)$ for if one of them was, we would have to have $a_{m3} = 1$

($m = 7, 8, 9$) which is impossible by $L.5$. As $a_{43} \neq -1$ and $a_{63} \neq -1$ we may suppose $a_{73} = -1$. By $L.3$ $a_{j3} = 0$ ($j = 1, 2, 3, 4$) so $a_{63} = 1 = a_{83} = a_{93}$. Now $a_{44} = 0$ for if $a_{44} = 1$ say, then by $L.3$ we must have $a_{54} = -1 = a_{64}$ and by $L.3$ the remaining spaces of $C.4$ are zeros so that $C.4$ does not represent a dodo. Thus $a_{44} = 0 = a_{45}$. Hence by $L.3$ we must have $a_{54} = 0 = a_{55}$ for if say $a_{54} = 1$ then the only possible position for a (-1) would be a_{74}. Further $a_{64} = 0 = a_{65}$ for if say $a_{64} = 1$ by $L.3$ we can only have $-1 = a_{84} = a_{94}$ which is impossible by $L.4$. Thus by $L.22$ we may suppose $a_{14} = 1$ so by $L.3$ we must have $a_{24} = -1 = a_{34}$. Now if $a_{74} = 0$ we may suppose by $L.22$ $a_{75} = 1$ so that by $L.3$ we can only have $a_{25} = -1 = a_{35}$, which is impossible by $L.4$. Thus $a_{74} \neq 0$ so $a_{74} = 1$, $a_{84} = a_{94} = 0$. Hence by $L.22$ both a_{85} and a_{95} are units so by $L.4$ we may suppose $a_{85} = 1 = -a_{95}$. By $L.3$ $a_{15} = 0 = a_{75}$ so we may suppose $a_{25} = 1 = -a_{35}$. Let $a_{86} = 1$ then by $L.2$ $a_{26} = -1 = a_{66}$ and by $L.3$ the remaining spaces of $C.6$ are zeros. Let $a_{97} = 1$ then by $L.2$ $a_{37} = -1 = a_{67}$ and by $L.3$ the remaining spaces of $C.7$ are zeros. However $R.4$ and $R.6$ now contradict $L.2$ so (A) cannot occur.

(B) We have $a_{53} \neq -1$, $a_{63} \neq -1$. By symmetry $a_{23} \neq -1$, $a_{33} \neq -1$ and by $L.17$ $a_{13} \neq -1$, $a_{43} \neq -1$ so we may suppose $a_{73} = a_{83} = -1$. By $L.3$ $a_{13} = 0 = a_{43}$. As at least one of a_{14} and a_{15} is a zero we may assume $a_{14} = 0$. However, we may also suppose $a_{44} = 0$ for if $a_{44} = 1$ clearly $a_{45} = 0$; then if $a_{15} = 0$ we merely interchange $C.4$ and $C.5$ whilst if $a_{15} = 1$ both $T.1$ and $T.4$ are naiks so that by $L.35$ we may assume $C.6$ to be a dodo. By $L.17$ $a_{16} = 0 = a_{46}$ so we interchange $C.4$ and $C.6$. Two cases now arise: (B_1) a_{j3} and a_{j4} are both units for at least one j from $j = 2, 3, 5, 6$ and (B_2) one of a_{j3} and a_{j4} is a zero for each j ($j = 2, 3, 5, 6$).

(B_1) By symmetry we may clearly suppose $a_{23} = 1 = a_{24}$. By $L.3$ we can only have $a_{34} = -1 = a_{94}$. By $L.3$ $a_{54} = 0 = a_{64}$ so we may suppose $a_{74} = 1$, $a_{84} = 0$. By $L.3$ $a_{33} = 0 = a_{93}$ so $a_{53} = 1 = a_{63}$. By $L.17$ $a_{25} = 0 = a_{75}$. Now $a_{15} = 0$ for if $a_{15} = 1$ by $L.3$ the only possible place for a (-1) would be a_{35}. Further $a_{45} = 0$ for if $a_{45} = 1$ we must by $L.3$ have $a_{55} = -1 = a_{65}$ which is impossible by $L.4$. Thus there can only be one more zero in $C.5$ so we may suppose $a_{55} = 1$. By $L.3$ we must have $a_{65} = -1 = a_{95}$. By $L.3$ $a_{35} = 0 = a_{85}$ so $C.5$ does not represent a dodo. Hence (B_1) cannot occur.

(B_2) At least one of a_{j3} and a_{j4} is a zero for each $j = 2, 3, 5, 6$.

Now at least two of the a_{j3} ($j = 2, 3, 5, 6$) are $(+1)$s, say a_{m3} and a_{l3}, then $a_{m4} = 0 = a_{l4}$. Thus if $a_{15} = 0 = a_{45}$ from (B_1) we would also have $a_{m5} = 0 = a_{l5}$ and then $C.4$ and $C.5$ would contradict $L.22$. Hence by symmetry we may suppose $a_{15} = 1$. By $L.3$ we must have $a_{25} = -1 = a_{35}$ so by $L.3$ $a_{j5} = 0$ ($j = 4$, 5, 6). By $L.4$ $a_{23} = a_{33} = 1$ is impossible so we may suppose $a_{23} = 0$. Thus at least one of a_{53} and a_{63} is a $(+1)$, say $a_{53} = 1$ then $a_{54} = 0$. Now $a_{24} \neq 0$ for if $a_{24} = 0$ by $L.23$ on $C.3$ and $C.4$ we have $a_{74} = 0 = a_{84}$ and so $C.4$ contains six zeros. Thus we may suppose $a_{24} = 1$. If $a_{33} = 0$ we have similarly that a_{34} is a unit. By $L.4$ $a_{34} \neq 1$ so $a_{34} = -1$. Clearly $a_{63} = 1 = a_{93}$. By $L.3$ $a_{64} = 0$ so we may suppose $a_{74} = 1$ then by $L.3$ $a_{94} = 0$ so $a_{84} = -1$. By $L.3$ $a_{75} = 0 = a_{85}$ so $a_{95} = 1$. However, we now have a contradiction to $L.6$ with $r_0 = 9$.

Thus $a_{33} \neq 0$ so $a_{33} = 1$. Hence $a_{34} = 0$ and by $L.3$ $a_{75} = 0 = a_{85}$ so $a_{95} = 1$. By $L.3$ $a_{64} \neq -1$, $a_{94} \neq -1$ so $a_{74} = -1 = a_{84}$ which is impossible by $L.4$.

Hence (B_2) cannot arise and so neither can (B) nor (b).

Consider (c). We may clearly suppose $a_{12} = -1 = a_{72}$ then by $L.3$ $a_{j2} = 0$ ($j = 4, 5, 6$). Clearly $a_{j3} \neq -1$ ($j = 1, 2, 3$) for if one of them is a (-1) we have $a_{j3} = 0$ ($j = 4, 5, 6$) since $a_{j3} \neq -1$ ($j = 4, 5, 6$) by the previous case and $a_{j3} \neq 1$ ($j = 4$, 5, 6) by $L.3$; however this is impossible by $L.21$. Two cases now arise: (i) at least one of the a_{j3} ($j = 4, 5, 6$) is a -1; (ii) $a_{j3} \neq -1$ ($j = 4, 5, 6$).

(i) We may clearly suppose $a_{43} = -1$ then by $L.3$ $a_{j3} = 0$ ($j = 1, 2, 3$). From (a) and (b) above the other (-1) of $C.3$ occurs amongst the a_{j3} ($j = 7, 8, 9$). Furthermore, if $a_{82} = 1 = a_{92}$ wherever we put the (-1) a zero must occur amongst the a_{j3} ($j = 7, 8, 9$) in which case we would have $a_{53} = 1 = a_{63}$. Hence by symmetry we may suppose $a_{22} = 1 = a_{32} = a_{82}$, $a_{92} = 0$. As in (b) (B) we may suppose $a_{14} = 0 = a_{44}$. Three cases now arise: (A) both a_{24} and a_{34} are units; (B) one of a_{24} and a_{34} is a unit and the other is a zero; (C) $a_{24} = 0 = a_{34}$.

(A) By $L.4$ $a_{24} = a_{34} \neq 0$ is impossible so one may suppose $a_{24} = 1 = -a_{34}$. By $L.3$ $a_{j4} = 0$ ($j = 5, 6, 7$) so we may further suppose $a_{84} = 1 = -a_{94}$. Now $a_{83} \neq -1$ for if $a_{83} = -1$, $a_{73} = 0 = a_{93}$ and $C.3$ contains five zeros. Also $a_{83} \neq 1$ for if $a_{83} = 1$ by $L.3$ $a_{73} \neq -1$, $a_{93} \neq -1$ so $C.3$ does not contain two (-1)s. Thus $a_{83} = 0$. Hence we must have $a_{53} = 1 = a_{63}$, and either $a_{73} = -1$, $a_{93} = 1$ or $a_{73} = 1 = -a_{93}$. Consider $C.5$: by $L.17$ $a_{25} = 0 = a_{35}$. Now $a_{15} = 0$ for if $a_{15} = 1$ then by $L.3$ we can only have $a_{75} = -1 = a_{95}$. By $L.3$ again the remaining spaces of $C.5$ are zeros whether $a_{73} = 1$ or -1 so that $C.5$ does not represent a dodo. Further $a_{45} = 0$ for if $a_{45} = 1$ by $L.3$ we must have $a_{85} = -1$ so $a_{75} \neq 1$, $a_{95} \neq 1$; thus we may suppose $a_{55} = 1$ and then $a_{75} = 0 = a_{95}$ by $L.3$ and once again $C.5$ does not represent a dodo. If $a_{85} = 1$ then by $L.3$ we can only have $a_{55} = -1 = a_{65}$ which is impossible by $L.4$ so we may suppose $a_{85} = 0$. Thus the remaining spaces of $C.5$ are units. Since $a_{73} = -a_{93} \neq 0$, by $L.3$ we must have $a_{75} = a_{95}$ so that $a_{55} = a_{65}$ which is impossible by $L.4$. Thus (A) cannot occur.

(B) We may clearly suppose $a_{24} = 1$, $a_{34} = 0$ then by $L.3$ we can only have $a_{84} = -1 = a_{94}$. Thus $a_{74} = 0$ so we may suppose $a_{54} = 1$, $a_{64} = 0$. By $L.17$ $a_{25} = 0$. Two cases now arise: (B_1) $a_{53} = 1$ and (B_2) $a_{53} \neq 1$.

(B_1) Suppose $a_{53} = 1$, then by $L.3$ $a_{83} \neq -1$, $a_{93} \neq -1$ so we must have $a_{73} = -1$. By $L.3$ $a_{83} = 0$ so $a_{63} = 1 = a_{93}$. By $L.17$ $a_{55} = 0$. If $a_{75} = 1$ then we can only have $-1 = a_{15} = a_{45}$ and then by $L.3$ the remaining spaces of $C.5$ are zeros so that $C.5$ does not represent a dodo. Hence $a_{75} = 0$. Thus $a_{15} = 0 = a_{45}$ for if either of them is a unit, say $+1$, then the only possible place for a (-1) is a_{95} for the case $a_{15} = 1$, and a_{85} for the case $a_{45} = 1$. Hence the remaining spaces of $C.5$ are units. By $L.3$ $a_{35} = a_{65}$ $(= 1$ say$)$ so $a_{85} = -1 = a_{95}$. Let $a_{96} = -1$ then by $L.2$ $a_{86} = 1 = a_{16}$ and by $L.3$ the remaining spaces of $C.6$ are zeros. Thus $R.4$ and $R.8$ contradict $L.2$ so (B_1) cannot arise.

(B_2) We have $a_{53} \neq 1$ so $a_{53} = 0$ and therefore $a_{63} = 1$ and the a_{j3} $(j = 7, 8, 9)$ are all units. By $L.3$ $a_{73} = a_{83}$ so $a_{73} = a_{83} = 1 = -a_{93}$. Now $a_{15} = 0$ for if $a_{15} = 1$ then by $L.3$ we must have $a_{75} = -1 = a_{95}$ and by $L.3$ the remaining spaces of $C.5$ are zeros so that $C.5$ does not represent a dodo. Similarly $a_{45} = 0$ for if $a_{45} = 1$ then by $L.3$ we can only have $a_{55} = -1 = a_{95}$ and by $L.3$ the remaining spaces of $C.5$ are zeros. Also if $a_{35} = 1$ then we must have $a_{85} = -1 = a_{95}$ and by $L.3$ the remaining spaces of $C.5$ are zeros. Hence $a_{35} = 0$. Further $a_{95} = 0$ for if $a_{95} = 1$ then by $L.3$ $C.5$ cannot contain any (-1)s. Thus the a_{j5} $(j = 5, 6, 7, 8)$ are all units. By $L.3$ $a_{75} = a_{85} = a_{55}$ which is impossible. Thus (B_2) cannot arise and so neither can (B).

(C) We have $a_{24} = 0 = a_{34}$. Now if $a_{53} = 1 = a_{63}$ then by (A) and (B) above we may by symmetry suppose $a_{54} = 0 = a_{64}$, so that $C.4$ would contain six zeros. Thus we may suppose $a_{53} = 1$, $a_{63} = 0$ and the a_{j3} $(j = 7, 8, 9)$ must all be units. By $L.3$ $a_{73} = a_{83}$ so $a_{73} = a_{83} = -a_{93} = 1$. Now $a_{94} = 0$ for if $a_{94} = 1$, by $L.3$ $C.4$ could contain at most one (-1). Thus a_{j4} $(j = 5, 6, 7, 8)$ are all units. By $L.3$ $a_{74} = a_{84} = 1$ say $a_{54} = a_{64} = -1$. However, we now have a contradiction to $L.6$ with $r_0 = 8$.

Hence (C) cannot arise and so neither can (i).

(ii) We have $a_{j3} \neq -1$ $(j = 4, 5, 6)$. Two cases immediately arise: (A) $a_{73} = -1$ and (B) $a_{73} \neq -1$.

(A) Suppose $a_{73} = -1$ then we may also suppose $a_{83} = -1$.

(A$_1$) Suppose $a_{13} = 1$ then by $L.3$ $a_{82} = 0$ so $a_{j2} = 1$ $(j = 2, 3, 9)$. Further by $L.3$ $a_{23} = 0 = a_{33} = a_{93}$ so we may suppose $a_{43} = 1 = a_{53}$, $a_{63} = 0$. Now if a_{74} or a_{75} is a unit $T.1$ and $T.7$ are naiks so by $L.35$ we may suppose $C.6$ is a dodo as well. Interchange $C.6$ with the column with the unit in $R.7$ so that we may suppose $a_{74} = 0 = a_{75}$. By $L.17$ $a_{14} = 0 = a_{15}$. Thus by $L.22$ at least one of a_{44}, a_{45}, a_{54} and a_{55} is a unit. By symmetry we may clearly suppose $a_{44} = 1$; by $L.17$ $a_{45} = 0$. By $L.3$ $a_{84} \neq -1$ so at least one of a_{54} and a_{64} is a (-1). Thus by $L.3$ $a_{24} = 0 = a_{34}$. Now if $a_{55} = 1$ then by $L.3$ we can only have $-1 = a_{95} = a_{65}$ so $a_{25} = 0 = a_{35}$ which is impossible by $L.22$. Hence $a_{55} = 0$.

If $a_{54} = 0$ then by $L.3$ $a_{84} = 1$ so $a_{65} = -1 = a_{94}$. By $L.22$ both a_{25} and a_{35} are units so by $L.4$ we may assume $a_{25} = 1 = -a_{35}$. By $L.3$ $a_{65} = 0$ so $a_{85} = -a_{95}$ which is impossible by $L.3$.

Thus $a_{54} \neq 0$ and by $L.4$ $a_{54} \neq 1$ so $a_{54} = -1$. By $L.3$ $a_{84} = 0$ so we may suppose $a_{64} = 1 = -a_{94}$. Now $a_{65} = 0$ for if $a_{65} = 1$ the only possible place for a (-1) in $C.5$ would be a_{85}. By $L.4$ $a_{25} = a_{35} \neq 0$ is impossible so we may suppose $a_{25} = 1 = -a_{35}$, $a_{85} = 1 = -a_{95}$. Let $a_{96} = -1$ then by $L.2$ $a_{36} = 1 = a_{56}$ and by $L.3$ the remaining spaces of $C.6$ are zeros. Let $a_{47} = 1$ then by $L.2$

$a_{67} = -1$ and by $L.3$ $a_{j7} = 0$ $(j = 1, 2, 3, 5, 9)$. Let $a_{28} = 1$, then by $L.2$ $a_{88} = -1$ and by $L.3$ $a_{j8} = 0$ $(j = 1, 3, 4, 5, 9)$. Thus we have

x	y	A	B	C	D	E	z
1	−1	1	0	0	0	0	0
1	1	0	0	1	0	0	1
1	1	0	0	−1	1	0	0
−1	0	1	1	0	0	1	0
−1	0	1	−1	0	1	0	0
−1	0	0	1	0	0	−1	
0	−1	−1	0	0	0		
0	0	−1	0	1	0		−1
0	1	0	−1	−1	−1	0	0

Choose the coordinate system shown. From boundedness we have: from $T.2$ $c_2 < 0$; from $T.3$ $d_2 < 0$; from $T.9$ $b_2 > 0$; from $T.5$ $a_2 > 0$; from $T.4$ $e_2 < 0$.

Thus if $a_{68} = 1$ $T.6$ is unbounded whilst if $a_{87} = 1$ $T.8$ is unbounded. By $L.3$ $a_{68} \neq -1$, $a_{87} \neq -1$ so we must have $a_{68} = 0 = a_{87}$. Let $a_{69} = 1$ then by $L.2$ we must have $a_{89} = -1$. Let $F = 0$ be the equation of the plane represented by $C.9$ then from $T.6$ $f_2 < 0$.

Suppose $a_{77} = 1$ then by $L.2$ we must have either $a_{78} = 1$ or $a_{79} = 1$ but in either case it is clear that $T.7$ is unbounded. Hence $a_{77} \neq 1$; by $L.3$ $a_{77} \neq -1$ so $a_{77} = 0$. Thus by $L.2$ on $R.6$ we must have $a_{79} = -1$ so that by $L.2$ on $R.8$ $a_{78} = 1$. Thus we have

A	x	y	B	C	D	E	F	z
1	−1	1	0	0	0	0	0	0
1	1	0	0	1	0	0	1	0
1	1	0	0	−1	1	0	0	0
−1	0	1	1	0	0	1	0	0
−1	0	1	−1	0	1	0	0	0
−1	0	0	1	0	0	−1	0	1
0	−1	−1	0	0	0	0	1	−1
0	0	−1	0	1	0	0	−1	−1
0	1	0	−1	−1	−1	0	0	0

Choose the coordinate system shown. From boundedness we have: from T.7 $f_2 > 0$; from T.8 $c_2 > 0$; from T.2 $a_2 < 0$; from T.3 $d_2 > 0$; from T.5 $b_2 > 0$. However T.9 is now unbounded, so (A$_1$) cannot occur.

Thus $a_{13} \neq 1$ so $a_{13} = 0$. If $a_{14} = 1$ then by $L.3$ we must have $a_{74} = -1$ so that both T.1 and T.7 are naiks. Thus by $L.35$ we may suppose $C.6$ is a dodo. Interchanging $C.4$ and $C.6$ we see that we may assume $a_{14} = 0 = a_{15}$. Now $a_{74} = 0 = a_{75}$ for if $a_{74} = 1$ say, then by $L.3$ there is only one possible place for a (-1) in $C.4$.

(A$_2$) Suppose $a_{22} = 1 = a_{32}$ then by $L.3$ $a_{23} = 0 = a_{33}$ so by $L.5$ we may suppose $a_{43} = 1 = a_{53} = a_{93}$, $a_{63} = 0$. Thus by $L.3$ $a_{92} = 0$ so $a_{82} = 1$. By $L.22$ at least one of a_{44}, a_{45}, a_{54} and a_{55} is a unit so let $a_{44} = 1$. By $L.3$ $a_{j4} \neq -1$ $(j = 2, 3, 8)$ so at least one of a_{54} and a_{64} is a (-1) so by $L.3$ $a_{24} = 0 = a_{34}$. Hence by $L.23$ $a_{84} = 0$ so by $L.4$ $a_{54} = -1$ and we may suppose $a_{64} = -1$, $a_{94} = 1$. By $L.17$ $a_{45} = 0 = a_{55}$ so at least one of a_{25} and a_{35} is a unit. Thus let $a_{25} = 1$. Now $a_{95} \neq -1$ for, if so, then by $L.3$ $a_{65} \neq 1$, $a_{85} \neq 1$ so that $a_{35} = 1$ which is impossible by $L.4$. Since $a_{65} \neq -1$ by $L.3$ we must have $a_{35} = -1 = a_{85}$. By $L.3$ $a_{65} = 0$ and $a_{95} \neq 1$ so $a_{95} = 0$; thus $C.5$ is not a dodo. Hence (A$_2$) cannot occur.

Thus at least one of a_{22} and a_{32} is a zero and we may clearly suppose $a_{32} = 0$ so $a_{22} = 1 = a_{82} = a_{92}$. By $L.3$ $a_{23} = 0 = a_{93}$. Hence by $L.5$ we may suppose $a_{33} = 1 = a_{43} = a_{53}$, $a_{63} = 0$. By $L.22$ at least one of a_{44}, a_{45}, a_{54}, and a_{55} is a unit so let $a_{44} = 1$. By $L.3$ $a_{84} \neq -1$ so at least one of a_{54} and a_{64} is a (-1) and so by $L.3$ $a_{24} = 0 = a_{34}$. By $L.17$ $a_{45} = 0$. If $a_{55} = 1$ then by $L.3$ we can only have $-1 = a_{65} = a_{95}$ so by $L.3$ $a_{25} = 0 = a_{35}$ which is impossible by $L.22$. Thus $a_{55} = 0$. Now if $a_{85} = 0$, a_{j5} $(j = 2, 3, 6, 9)$ are all units and by $L.3$ $a_{25} = a_{65} = a_{35}$ which is impossible. Hence we may suppose $a_{85} = 1$. By $L.17$ $a_{84} = 0$. Thus a_{j4} $(j = 5, 6, 9)$ are all units and by $L.4$ we must have $a_{54} = -1$ so we may suppose $a_{64} = -1$, $a_{94} = 1$. Now $a_{65} = 0$ for if a_{65} is a unit the only possible place for a unit of the opposite sign in $C.5$ is a_{85}. By $L.3$ $a_{35} \neq -1$ so $a_{35} = 1$ and $a_{25} = -1 = a_{95}$. Let $a_{96} = -1$ then by $L.2$ $a_{26} = 1 = a_{46}$ and by $L.3$ the remaining spaces of $C.6$ are zeros. Let $a_{57} = 1$ then by $L.2$ $a_{67} = -1$ and by $L.3$ $a_{j7} = 0$ $(j = 1, 2, 3, 4, 9)$. Let $a_{38} = 1$ then by $L.2$ $a_{18} = -1$

and by $L.3$ $a_{j8} = 0$ ($j = 2, 4, 5, 6, 8, 9$). Thus we have

x	y	A	B	z	C	D	E
1	−1	0	0	0	0	0	−1
1	1	0	0	−1	1	0	0
1	0	1	0	1	0	0	1
−1	0	1	1	0	1	0	0
−1	0	1	−1	0	0	1	0
−1	0	0	−1	0	0	−1	0
0	−1	−1	0	0	0		
0	1	−1	0	1	0		0
0	1	0	1	−1	−1	0	0

Choose the coordinate system shown. From boundedness we have: from $T.2$ $c_2 < 0$, $c_3 > 0$; from $T.9$ $b_2 < 0$, $b_3 > 0$; from $T.4$ $a_2 > 0$, $a_3 < 0$; from $T.5$ $d_2 < 0$, $d_3 > 0$.

Hence if $a_{87} = 1$, $T.8$ is unbounded in the z-direction. Thus $a_{87} \neq 1$ and by $L.3$ $a_{87} \neq -1$ so $a_{87} = 0$. Let $a_{69} = 1$ then by $L.2$ $a_{89} = -1$. Let $F = 0$ be the equation of the plane represented by $C.9$ then from $T.6$ $f_2 < 0$, $f_3 > 0$. $x = 0$ is a tem-plane so by $L.8$ each tetrahedron must have an intersection of positive area with $x = 0$. Consider the configuration on $x = 0$.

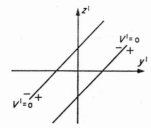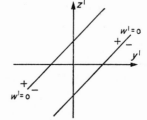

FIG. 16

From the above it is clear that $B^1 = 0$, $C^1 = 0$, $D^1 = 0$ and $F^1 = 0$ are of type $W^1 = 0$ whilst $A^1 = 0$ is of type $V^1 = 0$. Now each of $T^1.4$, $T^1.5$ and $T^1.6$ must have an area in $z^1 > 0$ and $z^1 < 0$ in order to have an area in common with both $T^1.2$ and $T^1.3$ as they must. Thus the intersection of each of $T^1.4$, $T^1.5$ and $T^1.6$ with the line $z^1 = 0$ must be a line of positive length.

Hence for $T^1.4$ we must have $a_4/a_2 < b_4/b_2$; for $T^1.5$ $b_4/b_2 < d_4/d_2$ and for $T^1.6$ $d_4/d_2 < f_4/f_2$.

Thus, $a_4/a_2 < b_4/b_2 < d_4/d_2 < f_4/f_2$ so that it is clear that $z^1 = 0$ does not occur in T^1.8.

From T^1.2 we must have $c_4/c_2 > 0$. Now from T^1.9 $B^1 = 0$ must close $y^1 \geqslant 0$, $C^1 \leqslant 0$, $z^1 \leqslant 0$ and so $b_4/b_2 > 0$ also. Hence $f_4/f_2 > 0$. T^1.8 must lie in $F^1 \leqslant 0$, $z^1 \geqslant 0$ and as $F^1 = 0$ has positive gradient it must now be in $y^1 > 0$. Thus neither $y^1 = 0$ nor $z^1 = 0$ can occur in T^1.8 which is impossible.

Hence (A) cannot occur.

(B) We have $a_{73} \neq -1$ so we may suppose $a_{83} = -1 = a_{93}$. Clearly we may assume $a_{82} = 1$ so by L.3 $a_{13} = 0 = a_{73}$. By L.5 $a_{j3} = 1$ ($j = 4, 5, 6$) is impossible so we may suppose $a_{23} = 1 = a_{43}$.

(B$_1$) Suppose $a_{14} = 1$. Then by L.3 we must have $a_{74} = -1$ so $a_{84} = 0$. Now one of a_{24}, a_{34} and a_{94} is a (-1) and by L.3 the other two must be zeros; also $a_{44} = 0$. Thus one of a_{54} and a_{64} is a $(+1)$, say $a_{54} = 1$. Hence by L.3 $a_{24} \neq -1$, $a_{34} \neq -1$ so $a_{94} = -1$. Further $a_{92} = 0$ so $a_{22} = 1 = a_{32}$. By L.3 and L.4 $a_{33} = 0$ and by L.3 $a_{53} = 0$, so $a_{63} = 1$. By L.17 $a_{15} = 0 = a_{25}$. Now $a_{35} = 0$ for if $a_{35} = 1$ we can only have $-1 = a_{85} = a_{95}$ and then by L.3 the remaining spaces of C.5 are zeros, which is impossible. Also $a_{95} = 0$ for if $a_{95} = 1$ we can only have $-1 = a_{75} = a_{85}$ so that by L.3 $a_{j5} = 0$ ($j = 4, 5, 6$) which is impossible. Further $a_{85} = 0$ for if $a_{85} = 1$ we can only have $-1 = a_{55}$. Hence, since by L.4 $a_{45} = a_{65} \neq 0$ is impossible, we may suppose $a_{45} = -a_{65} = 1$ so that $a_{55} = -a_{75} \neq 0$ which is impossible by L.3.

Thus (B$_1$) cannot arise, so $a_{14} \neq 1$ and we may assume $a_{14} = 0 = a_{15}$.

If $a_{24} = 1$ then we can only have $a_{34} = -1 = a_{74}$. By L.3 $a_{j4} = 0$ ($j = 4, 5, 6, 8$) so $a_{94} = 1$. Hence by L.3 $a_{22} = 0 = a_{92}$ so that C.2 does not represent a dotre.

Thus $a_{24} = 0 = a_{25}$.

(B$_2$) Suppose $a_{33} = 1$ so $a_{53} = 0 = a_{63}$. Then as above we must have $a_{34} = 0 = a_{35}$. By L.4 $a_{22} = a_{32} = 1$ is impossible so we may suppose $a_{22} = 1 = a_{92}$, $a_{32} = 0$. Now by L.4 $a_{8m} = a_{9m} \neq 0$ is impossible for $m = 4$ or 5. So if T.8/T.9 in C.l where $l \neq 4$ and $l \neq 5$ we may suppose by L.22 $a_{84} = 1 = a_{95}$; then by L.3 we can only have $a_{54} = -1 = a_{64} = a_{55} = a_{65}$ which is impossible by L.4. Hence T.8/T.9 in C.4 or C.5 and we may clearly suppose it is C.4. Let $a_{84} = 1 = -a_{94}$ then by L.3 $a_{44} = 0 = a_{74}$ so we may suppose $a_{54} = 1 = -a_{64}$. By L.17 $a_{85} = 0 = a_{95}$ and by L.3 $a_{55} = a_{65}$ so we may assume $a_{45} = -1 = a_{75}$, $a_{55} = 1 = a_{65}$.

10*

Let $a_{56} = 1$ then by $L.2$ $a_{86} = -1$ and by $L.3$ the remaining spaces of $C.6$ are zeros. Let $a_{67} = 1$ then by $L.2$ $a_{97} = -1$ and by $L.3$ the remaining spaces of $C.7$ are zeros. Let $a_{28} = 1$ then by $L.2$ $a_{38} = -1$ and by $L.3$ $a_{j8} = 0$ $(j = 4, 5, 6, 8, 9)$. Let $a_{49} = 1$ then by $L.2$ $a_{79} = -1$ and by $L.3$ $a_{j9} = 0$ $(j = 2, 5, 6, 8, 9)$. Thus we have

A	x	y	B	C	z	D	E	F
1	-1	0	0	0	0	0		
1	1	1	0	0	0	0	1	0
1	0	1	0	0	0	0	-1	
-1	0	1	0	-1	0	0	0	1
-1	0	0	1	1	1	0	0	0
-1	0	0	-1	1	0	1	0	0
0	-1	0	0	-1	0	0		-1
0	1	-1	1	0	-1	0	0	0
0	1	-1	-1	0	0	-1	0	0

Choose the coordinate system shown. From boundedness we have: from $T.8$ $b_3 > 0$; from $T.9$ $d_3 < 0$; from $T.5$ at least one of $a_3 > 0$ and $c_3 < 0$ holds; from $T.6$ at least one of $a_3 < 0$ and $c_3 > 0$ holds hence $a_3 c_3 > 0$; from $T.4$ $f_3 c_3 > 0$ and $f_3 a_3 > 0$; from $T.2$ $e_3 a_3 < 0$ so $e_3 c_3 < 0$ also.

Thus if $a_{78} = 1$ $T.7$ is unbounded in the z-direction so $a_{78} \neq 1$. By $L.3$ $a_{78} \neq -1$ so $a_{78} = 0$. Also if $a_{39} = 1$ $T.3$ is unbounded so $a_{39} \neq 1$. By $L.3$ $a_{39} \neq -1$ so $a_{39} = 0$. Let $a_{3.10} = 1$ then by $L.2$ $a_{7.10} = -1$. Clearly $a_{j.10} = 0$ $(j = 2, 4, 5, 6, 8, 9)$. Let $G = 0$ be the equation of the plane represented by $C.10$, then from $T.3$ $a_3 g_3 < 0$. Now if $a_{1.10} = -1$ then by $L.2$ we must have $a_{19} = 1$ and then $T.1$ is unbounded. Thus $a_{1.10} \neq -1$ so by $L.2$ we must have $a_{18} = 1$. Hence

x	y	z	A	B	C	D	E	F	G
1	-1	0	0	0	0	0	1		
1	1	1	0	0	0	0	1	0	0
1	0	1	0	0	0	0	-1	0	1
-1	0	1	0	-1	0	0	0	1	0
-1	0	0	1	1	1	0	0	0	0
-1	0	0	-1	1	0	1	0	0	0
0	-1	0	0	-1	0	0	0	-1	-1
0	1	-1	1	0	-1	0	0	0	0
0	1	-1	-1	0	0	-1	0	0	0

Choose the coordinate system shown. From boundedness we have: from T.2 $e_2 < 0$; from T.3 $g_2 < 0$; hence if $a_{1.10} = 1$ T.1 is unbounded, so by L.2 we must have $a_{19} = 1$. From T.1 $f_2 > 0$; from T.4 $b_2 > 0$; from T.5 at least one of $a_2 < 0$ and $c_2 < 0$ holds; from T.8 at least one of $a_2 < 0$ and $c_2 > 0$ holds. Hence $a_2 < 0$. From T.9 $d_2 > 0$. However, T.6 is now unbounded.

Thus (B$_2$) cannot occur so $a_{33} = 0$ and we may suppose $a_{53} = 1$, $a_{63} = 0$. By L.22 at least one of a_{44}, a_{45}, a_{54} and a_{55} is a unit, so we may clearly suppose $a_{44} = 1$ and then $a_{45} = 0$.

(B$_3$) Suppose $a_{54} = -1$, then by L.3 $a_{j4} = 0$ $(j = 3, 8, 9)$ so we may suppose $a_{64} = -1$, $a_{74} = 1$. By L.17 $a_{55} = 0$. By L.23 if $a_{65} = 0$ then $a_{75} = 0$ and C.5 contains six zeros which is impossible. Thus we may suppose $a_{65} = 1$, so by L.3 we can only have $-1 = a_{85} = a_{95}$. By L.3 $a_{75} = 0$ so $a_{35} = 1$. By L.4 $a_{92} = 0$ so $a_{22} = 1 = a_{32}$. Let $a_{26} = 1$ then by L.2 $a_{36} = -1$ and by L.3 the remaining spaces of C.6 are zeros. Let $a_{57} = 1$ then by L.2 $a_{67} = -1$ and by L.3 the remaining spaces of C.7 are zeros. Let $a_{48} = 1$ then by L.2 $a_{78} = -1$ and by L.3 $a_{j8} = 0$ $(j = 2, 3, 5, 6, 8)$. Let $a_{89} = 1$ then by L.2 $a_{99} = -1$ and by L.3 $a_{j9} = 0$ $(j = 2, 3, 4, 5, 6)$. Thus we have

x	y	z	A	B	C	D	E	F
1	-1	0	0	0	0	0		
1	1	1	0	0	1	0	0	0
1	1	0	0	1	-1	0	0	0
-1	0	1	1	0	0	0	1	0
-1	0	1	-1	0	0	1	0	0
-1	0	0	-1	1	0	-1	0	0
0	-1	0	1	0	0	0	-1	
0	1	-1	0	-1	0	0	0	1
0	0	-1	0	-1	0	0		-1

Choose the coordinate system shown. From boundedness we have: from T.2 $c_1 < 0$, $c_2 < 0$; from T.3 $b_1 < 0$, $b_2 < 0$; from T.8 $f_1 < 0$, $f_2 < 0$.

From T.5 $a_2 d_2 > 0$; from T.6 at least one of $a_2 < 0$ and $d_2 < 0$ holds. Thus both $a_2 < 0$ and $d_2 < 0$ hold. From T.4 $e_2 > 0$.

Now if $a_{98} = 1$ T.9 is unbounded so $a_{98} \neq 1$; by L.3 $a_{98} \neq -1$ so $a_{98} = 0$. If $a_{79} = 1$ T.7 is unbounded so $a_{79} \neq 1$; by L.3 $a_{79} \neq -1$ so $a_{79} = 0$. Let $a_{7.10} = 1$ then by L.2 $a_{9.10} = -1$ and by L.3 $a_{j.10} = 0$ $(j = 2, 3, 4, 5, 6, 8)$. Let $G = 0$ be the equation of the plane represented by $C.10$, then from T.7 $g_2 > 0$. Now if $a_{1.10} = -1$ by $L.2$ we must have $a_{19} = 1$ and then T.1 is unbounded. Thus $a_{1.10} \neq -1$ so by $L.2$ we must have $a_{18} = 1$.

From T.9 $g_1 > 0$; from T.5 at least one of $a_1 < 0$ and $d_1 > 0$ holds; from T.6 at least one of $a_1 < 0$ and $d_1 < 0$ holds. Hence $a_1 < 0$; from T.4 $e_1 > 0$. Thus if $a_{1.10} = 1$ T.1 is unbounded, so $a_{1.10} = 0$. Hence by $L.2$ $a_{19} = 1$ and we have

x	A	y	B	C	D	E	z	F	G
1	−1	0	0	0	0	0	1	1	0
1	1	1	0	0	1	0	0	0	0
1	1	0	0	1	−1	0	0	0	0
−1	0	1	1	0	0	0	1	0	0
−1	0	1	−1	0	0	1	0	0	0
−1	0	0	−1	1	0	−1	0	0	0
0	−1	0	1	0	0	0	−1	0	1
0	1	−1	0	−1	0	0	0	1	0
0	0	−1	0	−1	0	0	0	−1	−1

Choose the coordinate system shown. From boundedness we have: from T.4 $b_1 > 0$; from T.5 $e_1 > 0$; from T.6 $c_1 > 0$; from T.8 at least one of $a_1 > 0$ and $f_1 > 0$ holds; from T.1 at least one of $a_1 > 0$ and $f_1 < 0$ holds. Hence $a_1 > 0$; from T.2 $d_1 < 0$. However T.3 is now unbounded. Thus (B_3) does not occur and $a_{54} \neq -1$. By $L.4$ $a_{54} \neq 1$ so $a_{54} = 0$. Hence by $L.3$ we can only have $-1 = a_{64} = a_{74}$. By $L.3$ $a_{34} = 0 = a_{84}$ so $a_{94} = 1$. By $L.3$ $a_{92} = 0$ so $a_{22} = 1 = a_{32}$. Now if $a_{55} = 1$ by $L.3$ we can only have $-1 = a_{65} = a_{75}$ and then the remaining spaces of $C.5$ are zeros which is impossible. Thus $a_{55} = 0$. Hence by $L.22$ we may suppose $a_{35} = 1$. By $L.3$ we must have $-1 = a_{85} = a_{95}$ and the remaining spaces of $C.5$ are zeros which is impossible.

Thus (B) cannot occur and so neither can (ii), and hence neither can (c).

Hence we need only consider the case when two of a_{j2} $(j = 7, 8, 9)$ are (-1)s and two of a_{j3} $(j = 7, 8, 9)$ are (-1)s. Clearly we may suppose $a_{72} = -1 = a_{82}$. Two cases now arise: (i) $a_{73} = -1 = a_{83}$ and (ii) $a_{73} = -1 = a_{93}$.

(i) Suppose $a_{73} = -1 = a_{83}$. By $L.3$ $a_{92} = a_{93} = 1$ is impossible, so we may assume $a_{92} = 0$. By $L.5$ and symmetry we may therefore suppose $a_{12} = a_{22} = a_{42} = 1$, $a_{32} = a_{52} = a_{62} = 0$. Thus by $L.3$ $a_{13} = a_{23} = a_{43} = 0$. Now if $a_{74} = 1$ by $L.3$ we would have to have $-1 = a_{84}$ so that $C.4$ would contain six zeros which is impossible. Thus $a_{74} = 0 = a_{84} = a_{75} = a_{85}$. Thus by $L.22$ one of a_{14}, a_{15}, a_{24} and a_{25} is a unit so we may suppose $a_{14} = 1$. By $L.3$ at least one of a_{24} and a_{34} is a (-1) so $a_{j4} = 0$ $(j = 4, 5, 6)$. Hence a_{j4} $(j = 2, 3, 9)$ are all units. By $L.4$ $a_{24} \neq 1$ so we may suppose $a_{24} = -1 = a_{34}$, $a_{94} = 1$. By $L.17$ $a_{15} = 0 = a_{25}$. Further $a_{35} = 0$ for if $a_{35} = 1$ $C.5$ would contain no (-1)s. Thus the a_{j5} $(j = 4, 5, 6, 9)$ are all units. Three effective cases arise (A) $a_{33} = 0$ (B) $a_{93} = 0$ and (C) $a_{63} = 0$.

(A) Suppose $a_{33} = 0$ then $a_{j3} = 1$ $(j = 5, 6, 9)$. By $L.4$ $a_{55} = a_{65} \neq 0$ is impossible, so we may suppose $a_{45} = 1 = a_{55}$, $a_{65} = -1 = a_{95}$. Let $a_{46} = 1$ then by $L.2$ $a_{56} = -1$ and by $L.3$ the remaining units of $C.6$ are zeros. Let $a_{97} = -1$ then by $L.2$ $a_{17} = 1 = a_{67}$ and by $L.3$ the remaining spaces of $C.7$ are zeros. Thus we have

x	A	y	B	C	D	z
1	1	0	1	0	0	1
1	1	0	-1	0	0	0
1	0	0	-1	0	0	0
-1	1	0	0	1	1	0
-1	0	1	0	1	-1	0
-1	0	1	0	-1	0	1
0	-1	-1	0	0	0	0
0	-1	-1	0	0	0	0
0	0	1	1	-1	0	-1

Choose the coordinate system shown. From boundedness we have: from T.6 $c_1 < 0$, $c_3 > 0$; from T.5 $d_1 < 0$, $d_3 > 0$; from T.4 $a_1 > 0$, $a_3 < 0$; from T.9 $b_1 < 0$, $b_3 > 0$.

$y = 0$ is a tem-plane, so by $L.8$ each tetrahedron must have an intersection of positive area with $y = 0$. Consider the configuration on $y = 0$. From the above $A^1 = 0$, $B^1 = 0$, $C^1 = 0$ and $D^1 = 0$ all have positive gradients. (See FIG. 17, p. 152.)

From diagram (1) it is clear that $A^1 = 0$ must close $T^1.4$ so $A^1 = 0$ must have a gradient greater than that of $C^1 = 0$. Thus $a_4/a_3 > c_4/c_3 > 0$. Now for $z^1 = 0$ to occur in $T^1.9$ as it must, $B^1 = 0$ must have a gradient less than that of $C^1 = 0$ and $a_4/a_3 > c_4/c_3 > b_4/b_3$. Consider $T^1.1$ (see diagram (2)). Since $b_4/b_3 < a_4/a_3$ and $B^1 = 0$ has a gradient less than $C^1 = 0$ and a fortiori less than $A^1 = 0$, $T^1.1$ cannot be closed.

Hence (A) cannot arise.

(B) Suppose $a_{93} = 0$ then $a_{j3} = 1$ $(j = 3, 5, 6)$. By $L.4$ $a_{55} = a_{65} \neq 0$ is impossible, so we may suppose $a_{45} = 1 = a_{55}$, $a_{65} = -1 = a_{95}$. Let $a_{46} = 1$ then by $L.2$ $a_{56} = -1$ and by $L.3$ the remaining spaces of $C.6$ are zeros. Let $a_{67} = 1$ then by $L.2$ $a_{97} = -1$ and by $L.3$ $a_{j7} = 0$ $(j = 2, 3, 4, 5)$. Now if $a_{77} \neq 1$, $a_{87} \neq 1$ we have a contradiction to $L.6$ with $r_0 = 9$. Thus we may suppose $a_{77} = 1$, then by $L.3$ and $L.4$ $a_{87} = 0$. Let $a_{28} = 1$ then by $L.2$ $a_{38} = -1$ and by $L.3$ the remaining spaces of $C.8$ are zeros.

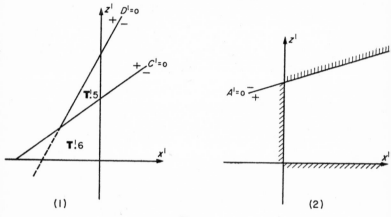

Fig. 17

Let $a_{79} = 1$ then by $L.2$ $a_{89} = -1$ and by $L.3$ $a_{j9} = 0$ $(j = 1, 2, 3, 4, 5, 6)$. Thus we have

x	A	y	B	z	C	D	E	F
1	1	0	1	0	0		0	0
1	1	0	-1	0	0	0	1	0
1	0	1	-1	0	0	0	-1	0
-1	1	0	0	1	1	0	0	0
-1	0	1	0	1	-1	0	0	0
-1	0	1	0	-1	0	1	0	0
0	-1	-1	0	0	0	1	0	1
0	-1	-1	0	0	0	0	0	-1
0	0	0	1	-1	0	-1	0	

Choose the coordinate system shown. From boundedness we have: from T.5 $c_1 < 0$; from T.4 $a_1 > 0$; from T.6 $d_1 > 0$; from T.2 at least one of $b_1 > 0$ and $e_1 < 0$ holds; from T.3 at least one of $b_1 > 0$ and $e_1 > 0$ holds. Hence $b_1 > 0$. Thus if $a_{17} = 1$ T.1 is unbounded, so $a_{17} \neq 1$. By $L.3$ $a_{17} \neq -1$ so $a_{17} = 0$. Let $a_{1.10} = 1$ then by $L.2$ $a_{9.10} = -1$ so $a_{99} = 0$. Hence by $L.2$ $a_{8.10} = 1$ so we have

A	x	y	B	C	D	E	F	G	z
1	1	0	1	0	0	0	0	0	1
1	1	0	-1	0	0	0	1	0	0
1	0	1	-1	0	0	0	-1	0	0
-1	1	0	0	1	1	0	0	0	0
-1	0	1	0	1	-1	0	0	0	0
-1	0	1	0	-1	0	1	0	0	0
0	-1	-1	0	0	0	1	0	1	0
0	-1	-1	0	0	0	0	0	-1	1
0	0	0	1	-1	0	-1	0	0	-1

Choose the coordinate system shown. From boundedness we have: from T.8 $g_2 < 0$; from T.7 $e_2 > 0$; from T.1 $a_2 b_2 < 0$; from T.2 $b_2 f_2 > 0$.

If $a_2 \geqslant 0$ then $b_2 < 0$ and $f_2 < 0$, so T.3 is unbounded.

Thus $a_2 < 0$ so $b_2 > 0$, $f_2 > 0$; from T.6 $c_2 > 0$; from T.5 $d_2 > 0$. However T.4 is now unbounded, so (B) cannot arise.

(C) Suppose $a_{63} = 0$ then $a_{j3} = 1$ ($j = 3, 5, 9$). Let $a_{16} = 1$ then by $L.2$ $a_{96} = -1$ and by $L.3$ $a_{j6} = 0$ ($j = 2, 3, 7, 8$). Clearly we may suppose $a_{95} = 1$. Now a_{65} and a_{66} cannot both be units for if they are, we have a contradiction to $L.6$ with $r_0 = 6$. Since a_{65} is a unit, $a_{66} = 0$. Hence by $L.2$ on $R.9$ $a_{65} = -1$. Let $a_{67} = -1$, $a_{68} = 1$ then by $L.6$ we may suppose $a_{77} = 1 = -a_{88}$. By $L.3$ $a_{j7} = a_{j8} = 0$ ($j = 1, 2, 3, 9$). Let $a_{29} = 1$ then by $L.2$ $a_{39} = -1$ and by $L.3$ the remaining spaces of $C.9$ are zeros. Thus we have

x	y	A	B	C	z	D	E	F
1	1	0	1	0	1	0	0	0
1	1	0	-1	0	0	0	0	1
1	0	1	-1	0	0	0	0	-1
-1	1	0	0					0
-1	0	1	0					0
-1	0	0	0	-1	0	-1	1	0
0	-1	-1	0	0	0	1		0
0	-1	-1	0	0	0		-1	0
0	0	1	1	1	-1	0	0	0

Choose the coordinate system shown. From boundedness we have: from T.1 $b_1 < 0$, $b_3 < 0$; from T.2 $f_1 < 0$, $f_3 < 0$; from T.3 $a_1 < 0$, $a_3 < 0$; from T.9 $c_1 > 0$, $c_3 > 0$.

Now if $a_{45} = 1$ by L.2 $a_{46} = 1$ and T.4 is unbounded in the z-direction. Thus $a_{45} = -1$, $a_{55} = 1$ and by L.2 $a_{56} = 1$. By L.3 $a_{46} = 0$. By symmetry and L.2 we may clearly suppose $a_{47} = 1$. By L.3 $a_{57} = 0 = a_{58} = a_{87}$. By L.1 $a_{48} = 0$.

From T.4 $d_1 > 0$, $d_3 > 0$; from T.6 $e_1 > 0$, $e_3 > 0$. Thus if $a_{78} = 1$ T.7 is unbounded in the z-direction. By L.4 $a_{78} \neq -1$ so $a_{78} = 0$. Let $a_{7.10} = 1$ then by L.2 $a_{8.10} = -1$ and clearly the remaining spaces of $C.10$ are zeros. Thus we have

x	y	A	B	C	z	D	E	F	G
1	1	0	1	0	1	0	0	0	0
1	1	0	−1	0	0	0	0	1	0
1	0	1	−1	0	0	0	0	−1	0
−1	1	0	0	−1	0	1	0	0	0
−1	0	1	0	1	1	0	0	0	0
−1	0	0	0	−1	0	−1	1	0	0
0	−1	−1	0	0	0	1	0	0	1
0	−1	−1	0	0	0	0	−1	0	−1
0	0	1	1	1	−1	0	0	0	0

$y = 0$ is a tem-plane so by L.8 every tetrahedron must have an intersection of positive area with $y = 0$. Consider thecon figuration on $y = 0$, then in order that $T^1.7$ and $T^1.8$ should have an area in common with both $T^1.1$ and $T^1.4$ as they must, $T^1.7$ and $T^1.8$ must have areas in both $x^1 > 0$ and $x^1 < 0$. Thus the intersection of each of $T^1.7$ and $T^1.8$ with the line $x^1 = 0$ must be a line of positive length. From the above $A^1 = 0$, $B^1 = 0$, $C^1 = 0$, $D^1 = 0$, $E^1 = 0$ and $F^1 = 0$ all have negative gradients. (See FIG. 18, p. 155.)

Now the figure defined by $A^1 \geqslant 0$, $x^1 \leqslant 0$, $z^1 \geqslant 0$ is clearly not closed. Hence $C^1 = 0$ must close $T^1.5$; as $C^1 = 0$ has negative gradient it cannot do so by joining $x^1 = 0$ to $z^1 = 0$. Thus $C^1 = 0$ joins $A^1 = 0$ to one of $x^1 = 0$ and $z^1 = 0$, but in either case we must have $a_4/a_3 > c_4/c_3$. Consider $T^1.4$; then clearly $D^1 = 0$ closes $T^1.4$ and we must have $c_4/c_3 > d_4/d_3$. Consider $T^1.6$; clearly $E^1 = 0$ closes $T^1.6$ and we must have $c_4/c_3 > e_4/e_3$ so $a_4/a_3 > c_4/c_3 > e_4/e_3$.

We therefore arrive at the situation in diagram (2). Hence no point of $x^1 = 0$ lies in $T^1.8$ which contradicts the requirement that the intersection of $T^1.8$ with $x^1 = 0$ is a line of positive length.

Hence (C) cannot occur and so neither can (i).

(ii) We now have $a_{73} = -1 = a_{93}$. By $L.3$ $a_{92} = a_{83} = 1$ is impossible, so by symmetry we may suppose $a_{92} = 0$. Hence by $L.5$ we may suppose $a_{12} = a_{22} = a_{42} = 1$, $a_{32} = a_{52} = a_{62} = 0$. By $L.3$ $a_{13} = 0 = a_{23} = a_{43}$.

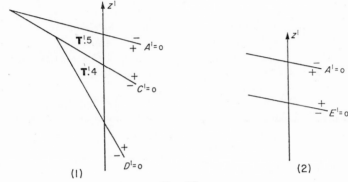

FIG. 18

(A) Suppose $a_{14} = 1 = -a_{24}$, then by $L.3$ $a_{j4} = 0$ ($j = 4, 5, 6, 7, 8$) so we may suppose $a_{34} = -1, a_{94} = 1$ and by $L.3$ $a_{33} = 0$. Thus $a_{53} = a_{63} = a_{83} = 1$. By $L.17$ $a_{15} = 0 = a_{25}$. Now $a_{35} = 0$ for if $a_{35} = 1$ we can only have $-1 = a_{75} = a_{85}$, and then by $L.3$ the remaining spaces of $C.5$ are zeros which is impossible. By $L.23$ on $C.3$ and $C.5$ we have $a_{75} = 0 = a_{95}$ so that the a_{j5} ($j = 4, 5, 6, 8$) are all units. By $L.3$ $a_{85} = a_{45}$ so $a_{55} = a_{65}$ which is impossible by $L.4$. Thus (A) cannot arise.

(B) Suppose $a_{14} = 1$ then by (A) $a_{24} \neq -1$ and by $L.4$ $a_{24} \neq 1$ so $a_{24} = 0$. Thus we can only have $-1 = a_{34} = a_{94}$. By $L.3$ $a_{j4} = 0$ ($j = 4, 5, 6$) and by $L.17$ $a_{15} = 0$.

(B₁) Suppose $a_{74} = 1$ then by $L.3$ $a_{33} = 0$ so $a_{j3} = 1$ ($j = 5, 6, 8$). Clearly $a_{75} = 0$. If $a_{45} = 1$ we can only have $-1 = a_{55} = a_{95}$ since $a_{55} = a_{65} \neq 0$ is impossible by $L.4$ and then the remaining spaces of $C.5$ are zeros by $L.3$. Thus $a_{45} = 0$. If $a_{55} = 1$ then we can only have $-1 = a_{65} = a_{85}$ and then the remaining spaces of $C.5$ are zeros by $L.3$. Thus $a_{55} = 0$ and by symmetry

$a_{65} = 0$. Thus the a_{j5} $(j = 2, 3, 8, 9)$ are all units and by $L.3$ $a_{25} = a_{85} = a_{95}$ which is impossible.

Thus $a_{74} \neq 1$ so $a_{74} = 0$, $a_{84} = 1$. By $L.3$ $a_{83} = 0$ so $a_{j3} = 1$ $(j = 3, 5, 6)$. By $L.17$ $a_{35} = 0$. Thus $a_{25} = 0$ for if $a_{25} = 1$ by $L.3$ there could only be one (-1) in $C.5$. If $a_{45} = 1$ we can only have $-1 = a_{55} = a_{95}$ since $a_{55} = a_{65} \neq 0$ is impossible by $L.4$ and then the remaining spaces of $C.5$ are zeros by $L.3$. Thus $a_{45} = 0$. By $L.23$ on $C.3$ and $C.5$ $a_{75} = a_{95} = 0$ which is impossible since $C.5$ now contains six zeros.

Thus (B) cannot arise.

Hence we may suppose $a_{14} = 0 = a_{15} = a_{25}$. Thus by $L.36$ we cannot have both a_{44} and a_{45} zeros. Thus suppose $a_{44} = 1$, then by $L.17$ $a_{45} = 0$. Hence by $L.23$ on $C.3$ and $C.5$ we have $a_{75} = 0 = a_{95}$. Thus the a_{j5} $(j = 3, 5, 6, 8)$ are all units and by $L.3$ $a_{55} = a_{35} = a_{65}$ which is impossible.

Hence (ii) cannot occur and we have proved the following lemma:

LEMMA 37. It is not possible for a 9-con containing ten D_m-planes to contain a tetre, two dotres and two dodos.

Hence by $L.35$ we have:

LEMMA 38. If a 9-con containing ten D_m-planes, one of which is a tetre, exists, then it can contain at most one naik.

All the permatrices of this chapter have been eliminated by arguments which do not involve the tetrahedra which are naiks, so by the remarks of Chapter Four we see that a 9-con containing eleven D_m-planes, one of which is a tetre, cannot exist. Hence by Theorem 5 we have:

THEOREM 6. If a 9-con containing a tetre exists, it must contain exactly ten D_m-planes (m not necessarily being a fixed integer).

CHAPTER SEVEN

ON THE NON-EXISTENCE OF A 9-CON CONTAINING A TETRE

WE BEGIN the chapter by proving a lemma which would more appropriately be situated in Chapter Eight. However, it owes its position here to the fact that a variant of it is used in the proof of Lemma 40. By using Lemma 40 and the concept of a surplus we enumerate the sets of nine D_m-planes which together with a tetre may be contained in a 9-con. By this means we show that a 9-con containing ten D_m-planes, one of which is a tetre cannot exist, so that by Theorem 6 we have:

THEOREM 7. If a 9-con exists, then it cannot contain a tetre. We require the following lemma.

LEMMA 39. If a 9-con contains a chardho, all four of whose faces lie in dodos, then the matrix representation of the 9-con must contain a minor equivalent to one of the following:

G_1				G_2				G_3			
1	1	1	1	1	1	1	1	1	1	1	1
1	-1	0	1	1	-1	0	0	1	-1	0	0
-1	0	1	0	-1	0	1	0	-1	0	0	1
-1	0	0	0	-1	0	0	1	-1	0	0	0
0	-1	0	0	0	-1	0	0	0	-1	0	0
0	1	-1	0	0	1	-1	0	0	1	-1	0
0	0	-1	0	0	0	-1	0	0	0	-1	0
0	0	0	-1	0	0	0	-1	0	0	1	-1
0	0	0	-1	0	0	0	-1	0	0	0	-1

Proof. We may suppose $R.1$ represents the chardho and $C.1$, $C.2$, $C.3$ and $C.4$ the dodos. Hence we may assume $a_{1j} = 1$ $(j = 1, 2, 3, 4)$, $a_{1j} = 0$ $(j > 4)$. By elementary transformations we can arrange that $a_{21} = 1$, $a_{31} = a_{41} = -1$, $a_{j1} = 0$ $(j > 4)$. By $L.2$ we may suppose $a_{22} = -1$ so by $L.3$ $a_{32} = 0 = a_{42}$. Thus by elementary transformations we can arrange $a_{52} = -1, a_{62} = 1$, $a_{j2} = 0$ $(j > 6)$. By $L.3$, $a_{j3} \neq -1$, $a_{j4} \neq -1$ $(j = 2, \ldots 5)$.

Hence by symmetry we may suppose $a_{63} = -1 = a_{73}$. By $L.3$ $a_{23} = 0 = a_{53}$, $a_{j4} \neq -1$ ($j = 2, \ldots 7$) so $a_{84} = -1 = a_{94}$.

Clearly there are only two effective cases for the remaining $(+1)$ of $C.3$, namely (a) $a_{33} = 1$ and (b) $a_{83} = 1$.

(a) Suppose $a_{33} = 1$. Now if the remaining $(+1)$ of $C.4$ is one of a_{24}, a_{34} and a_{64} we have a minor equivalent to (G_1), whilst if it is one of a_{44}, a_{54} and a_{74} we have a minor equivalent to (G_2).

(b) Suppose $a_{83} = 1$ then by $L.3$ $a_{64} = 0 = a_{74}$. Now if $a_{24} = 1$ we have a minor equivalent to (G_1) whilst if $a_{54} = 1$ we have a minor equivalent to (G_2). Finally if a_{34} or a_{44} is the remaining $(+1)$ of $C.4$ we have a minor equivalent to (G_3).

LEMMA 40. If a tetre, a dotre and four dodos occur amongst the D_m-planes of a 9-con then these six D_m-planes cannot contain all four faces of a chardho.

Proof. Suppose the lemma is false; we may clearly assume that the chardho is represented by $R.1$ and that $a_{1j} = 1$ ($j = 1, 2, 3, 4$), $a_{1j} = 0$ ($j > 4$). Since a face of a chardho clearly cannot lie in a tetre we need only consider the cases when a chardho has its faces contained in either four dodos or a dotre and three dodos. In the former case by $L.39$ there are only three non-equivalent matrix representations of the first four columns. In the latter case a matrix representation of the first four columns must clearly be equivalent to one of the G_i (of $L.39$) with an extra unit in one of the columns. Hence we consider the G_i of $L.39$, omitting the zeros which do not follow by $L.3$ and show that none of them leads to a 9-con. We suppose that $C.5$ represents the tetre and $C.6$ the remaining dodo or dotre.

Consider (G_1): we have

$$
\begin{array}{rrrr}
1 & 1 & 1 & 1 \\
1 & -1 & 0 & 1 \\
-1 & 0 & 1 & \\
-1 & 0 & & \\
& -1 & 0 & \\
0 & 1 & -1 & \\
0 & & -1 & \\
& 0 & & -1 \\
& 0 & & -1 \\
\end{array}
$$

The zeros all follow from $L.3$. By $L.17$ $a_{25} = 0$.

(i) Suppose $a_{72} = 1$ then $C.l$ $(l = 1, 3, 4, 6)$ are all dodos so that the remaining spaces of $C.1$, $C.3$ and $C.4$ are all zeros. By $L.17$ $a_{26} = 0$. As there is only one more zero in $C.5$ by symmetry we may suppose $a_{65} = 1$. Now if $a_{75} = -1$, by $L.3$ $a_{35} = 0 = a_{55}$, so that $C.5$ contains at most five units. Thus $a_{75} \neq -1$; by $L.4$ $a_{75} \neq 1$ so $a_{75} = 0$. Thus the remaining spaces of $C.5$ are units. By $L.3$ $a_{35} = a_{65} = a_{55}$ so we must have $a_{45} = -1 = a_{85} = a_{95}$. By $L.17$ $a_{36} = 0 = a_{66}$. Now if $a_{56} = 1$ by $L.3$ no (-1)s can occur in $C.6$ so $a_{56} = 0$. Thus the a_{j6} $(j = 4, 7, 8, 9)$ are all units. By $L.4$ $a_{86} = a_{96} \neq 0$ is impossible so we may suppose $a_{86} = 1 = -a_{96}$ and by symmetry $a_{46} = 1 = -a_{76}$. Let $a_{77} = -1$, then by $L.2$ $a_{67} = 1 = a_{97}$ and by $L.3$ the remaining spaces of $C.7$ are zeros. Let $a_{48} = 1$ then by $L.2$ $a_{88} = -1$ and by $L.3$ the remaining spaces of $C.8$ are zeros. Thus we have

A	x	y	B	z	C	D	E
1	1	1	1	0	0	0	0
1	-1	0	1	0	0	0	0
-1	0	1	0	1	0	0	0
-1	0	0	0	-1	1	0	1
0	-1	0	0	1	0	0	0
0	1	-1	0	1	0	1	0
0	1	-1	0	0	-1	-1	0
0	0	0	-1	-1	1	0	-1
0	0	0	-1	-1	-1	1	0

Choose the coordinate system shown. From boundedness we have: T.6 $d_1 < 0$, $d_2 > 0$; from T.7 $c_1 > 0$, $c_2 < 0$; from T.9 $b_1 < 0$, $b_2 > 0$; from T.8 $e_1 > 0$, $e_2 < 0$; from T.4 $a_1 > 0$, $a_2 < 0$.

Now $z = 0$ is a tem-plane so by $L.8$ each tetrahedron must have an intersection of positive area with $z = 0$. Thus consider the configuration on $z = 0$.

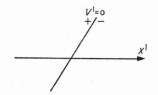

FIG. 19

From the above it is clear that $B^1 = 0$ and $D^1 = 0$ are of type $V^1 = 0$ whilst $A^1 = 0$, $C^1 = 0$ and $E^1 = 0$ are of type $W^1 = 0$.

Now each of $T^1.4$, $T^1.8$ and $T^1.9$ must have an area in both $y^1 > 0$ and $y^1 < 0$ if each of them is to have an area in common with both $T^1.3$ and $T^1.6$ as they must. Thus the intersection of each of them with the line $y^1 = 0$ is a line of positive length. Hence for $T^1.8$ we must have $e_4/e_1 > b_4/b_1$ and $e_4/e_1 > c_4/c_1$. Similarly for $T^1.4$ we must have $a_4/a_1 > e_4/e_1$.

Hence $a_4/a_1 > b_4/b_1$ so that $y^1 = 0$ clearly does not occur in $T^1.1$. Further $c_4/c_1 \geqslant 0$ for, if $c_4/c_1 < 0$, $x^1 \geqslant 0$, $y^1 \leqslant 0$ would lie in $C^1 > 0$ so that $T^1.7$ would not exist. But $a_4/a_1 > e_4/e_1 > c_4/c_1 \geqslant 0$ so $a_4/a_1 > 0$. Now $T^1.1$ must lie in $A^1 \geqslant 0$, $y^1 \geqslant 0$ which lies in $x^1 > 0$ since $A^1 = 0$ is of type $W^1 = 0$ and $a_4/a_1 > 0$. Hence $x^1 = 0$ cannot occur in $T^1.1$. As $y^1 = 0$ does not occur in $T^1.1$, from the above $T^1.1$ cannot exist which is impossible.

Hence (i) cannot arise and we may suppose $a_{72} = 0$ for $a_{72} \neq$ —1 by $L.3$.

(ii) Suppose $a_{35} = 1 = a_{65}$ then by $L.3$ $a_{55} \neq$ —1, $a_{75} \neq$ —1 so we must have $a_{45} = -1 = a_{85} = a_{95}$. Hence by $L.3$ $a_{81} = a_{91} = 0 = a_{43} = a_{83} = a_{93} = a_{34} = a_{64}$. By $L.17$ $a_{36} = 0 = a_{66}$. Now one of a_{55} and a_{75} is $(+1)$ and the other is zero. Let the $(+1)$ be a_{k5} and the zero a_{l5}. Now $a_{26} = 0$ for if $a_{26} = 1$ by $L.2$ we must have $a_{56} = -1 = a_{76}$, i.e. $a_{k6} = -1$ and so by $L.3$ $a_{46} = 0 = a_{86} = a_{96}$ and $C.6$ then contains six zeros. Thus by symmetry we may now suppose $a_{86} = 1$. By $L.3$ $a_{k6} \neq$ —1 so at least one of a_{46} and a_{96} is a (-1). Hence by $L.3$ $a_{k6} \neq 1$ so $a_{k6} = 0$. Thus a_{96} is a unit; by $L.4$ $a_{96} \neq 1$ so $a_{96} = -1$ and by symmetry we may suppose $a_{46} = 1 = -a_{16}$. Hence by $L.3$ $a_{51} = 0 = a_{j4}$ $(j = 4, 5, 7)$ so that none of the first six columns represent a dotre. Thus (ii) cannot arise.

(iii) Suppose $a_{35} = 1$ then by $L.17$ $a_{34} = 0 = a_{36}$ and by (ii) $a_{65} \neq 1$. By $L.3$ $a_{65} \neq$ —1 so $a_{65} = 0$, and the remaining spaces of $C.5$ are units. By $L.3$ $a_{75} = a_{35} = 1$. Let a_{2l} be the remaining unit of $R.2$, then by $L.2$ $a_{5l} = a_{7l} = -a_{2l}$ and by $L.3$ $a_{3l} = 0 = a_{6l}$. Since a_{55} is a unit it follows from $L.3$ whether $a_{55} = 1$ or $a_{55} = -1$ that $a_{jl} = 0$ $(j = 4, 8, 9)$. Thus $C.l$ represents a doun so we may suppose $l = 7$ and put $a_{26} = 0$. Let a_{7m} be the remaining unit of $R.7$ then by $L.2$ $a_{6m} = -a_{7m}$ and by $L.3$ $a_{3m} = 0$. Hence if

$a_{55} = 1$, by $L.2$ $a_{5m} = -a_{7m}$ so that $R.3$ and $R.5$ contradict $L.2$. Thus $a_{55} \neq 1$ so $a_{55} = -1$.

If $a_{45} = 1$ then $a_{85} = -1 = a_{95}$ so by $L.6$ we must have $a_{54} = 1$. Hence $C.4$ represents the dotre, so $C.3$ represents a dodo; thus $a_{j3} = 0$ $(j = 4, 8, 9)$. By $L.2$ therefore $a_{4m} = -a_{7m}$, so by $L.3$ $a_{8m} = 0 = a_{9m}$. Hence by $L.6$ we must have $a_{64} = 1$ which is impossible because $C.4$ then contains four $(+1)$s.

Thus $a_{45} \neq 1$ so $a_{45} = -1$ and we may suppose $a_{85} = 1 = -a_{95}$. By $L.3$ $a_{j1} = 0$ $(j = 5, 8, 9)$, $a_{43} = 0 = a_{93}$, $a_{j4} = 0$ $(j = 4, 5, 7)$. If $a_{76} = 1$, by $L.3$ we must have $-1 = a_{66} = a_{86}$ so by $L.3$ $a_{j6} = 0$ $(j = 4, 5, 9)$ which is impossible. Thus $a_{76} = 0$. Hence if $a_{86} = 1$, by $L.3$ we can only have one (-1) in $C.6$; thus $a_{86} = 0$ and a_{j6} $(j = 4, 5, 6, 9)$ are all units.

By $L.3$ $a_{56} = a_{66} = 1$ so $a_{46} = a_{96} = -1$. By $L.3$ $a_{64} = 0$ so the only possibility for a dotre is $C.3$; hence $C.3$ must represent a dotre and we have $a_{83} = 1$. Let $a_{48} = 1$, then by $L.2$ $a_{98} = -1$ and by $L.3$ the remaining spaces of $C.8$ are zeros. Let $a_{39} = 1$, then by $L.2$ $a_{89} = -1$ and by $L.3$ the remaining spaces of $C.9$ are zeros. Thus

x	A	y	z	B	C	D	E	F
1	1	1	1	0	0	0	0	0
1	-1	0	1	0	0	1	0	0
-1	0	1	0	1	0	0	0	1
-1	0	0	0	-1	-1	0	1	0
0	-1	0	0	-1	1	-1	0	0
0	1	-1	0	0	1	0	0	0
0	0	-1	0	1	0	-1	0	0
0	0	1	-1	1	0	0	0	-1
0	0	0	-1	-1	-1	0	-1	0

Choose the coordinate system shown. From boundedness we have: from $T.1$ $a_2 < 0$; from $T.2$ $d_2 < 0$; from $T.3$ at least one of $b_2 < 0$ and $f_2 < 0$ holds; from $T.8$ at least one of $b_2 < 0$ and $f_2 > 0$ holds; hence $b_2 < 0$. From $T.5$ $c_2 < 0$; from $T.4$ $e_2 < 0$. However $T.9$ is now unbounded so (iii) cannot occur.

Hence we must have $a_{35} = 0$ so the remaining spaces of $C.5$ are units. Let a_{2l} be the remaining unit of $R.2$ then by $L.2$ $a_{5l} = a_{7l} = -a_{2l}$ and by $L.3$ $a_{3l} = 0 = a_{6l}$. Now if $a_{jl} = a_{2l}$ for j one of 4, 8 and 9 then in $C.5$ we have by $L.3$ $a_{75} = a_{j5} = a_{55} = a_{65}$ which is impossible. By $L.3$ $a_{jl} \neq -a_{2l}$ so $a_{jl} = 0$ $(j = 4, 8, 9)$

and $C.l$ represents a doun. Thus we may suppose $l = 7$ and put $a_{27} = 1$, $a_{57} = -1 = a_{77}$ and $a_{26} = 0$. Now by $L.3$ $a_{55} = a_{65}$ so we may suppose $a_{55} = a_{65} = 1$.

If $a_{75} = 1$, by letting the remaining unit of $R.7$ be a_{7m} we have by $L.2$ $a_{5m} = a_{6m} = -a_{7m}$, so by $L.3$ $a_{3m} = 0$. However, $R.3$ and $R.5$ now contradict $L.2$.

Thus $a_{75} \neq 1$ so $a_{75} = -1$. By $L.17$ $a_{66} = 0$.

If $a_{45} = 1$ then $a_{85} = -1 = a_{95}$ so by $L.3$ $a_{83} = 0 = a_{93}$. Hence by $L.6$ we must have $a_{74} = 1$, so by $L.17$ $a_{76} = 0$. Thus at least one of a_{86} and a_{96} is a unit so put $a_{86} = 1$. By $L.3$ we can only have $-1 = a_{96} = a_{36}$ and then by $L.3$ $a_{46} = 0 = a_{56}$ so that $C.6$ represents a doun, contradicting its definition.

Thus $a_{45} \neq 1$ so $a_{45} = -1$ and we may suppose $a_{85} = 1 = -a_{95}$. Now $a_{86} = 0$ for if $a_{86} = 1$ by $L.3$ we can only have $-1 = a_{36} = a_{56}$ so by $L.3$ again $a_{j6} = 0$ $(j = 4, 7, 9)$ which is impossible. Hence $a_{56} = 0$ for if $a_{56} = 1$ there can be at most one (-1) in $C.6$. Thus a_{j6} $(j = 3, 4, 7, 9)$ are all units. By $L.3$ $a_{36} = a_{76}$ $(= 1$ say$)$ so $a_{46} = a_{96} = -1$. Hence by $L.3$ the remaining spaces of $C.1$, $C.3$ and $C.4$ are all zeros so that none of the first six columns represent a dotre which is impossible.

Thus (G_1) does not lead to a 9-con.

Now consider (G_3)

$$
\begin{array}{cccc}
1 & 1 & 1 & 1 \\
1 & -1 & 0 & \\
-1 & 0 & & 1 \\
-1 & 0 & & \\
& -1 & 0 & \\
& 1 & -1 & 0 \\
& & -1 & 0 \\
0 & & 1 & -1 \\
0 & & & -1 \\
\end{array}
$$

Clearly the zeros follow from $L.3$. Now we may also suppose $a_{24} = 0 = a_{33} = a_{61} = a_{82}$ for if any of them are $(+1)$s we have a case equivalent to the one for (G_1); none of them are (-1)s by $L.3$.

We now remark that each of the cases (a) $a_{35} = \pm 1$, (b) $a_{65} = \pm 1$ and (c) $a_{85} = \pm 1$ is equivalent to the case $a_{25} = \pm 1$. As at most two of the a_{j5} $(j = 2, 3, 6, 8)$ can be zeros we may clearly suppose $a_{25} = 1$. By $L.3$ $a_{35} \neq -1$, $a_{45} \neq -1$ and $a_{65} \neq -1$

so three of the a_{j5} $(j = 5, 7, 8, 9)$ are (-1)s. Thus at least one of a_{85} and a_{95} is a (-1) so by $L.3$ $a_{35} = 0$. Further at least one of a_{55} and a_{85} is a (-1) so by $L.3$ $a_{65} = 0$. Hence the remaining spaces of $C.5$ are units. By $L.3$ $a_{45} = a_{25} = 1$ and $a_{75} = a_{85}$. Thus $a_{75} = a_{85} = -1$, otherwise $C.5$ would contain four $(+1)$s. By $L.3$ $a_{43} = 0 = a_{44} = a_{71} = a_{72}$ and, since $a_{55} = a_{95} \neq 0$, $a_{92} = 0 = a_{54}$. By $L.17$ $a_{26} = 0 = a_{86}$.

Now if $a_{55} = 1 = -a_{95}$, by $L.3$ and $L.4$ we have $a_{51} = 0 = a_{93}$ whilst if $a_{95} = 1 = -a_{55}$ by $L.3$ $a_{51} = 0 = a_{93}$.

Hence $a_{51} = 0 = a_{93}$ so the first four columns all represent dodos; hence $C.6$ represents a dotre. Clearly the cases $a_{56} = \pm 1$ and $a_{96} = \pm 1$ are equivalent so as both cannot be zero we may suppose $a_{96} = 1$. Hence by $L.3$ whether $a_{95} = 1$ or -1 we must have $-1 = a_{66}$. Thus by $L.3$ $a_{56} = 0$ so a_{j6} $(j = 3, 4, 7)$ are all units. By $L.3$ $a_{36} = a_{96} = 1$ and $a_{46} = a_{76}$. Thus $a_{46} = a_{76} = -1$ otherwise $C.6$ contains four $(+1)$s. But by $L.3$ on $R.4$ $a_{95} \neq -1$ and on $R.7$ $a_{95} \neq 1$. Thus $a_{95} = 0$ and $C.5$ does not represent a tetre.

Hence (G_3) does not lead to a 9-con.

Finally consider (G_2)

$$
\begin{array}{cccc}
1 & 1 & 1 & 1 \\
1 & -1 & 0 & \\
-1 & 0 & 1 & \\
-1 & 0 & & 1 \\
& -1 & 0 & \\
0 & 1 & -1 & \\
0 & & -1 & \\
0 & & & -1 \\
0 & & & -1 \\
\end{array}
$$

Clearly the zeros follow from $L.3$. Now we may also suppose $a_{24} = 0 = a_{34} = a_{43} = a_{64}$ for if any of them are $(+1)$s we have a case equivalent to the case for (G_1). Further we may assume $a_{83} = 0 = a_{93}$ otherwise we have a case equivalent to the case for (G_3).

(i) Suppose $a_{25} = 1 = a_{35}$ then by $L.3$ $a_{j5} \neq -1$ $(j = 4, 6, 7)$ so $a_{m5} = -1$ $(m = 5, 8, 9)$. By $L.3$ $a_{45} = 0 = a_{65}$ so $a_{75} = 1$. Further by $L.3$ $a_{51} = 0 = a_{74} = a_{j2}$ $(j = 7, 8, 9)$. By $L.17$ $a_{26} = 0 = a_{36}$. Now if $a_{86} = -a_{96} \neq 0$ by $L.3$ $a_{46} = 0 = a_{76}$ so that $a_{56} = -a_{66}$ which is impossible by $L.3$. Since $a_{86} = a_{96} \neq 0$ is impossible

11*

by $L.4$ we may suppose $a_{96} = 0$. Further a_{86} is a unit, for if $a_{86} = 0$, by $L.6$ $a_{66} = 0$ also and $C.6$ contains six zeros which is impossible. Thus let $a_{86} = 1$, then by $L.3$ we can only have $-1 = a_{56} = a_{66}$ so $a_{76} = 0$ and $a_{54} = 0$. However none of the columns represent a dotre so the case does not arise.

(ii) Suppose $a_{25} = 1$; by $L.3$ $a_{35} \neq -1$ so by (i) we may suppose $a_{35} = 0$. By $L.3$ $a_{45} \neq -1$, $a_{65} \neq -1$ so at least one of a_{85} and a_{95} is a (-1) and so by $L.3$ $a_{45} = 0$ and the remaining spaces of $C.5$ are units. By $L.3$ $a_{55} = a_{65} = a_{25} = 1$ so $a_{j5} = -1$ ($j = 7, 8, 9$). By $L.3$ $a_{54} = 0 = a_{j2}$ ($j = 7, 8, 9$). By $L.4$ $a_{51} = 0$ and by $L.17$ $a_{26} = 0 = a_{66}$. Now if $a_{86} = -a_{96} \neq 0$, by $L.3$ $a_{46} = 0 = a_{56}$ so $a_{36} = -a_{76} \neq 0$ which is impossible by $L.3$. Since $a_{86} = a_{96} \neq 0$ is impossible by $L.4$ we may suppose $a_{96} = 0$. Further a_{86} is a unit for if $a_{86} = 0$, by $L.6$ $a_{36} = 0$ also and $C.6$ contains six zeros. Hence let $a_{86} = 1$, so by $L.3$ we can only have $-1 = a_{36} = a_{76}$. By $L.3$ $a_{74} = 0 = a_{56}$. However none of the columns represent a dotre so the case cannot occur.

Thus $a_{25} = 0$.

(iii) Suppose $a_{35} = 1 = a_{65}$, then by $L.3$ $a_{55} \neq -1$, $a_{75} \neq -1$ so $a_{j5} = -1$ ($j = 4, 8, 9$). Now $a_{51} = 0$ for if $a_{51} = 1$ both $T.3$ and $T.4$ are naiks which is impossible by $L.38$. By $L.17$ $a_{j6} = 0$ ($j = 3, 4, 6$) so at least one of a_{86} and a_{96} is a unit. Hence let $a_{86} = 1$. Now one of a_{55} and a_{75} is a $(+1)$ and the other is a zero. Let a_{l5} be the $(+1)$ and a_{m5} the zero, then by $L.3$ $a_{l4} = 0$.

If $a_{96} = -1$, by $L.3$ $a_{16} = 0$ so we may suppose by symmetry $a_{26} = 1 = -a_{m6}$. By $L.17$ $a_{82} = 0 = a_{92}$ and by $L.3$ $a_{m4} = 0$. Thus the only column that can represent a dotre is $C.2$ so we must have $a_{72} = 1$. Hence by $L.3$ $a_{76} \neq -1$ so $l = 7$, $m = 5$, i.e. $a_{75} = 1$ which is impossible by $L.4$.

Thus $a_{96} \neq -1$; by $L.4$ $a_{96} \neq 1$ so $a_{96} = 0$. By $L.17$ $a_{82} = 0$. By $L.3$ we can only have $-1 = a_{26} = a_{m6}$ so $a_{16} = 1$. Also, by $L.3$, $a_{m4} = 0$ so $C.2$ is the only column that can represent a dotre.

As $a_{m6} = -a_{16} \neq 0$, by $L.3$ $a_{72} = 0$ so we must have $a_{92} = 1$. Hence by $L.3$ $a_{55} = 0$ so $a_{75} = 1 = a_{76}$, $a_{56} = -1$. Let $a_{67} = 1$ then by $L.2$ $a_{77} = -1$ and the remaining spaces of $C.7$ are zeros by $L.3$. Let $a_{88} = 1$ then by $L.2$ $a_{98} = -1$ and by $L.3$ the remaining spaces of $C.8$ are zeros.

Let $a_{29} = 1$ then by $L.2$ $a_{59} = -1$ and by $L.3$ $a_{j9} = 0$ ($j = 6$, 7, 8, 9). Finally let $a_{5.10} = -1$. Thus we have

A	x	B	y	z	C	D	E	F	G
1	1	1	1	0	0	0	0	0	0
1	-1	0	0	0	-1	0	0	1	
-1	0	1	0	1	0	0	0		
-1	0	0	1	-1	0	0	0		
0	-1	0	0	0	-1	0	0	-1	-1
0	1	-1	0	1	0	1	0	0	
0	0	-1	0	1	1	-1	0	0	
0	0	0	-1	-1	1	0	1	0	
0	1	0	-1	-1	0	0	-1	0	

Choose the coordinate system shown. From boundedness we have: from $T.9$ $e_2 < 0$, $e_3 < 0$; from $T.8$ $c_2 > 0$, $c_3 > 0$; from $T.6$ $b_2 d_2 > 0$ and at least one of $b_3 > 0$ and $d_3 < 0$ holds; from $T.7$ at least one of $b_2 > 0$ and $d_2 > 0$ holds and at least one of $b_3 > 0$ and $d_3 > 0$ holds. Hence we must have $b_2 > 0$, $b_3 > 0$. From $T.1$ $a_2 < 0$, $a_3 < 0$; from $T.2$ $f_2 > 0$, $f_3 > 0$.

Now if $a_{39} = 1$, $T.3$ is unbounded in the y-direction so $a_{39} \neq 1$. Thus by $L.2$ we must have $a_{3.10} = 1$. Further if $a_{49} = 1$, $T.4$ is unbounded in the y-direction so $a_{49} \neq 1$. Thus by $L.2$ we must have $a_{4.10} = 1$. From $T.3$ $g_2 < 0$, $g_3 < 0$.

Now $x = 0$ is a tem-plane so by $L.8$ each tetrahedron must have an intersection of positive area, with $x = 0$. Thus consider the configuration on $x = 0$.

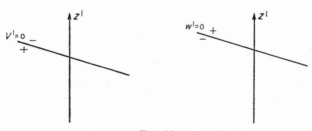

Fig. 20

From the above it is clear that $A^1 = 0$, $E^1 = 0$ and $G^1 = 0$ are of type $V^1 = 0$ whilst $B^1 = 0$, $C^1 = 0$ and $F^1 = 0$ are of type $W^1 = 0$.

If $c_4/c_3 > 0$ then clearly $y^1 \leqslant 0$, $z^1 \leqslant 0$ lies in $C^1 < 0$ so that T.8 does not have an intersection with $x = 0$ which is impossible. Thus $c_4/c_3 \leqslant 0$.

Now each of $T^1.2$ and $T^1.5$ must have an area in both $z^1 > 0$ and $z^1 < 0$ if they are to have an area in common with both $T^1.6$ and $T^1.9$ as they must. Thus the intersection of each with the line $z^1 = 0$ is a line of positive length. Hence for $T^1.2$ we must have $f_4/f_3 < a_4/a_3$ and for $T^1.5$ both $g_4/g_3 < f_4/f_3$ and $g_4/g_3 < c_4/c_3 \leqslant 0$.

Since $g_4/g_3 < 0$, $z^1 = 0$ does not lie in $y^1 \geqslant 0$, $G^1 \geqslant 0$ so it cannot occur in $T^1.4$.

But as $g_4/g_3 < f_4/f_3 < a_4/a_3$ no point of $y^1 = 0$ can occur in $A^1 \leqslant 0$, $G^1 \geqslant 0$ so $y^1 = 0$ also cannot occur in $T^1.4$.

Hence T.4 does not have an intersection with $x = 0$ which is impossible. Thus (iii) cannot arise.

(iv) Suppose $a_{35} = 1$, then from (iii) $a_{65} \neq 1$. By $L.3$ $a_{65} \neq -1$ so $a_{65} = 0$ and the a_{j5} $(j = 4, 5, 7, 8, 9)$ are all units. By $L.3$ $a_{85} = a_{45} = a_{95} = -1$ otherwise we have four $(+1)$s in $C.5$ and so $a_{55} = 1 = a_{75}$. By $L.17$ $a_{36} = 0 = a_{46}$ and by $L.3$ $a_{51} = 0 = a_{82} = a_{92} = a_{54} = a_{74}$. Now if $a_{56} = 1$, by $L.3$ we can only have $-1 = a_{26} = a_{76}$ and then by $L.3$ $a_{j6} = 0$ $(j = 6, 8, 9)$ and $C.6$ represents a doun. Thus $a_{56} = 0$. Hence at least one of a_{86} and a_{96} is a unit so let $a_{86} = 1$. If $a_{96} = -1$, by $L.3$ $a_{76} = 0$ so $a_{26} = -a_{66}$ which is impossible by $L.3$. Thus $a_{96} \neq -1$. By $L.4$ $a_{96} \neq 1$ so $a_{96} = 0$. Hence the a_{j6} $(j = 2, 6, 7)$ are all units. By $L.3$ $a_{76} = a_{86} = 1$ so $a_{26} = -1 = a_{66}$. By $L.3$ $a_{72} = 0$ so that none of the first six columns represent a dotre. Hence (iv) cannot arise.

Thus we may now suppose $a_{35} = 0$, so the remaining spaces of $C.5$ are units. By $L.3$ $a_{45} = a_{85} = a_{95} = 1$ say, then $a_{j5} = -1$ $(j = 5, 6, 7)$. By $L.17$ $a_{46} = 0 = a_{66}$. By $L.3$ $a_{51} = 0 = a_{82} = a_{92} = a_{54} = a_{74}$. By $L.4$ $a_{72} = 0$ so that $C.6$ must represent the dotre. Hence at least one of a_{86} and a_{96} is a unit so let $a_{86} = 1$. Now $a_{96} \neq 1$ by $L.4$ and $a_{96} \neq -1$ for, if it is, by $L.3$ $a_{56} = 0 = a_{76}$ and $C.6$ does not represent a dotre. Thus $a_{96} = 0$ so the a_{j6} $(j = 2, 3, 5, 7)$ are all units. By $L.3$ we have $a_{36} = a_{76} = a_{86} = a_{56}$ which is clearly impossible.

Hence (G_2) does not lead to a 9-con and the lemma is proved.

We now analyse the sets of nine D_m-planes which together with a tetre may be contained in a 9-con. By $L.31$ at most two of the planes can be dotres. Further at most one of them is a uno for if two unos did occur, then by $L.18$ at least two naiks would occur in the 9-con and this is impossible by $L.38$. As unos and dotres are the only D_m-planes to have a surplus of zero at least six of the D_m-planes must have a positive surplus.

Now the nine D_m-planes other than the tetre have a total surplus of $36 - 30 + 3 = 9$. It therefore follows that two of them cannot be treuns for, as treuns have a surplus of 3, if two did occur, at most five of the D_m-planes could have a positive surplus which contradicts the above.

(i) Consider the case when two dotres occur with the tetre. Then the remaining seven D_m-planes contain 20 faces and have a total surplus of 9. By $L.37$ at most one of them can be a dodo so at most two D_4-planes can occur.

(a) Suppose two D_4-planes occur then we must have one treun and one dodo so that the five undetermined D_m-planes contain 12 faces and have a total surplus of $9 - 3 - 1 = 5$. Thus at least two of them are D_3-planes. However as a treun, a dodo and two D_3-planes have a surplus of at least 8, at most five of the D_m-planes can have a positive surplus, which contradicts the above.

(b) Suppose at most one D_4-plane occurs. Then six of the other undetermined D_m-planes contain at least 16 faces. Thus at least four of them are D_3-planes. Since D_3-planes have a surplus of at least 2, it therefore follows that at most five D_m-planes have a positive surplus which again contradicts the above.

Hence (i) cannot occur.

(ii) Suppose no dotres occur with the tetre. Then the nine undetermined D_m-planes contain 30 faces and have a total surplus of 9. As at most one uno can occur, at least eight of these planes must have a positive surplus. Hence a treun cannot occur for, if it did, as treuns have a surplus of 3, at most seven of the D_m-planes would have a positive surplus. Now as no treuns or dotres occur with the tetre, the 9-con clearly cannot contain any dhoats or naiks, so no unos can occur amongst the D_m-planes for, if one did, a naik would have to occur in the 9-con by $L.18$.

Hence all the nine undetermined D_m-planes must have a positive surplus. So each of them must have a surplus of 1, i.e.

each must either be a dodo or a unun. Hence as they must contain 30 faces we can only have six dodos and three ununs.

Thus consider the set of D_m-planes consisting of one tetre, three ununs and six dodos. Let $C.1$ represent the tetre with $a_{j1} = 1$ ($j = 1, 2, 3$), $a_{j1} = -1$ ($j = 4, 5, 6$), $a_{j1} = 0$ ($j = 7, 8, 9$) and $C.2$, $C.3$ and $C.4$ the ununs. Clearly none of $T.l$ ($l = 1, \ldots 6$) can be chardhos and from the above none of them are naiks, or dhoats either. Thus each of them is a thaik so that each $R.l$ ($l = 1, \ldots 6$) must have one and only one unit in columns 2, 3 and 4. As these columns only contain two units each we may clearly suppose $a_{12} = 1$, $a_{32} = 0$ so that we may further assume $a_{33} = 1$. Now by $L.3$ $a_{j1} \neq -1$ ($j = 4, 5, 6$; $l = 2, 3$) so one of $R.4$, $R.5$ and $R.6$ does not have a unit in columns 2, 3 and 4 which contradicts the above.

Hence the set does not lead to a 9-con and (ii) cannot arise.

(iii) Finally consider the case when one and only one dotre occurs with the tetre. Then the eight undetermined D_m-planes contain 25 faces and have a total surplus of 9. As at most one uno can occur, at least seven of them must have a positive surplus. Hence as a D_3-plane has a surplus of at least 2, at most two D_3-planes can occur amongst them. Thus at least four of the D_m-planes must be D_4-planes. From the above at most one of them can be a treun so we must have at least three dodos.

(a) Suppose a treun does occur, then we have at least three dodos and the four undetermined D_m-planes have a total surplus of $9 - 3 - 3 = 3$. Hence one of them must be a uno so that the three undetermined D_m-planes contain 8 faces and have a total surplus of 3. Thus each of them has a surplus of 1, i.e. each is either a dodo or a unun. Thus as they contain 8 faces we can only have a dodo and two ununs. Hence the set S_a of D_m-planes obtained is one tetre, one dotre, four dodos, one treun, two ununs and a uno. As S_a contains a uno the 9-con contains a naik by $L.18$. Consider the matrix representation of S_a. As S_a contains only one tetre, one dotre and one treun there are only nine tripts in the matrix. Since one of the rows represents a naik two tripts must lie in the same row, so there is at least one row that contains no tripts. By $L.17$ therefore this row represents a chardho. However as S_a does not contain a doun the faces of this chardho must be contained in the dotre and four dodos. Hence by $L.40$ S_a does not lead to a 9-con.

Hence a treun does not occur and we have at least four dodos. Thus the four undetermined D_m-planes contain 9 faces and have a total surplus of 5. Now a dodo cannot occur amongst them for, if it did, the other three would contain 5 faces so that one of them would be a uno and the other two would be D_2-planes. By $L.38$ the D_2-planes cannot be nodos so they must both be ununs; but as the total surplus of a dodo, a uno and two ununs is only 3 this is impossible. Hence at least one D_3-plane occurs; by $L.38$ it cannot be a notre so it must be a doun. Thus the three undetermined D_m-planes contain 6 faces and have a surplus of 3.

Hence either (b) a uno occurs so that the other two D_m-planes are a D_3-plane and a D_2-plane and therefore a doun and a unun; or (c) a uno does not occur so that each of the three has a surplus of 1; thus since none of them can be a dodo we have three ununs.

Consider firstly the set S_b of D_m-planes that is obtained from (b), namely one tetre, one dotre, four dodos, two douns a unun and a uno. Since S_b contains a uno the 9-con contains a naik by $L.18$. Consider the matrix representation of S_b. As S_b contains only one tetre, one dotre and no treuns there are only eight tripts in the matrix. Since one of the rows represents a naik two tripts must lie in the same row so there are at least two rows that contain no tripts. By $L.17$ these rows must represent chardhos so that at least two chardhos occur in the 9-con. However by $L.40$ at most two chardhos can occur for, if there are three, the four faces of at least one of them must be contained in the dotre and four dodos since S_b contains only two douns. Hence two and only two chardhos occur in the 9-con and by $L.40$ one face from each of them must be contained in the douns.

Let $C.1$ represent the tetre with $a_{j1} = 1$ $(j = 1, 2, 3)$, $a_{j1} = -1$ $(j = 4, 5, 6)$ and $a_{j1} = 0$ $(j = 7, 8, 9)$ and $C.2$, which we assume contains only two (-1)s, the dotre. Clearly we may suppose $R.1$ represents the naik so that we must have $a_{12} = -1$. Further we may assume $R.8$ and $R.9$ represent the two chardhos. Hence as $R.7$ does not represent a chardho we must have $a_{72} = -1$. Thus by $L.3$ $a_{j2} = 0$ $(j = 4, 5, 6)$ so we may suppose $a_{22} = 1 = a_{82}$, the other $(+1)$ being either a_{32} or a_{92}. Let $a_{13} = 1$, then as $\mathbf{T}.1$ is a naik $C.3$ contains two (-1)s. Clearly by $L.3$, $a_{73} = -1$ is one of them so by $L.3$ we have $a_{23} = 0 = a_{83}$.

Now if $a_{92} = 1$ then $a_{32} = 0$, and by $L.3$ $a_{93} = 0$ so we can only have $-1 = a_{33}$. However by $L.3$ $a_{j3} = 0$ $(j = 4, 5, 6)$ so that $C.3$ represents a doun and so one of the chardhos cannot have a face contained in a doun since S_b contains only two douns.

Thus $a_{92} \neq 1$ so $a_{92} = 0$, $a_{32} = 1$. By $L.3$ $a_{33} = 0$ and we can only have $-1 = a_{93}$. Since $\mathbf{T}.9$ is a chardho another $(+1)$ must occur in $C.3$ and by symmetry we may suppose $a_{43} = 1$. By $L.2$ we may suppose $a_{24} = 1 = -a_{34}$ then by $L.3$ $a_{j4} = 0$ $(j = 1, 4, 5, 6, 7)$. Let $a_{25} = 1$ then by $L.3$ and $L.4$ $a_{35} = 0$ so we may let $a_{36} = 1$. Clearly $a_{15} = a_{16} = a_{26} = 0$.

Now if $a_{84} = 0 = a_{94}$ then by $L.2$ we must have $a_{j5} = -1 = a_{j6}$ $(j = 8, 9)$. As $\mathbf{T}.8$ and $\mathbf{T}.9$ are chardhos $\mathbf{T}.8/\mathbf{T}.9$ in a dodo and further both $C.5$ and $C.6$ must contain another $(+1)$. Hence the faces of $\mathbf{T}.9$ are contained in four dodos so by $L.40$ the case does not lead to a 9-con.

Thus $a_{84} = 0 = a_{94}$ is impossible. However if either a_{84} or a_{94} is a $+1$ (or -1) then another -1 $(+1)$ must also occur in $C.4$ because $\mathbf{T}.8$ and $\mathbf{T}.9$ are chardhos. Hence by symmetry we may suppose $a_{84} = 1 = -a_{94}$. Thus by $L.2$ $a_{85} = -1 = a_{96}$ and by $L.3$ $a_{75} = 0 = a_{95} = a_{86} = a_{46}$. By $L.3$ no more (-1)s can occur in either $C.5$ or $C.6$ so $C.5$ and $C.6$ must both be douns for neither can be a unun since $\mathbf{T}.8$ and $\mathbf{T}.9$ are chardhos. Hence we may suppose $C.7$ and $C.8$ represent the two remaining dodos and $C.9$ the unun. By $L.1$ $a_{ij} = 0$ $(j = 7, 8, 9; i = 1, 2, 3)$ and by $L.17$ $a_{89} = 0 = a_{99}$. Now by $L.17$ and $L.1$ none of $R.4$, $R.7$, $R.8$ and $R.9$ can have units in both $C.7$ and $C.8$. Hence both $R.5$ and $R.6$ have units in both $C.7$ and $C.8$.

Clearly we may suppose $a_{57} = -1 = a_{58}$. By $L.3$ $a_{67} = 1 = a_{68}$ is impossible and by $L.4$ we cannot have $a_{67} = -1 = a_{68}$ so we may suppose $a_{67} = -1$, $a_{68} = 1$. By $L.3$ $a_{49} = -a_{79} \neq 0$ is impossible so one of a_{59} and a_{69} is a unit. By symmetry we may suppose $a_{69} = -1$. By $L.3$ $a_{59} = 0$ and by $L.1$ $a_{65} = 0 = a_{66}$. Two cases now arise: (α) $a_{55} = 1$ and (β) $a_{55} \neq 1$.

(α). Suppose $a_{55} = 1$ then $a_{56} = 0$. By $L.3$ $a_{87} \neq 1$ so by $L.2$ we must have $a_{88} = -1$. By $L.3$ $a_{98} \neq 1$ so by $L.2$ on $R.5$ $a_{97} = 1$. As $C.5$ and $C.6$ are douns we have $a_{45} = 0$, $a_{76} = 1$. Thus by $L.2$ $a_{48} = 1$ so by $L.3$ $a_{47} \neq 1$ and so by $L.2$ $a_{49} = 1$. Thus $a_{78} = 0 =$

a_{79} so $a_{77} = 1$. Hence we have

A	x	y	B	C	D	z	E	F
1	−1	1	0	0	0	0	0	0
1	1	0	1	1	0	0	0	0
1	1	0	−1	0	1	0	0	0
−1	0	1	0	0	0	0	1	1
−1	0	0	0	1	0	−1	−1	0
−1	0	0	0	0	0	−1	1	−1
0	−1	−1	0	0	1	1	0	0
0	1	0	1	−1	0	0	−1	0
0	0	−1	−1	0	−1	1	0	0

Choose the coordinate system shown. From boundedness we have: from T.7 $d_3 < 0$; from T.9 $b_3 > 0$; from T.3 $a_3 > 0$; from T.2 $c_3 < 0$; from T.5 $e_3 < 0$; from T.4 $f_3 > 0$. However T.6 is now unbounded so (α) cannot occur.

(β) Suppose $a_{55} \neq 1$, then clearly $a_{55} = 0$, $a_{45} = 1$. As $C.10$ represents the uno $a_{5.10} = 0$ so a_{56} is a unit. By $L.3$ $a_{56} \neq -1$ so $a_{56} = 1$. Thus $a_{76} = 0$. By $L.3$ $a_{97} \neq 1$ so by $L.2$ $a_{98} = -1$. By $L.3$ $a_{88} \neq 1$ so by $L.2$ on $R.5$ $a_{87} = 1$. Also by $L.2$ on $R.9$ $a_{78} = 1$ so $a_{48} = 0$ and so by $L.2$ $a_{47} = 1$, $a_{77} = 0$ and $a_{79} = 1$. Thus we have

x	y	A	B	z	C	D	E	F
1	−1	1	0	0	0	0	0	0
1	1	0	1	1	0	0	0	0
1	1	0	−1	0	1	0	0	0
−1	0	1	0	1	0	1	0	0
−1	0	0	0	0	1	−1	−1	0
−1	0	0	0	0	0	−1	1	−1
0	−1	−1	0	0	0	0	1	1
0	1	0	1	−1	0	1	0	0
0	0	−1	−1	0	−1	0	−1	0

Choose the coordinate system shown. From boundedness we have: from T.2 $b_1 < 0$; from T.3 $c_1 < 0$; from T.8 $d_1 > 0$; from T.5 $e_1 < 0$; from T.6 $f_1 < 0$; from T.7 $a_1 < 0$. However T.9 is now unbounded so (β) cannot arise.

Hence S_b cannot lead to a 9-con.

Finally consider the set S_c of D_m-planes that is obtained from (c), namely one tetre, one dotre, four dodos, one doun and three ununs. By $L.40$ therefore at most one chardho can occur, for if there are two, at least one of them must have its four faces contained in the dotre and four dodos since S_c contains only one doun. Now consider the matrix representation of S_c. As S_c contains only one tetre, one dotre and no treuns there are only eight tripts in the matrix. Since there is at most one chardho at least eight of the rows must contain at least one tript. However as there are only eight it is clear that eight of the rows contain one and only one tript so they must all represent thaiks, whilst the ninth contains none and so represents a chardho. Thus the 9-con, if it exists, consists of one chardho and eight thaiks. Clearly by $L.40$ the chardho must have a face contained in the doun.

Let $C.1$ represent the doun with $a_{11} = -1$, $a_{21} = 1 = a_{31}$, $a_{j1} = 0$ $(j = 4, \ldots 9)$. Then from the above $T.1$ is the chardho. Let $C.2$, $C.3$ and $C.4$ represent the ununs. By $L.17$ $a_{1j} = 0$ $(j = 2, 3, 4)$. Now by $L.17$ a row representing a thaik contains one and only one sipt. Hence as $T.l$ $(l = 2, \ldots 9)$ are all thaiks each row $R.l$ $(l = 2, \ldots 9)$ contains one and only one unit in the first four columns. Thus we may suppose $a_{42} = 1 = -a_{52}$, $a_{63} = 1 = -a_{73}$, $a_{84} = 1 = -a_{94}$ and the remaining spaces of $C.2$, $C.3$ and $C.4$ are zeros. Let $C.5$ which we suppose contains only two (-1)s represent the dotre and $C.6$ the tetre. By $L.17$ $a_{16} = 0$. Thus $C.l$ $(l = 7, \ldots 10)$ represent the dodos.

(A) Suppose $a_{35} = -1$. Now if it happens that $a_{25} = -1$ then, from the above, the six units of $C.6$ must lie in the rows $R.l$ $(l = 4, \ldots 9)$; however by $L.3$ $a_{46} = a_{56}$, $a_{66} = a_{76}$ and $a_{86} = a_{96}$ so there would have to be four units of the same sign in $C.6$ which is impossible. Thus $a_{25} \neq -1$ so a_{26} must be a unit. Further as $a_{25} \neq -1$, by symmetry we may suppose $a_{45} = -1$. Hence the units of $C.6$ lie in rows $R.l$ $(l = 2, 5, 6, 7, 8, 9)$. By $L.3$ $a_{66} = a_{76}$, $a_{86} = a_{96}$ so by symmetry we may assume $a_{j6} = 1$ $(j = 2, 6, 7)$ and $a_{16} = -1$ $(l = 5, 8, 9)$. Clearly by $L.3$ $a_{15} = 0 = a_{55}$.

If $a_{65} = a_{75} = 1$ let $a_{67} = 1$; by $L.3$ and $L.4$ $a_{77} = 0$ so let $a_{78} = 1$. Clearly $a_{68} = 0$. By $L.2$ we must have $a_{j7} = -1 = a_{j8}$ $(j = 1, 2)$. Thus the four units of $R.2$ are determined; however by $L.3$ $a_{37} \neq 1$, $a_{38} \neq 1$ so $R.2$ and $R.3$ contradict $L.2$. Thus at least one of a_{65} and a_{75} is a zero and we may assume $a_{75} = 0$.

If $a_{85} = 1 = a_{95}$ let $a_{87} = 1$; by $L.3$ and $L.4$ $a_{97} = 0$ so let $a_{98} = 1$. Clearly $a_{88} = 0$. By $L.2$ we must have $a_{j7} = -1 = a_{j8}$ ($j = 1, 5$). Thus the four units of $R.5$ are determined; however $R.1$ and $R.5$ contradict $L.2$. Thus at least one of a_{85} and a_{95} is a zero and we may assume $a_{95} = 0$.

Hence we must have $a_{25} = 1 = a_{65} = a_{85}$. Let $a_{27} = 1$ then by $L.2$ $a_{67} = -1 = a_{77}$. By $L.3$ $a_{j7} = 0$ ($j = 3, 4, 5, 8, 9$) so we must have $a_{17} = 1$. Let $a_{78} = 1$, then by $L.2$ $a_{38} = -1 = a_{48}$ and by $L.3$ $a_{j8} = 0$ ($j = 1, 2, 6, 8$). As only two columns remain both a_{19} and $a_{1.10}$ are units so we may suppose $a_{19} = 1 = a_{1.10}$.

Clearly $a_{j9} = 0 = a_{j.10}$ ($j = 2, 6, 7$). By symmetry we may suppose $T.3/T.4$ in $C.9$. As $a_{39} \neq -1$ by $L.3$, we have $a_{39} = 1 = -a_{49}$. Clearly $a_{3.10} = a_{4.10} = 0$. By $L.3$ $a_{8.9} = 0$ so by $L.2$ on $R.1$ $a_{8.10} = -1$. By $L.2$ on $R.8$ $a_{5.10} = 1$ so $a_{9.10} = -1$. By $L.3$ $a_{58} = 0$ so $a_{98} = 1$, $a_{59} = -1$. Thus we have

A	B	C	D	x	y	z	E	F	G
-1	0	0	0	0	0	1	0	1	1
1	0	0	0	1	1	1	0	0	0
1	0	0	0	-1	0	0	-1	1	0
0	1	0	0	-1	0	0	-1	-1	0
0	-1	0	0	0	-1	0	0	-1	1
0	0	1	0	1	1	-1	0	0	0
0	0	-1	0	0	1	-1	1	0	0
0	0	0	1	1	-1	0	0	0	-1
0	0	0	-1	0	-1	0	1	0	-1

Choose the coordinate system shown. From boundedness we have: from $T.2$ $a_3 < 0$; from $T.6$ $c_3 > 0$; from $T.7$ $e_3 > 0$; from $T.3$ $f_3 > 0$; from $T.1$ $g_3 < 0$; from $T.9$ $d_3 > 0$. However $T.8$ is now unbounded so (A) cannot occur.

Hence we have $a_{35} \neq -1$ and by symmetry $a_{25} \neq -1$. Thus we may suppose by symmetry $a_{45} = -1$.

(B) Suppose $a_{55} = -1$. Thus the units of $C.6$ lie in $R.l$ ($l = 2$, 3, 6, 7, 8, 9) and $a_{46} = 0 = a_{56}$. By $L.3$ $a_{66} = a_{76}$ and $a_{86} = a_{96}$ so by symmetry we may suppose $a_{j6} = 1$ ($j = 2, 6, 7$) and $a_{16} = -1$ ($l = 3, 8, 9$).

(B$_1$) Suppose $a_{65} = 1 = a_{75}$. Let $a_{67} = 1$ then by $L.3$ and $L.4$ $a_{77} = 0$ so let $a_{78} = 1$. Hence by $L.2$ we have $a_{j7} = -1 = a_{j8}$ ($j = 1, 2$) so by $L.3$ $a_{l7} = 0 = a_{l8}$ ($l = 3, 8, 9$). Hence by symmetry we may suppose $a_{47} = 1$, $a_{57} = 0$. Thus by $L.3$ $a_{48} = 0$ so $a_{58} = 1$. Further by $L.3$ $a_{15} = 0 = a_{25}$. Let $a_{19} = 1$ then by $L.2$ $a_{89} = -1 = a_{99}$. Clearly $a_{1.10} = 0 = a_{j9} = a_{j.10}$ $(j = 2, 6, 7)$. Now by $L.3$ and $L.4$ $a_{8.10}$ and $a_{9.10}$ cannot both be units and neither can both a_{85} and a_{95}. Thus we may suppose $a_{85} = 1 = a_{9.10}$, $a_{95} = 0 = a_{8.10}$. Clearly $a_{35} = 0$ now. By $L.2$ on $R.8$ $a_{39} = 1$ so $a_{49} = 0 = a_{59}$. By $L.2$ on $R.9$ $a_{4.10} = -1 = a_{5.10}$ so $a_{3.10} = 1$. Thus we have

A	B	C	D	x	y	z	E	F	G
-1	0	0	0	0	0	-1	-1	1	0
1	0	0	0	0	1	-1	-1	0	0
1	0	0	0	0	-1	0	0	1	1
0	1	0	0	-1	0	1	0	0	-1
0	-1	0	0	-1	0	0	1	0	-1
0	0	1	0	1	1	1	0	0	0
0	0	-1	0	1	1	0	1	0	0
0	0	0	1	1	-1	0	0	-1	0
0	0	0	-1	0	-1	0	0	-1	1

Choose the coordinate system shown. From boundedness we have: from $T.6$ $c_1 < 0$; from $T.7$ $e_1 < 0$; from $T.2$ $a_1 < 0$; from $T.1$ $f_1 < 0$; from $T.3$ $g_1 > 0$; from $T.4$ $b_1 > 0$. However $T.5$ is now unbounded and so (B_1) does not occur.

By symmetry we have that $a_{85} = 1 = a_{95}$ cannot arise either; thus we may suppose $a_{75} = 0 = a_{95}$.

(B_2) Suppose $a_{25} = 1 = a_{35}$. Let $a_{27} = 1$, then by $L.3$ and $L.4$ $a_{37} = 0$ so let $a_{38} = 1$. By $L.1$ $a_{28} = 0 = a_{j9} = a_{j.10}$ $(j = 2, 3)$. By $L.2$ we must have $a_{67} = -1 = a_{77} = a_{88} = a_{98}$. By $L.3$ $a_{87} = 0 = a_{97} = a_{68} = a_{78}$. Now at least one of a_{65} and a_{85} is a zero and by symmetry we may suppose $a_{85} = 0$. Let $a_{89} = 1$ then by $L.3$ and $L.4$ $a_{99} = 0$ so $a_{9.10} = 1$. By $L.1$ $a_{8.10} = 0$. By symmetry we may suppose $a_{7.9} = 1$, $a_{7.10} = 0$. By $L.3$ and $L.4$ $a_{69} = 0$ so at least one of a_{49} and a_{59} is a (-1). We may clearly suppose $a_{49} = -1$. Thus by $L.3$ $a_{48} = 0 = a_{47}$. By $L.2$ on $R.9$ therefore we have $a_{4.10} = -1$. Hence $a_{59} = 0$ for if $a_{59} = -1$ exactly as for $a_{49} = -1$ we would have $a_{58} = 0 = a_{57}$ so that $a_{5.10} = -1$ which is impossible by $L.4$. Thus $a_{19} = -1$. By $L.3$ $a_{17} = 0 = a_{18}$. By $L.2$ on $R.9$ $a_{1.10} = -1$ so by $L.2$ on $R.4$ $a_{15} = 1$. Thus $a_{65} = 0$ so $a_{6.10} = 1$. Hence $a_{5.10} = 0$ so $a_{57} = 1 =$

a_{58}. Thus we have

x	A	B	C	D	E	F	G	y	z
-1	0	0	0	1	0	0	0	-1	-1
1	0	0	0	1	1	1	0	0	0
1	0	0	0	1	-1	0	1	0	0
0	1	0	0	-1	0	0	0	-1	-1
0	-1	0	0	-1	0	1	1	0	0
0	0	1	0	0	1	-1	0	0	1
0	0	-1	0	0	1	-1	0	1	0
0	0	0	1	0	-1	0	-1	1	0
0	0	0	-1	0	-1	0	-1	0	1

Choose the coordinate system shown. From boundedness we have: from T.1 $d_1 > 0$; from T.4 $a_1 > 0$; from T.3 at least one of $e_1 > 0$ and $g_1 < 0$ holds. Now $e_1 g_1 < 0$, for if $e_1 g_1 \geqslant 0$, from T.8 we must have $c_1 e_1 > 0$ and then T.9 is unbounded. Hence we must have both $e_1 > 0$ and $g_1 < 0$.

From T.2 $f_1 < 0$. However T.5 is now unbounded and so (B$_2$) does not occur.

Thus at least one of a_{65} and a_{85} is a ($+1$). By symmetry we may suppose $a_{65} = 1$. Let $a_{67} = 1$ then by L.2 $a_{17} = -1 = a_{27}$ so by L.3 $a_{j7} = 0$ ($j = 3, 8, 9$). By L.1 $a_{6l} = 0$ ($l = 8, 9, 10$).

(B$_3$) Suppose one of a_{47} and a_{57} is a ($+1$). We may clearly assume $a_{47} = 1$ and then $a_{57} = 0 = a_{77}$. By L.3 $a_{15} = 0 = a_{25}$ so $a_{35} = 1 = a_{85}$. Let $a_{88} = 1$ then by L.2 $a_{18} = -1 = a_{38}$ so by L.3 $a_{j8} = 0$ ($j = 2, 4, 5, 7$) so $a_{98} = 1$. By L.1 $a_{j9} = 0 = a_{j.10}$ ($j = 3, 8$). Let $a_{19} = -1$ then $a_{1.10} = 0$ and by L.2 $a_{59} = 1 = a_{79}$. By L.3 $a_{49} = 0 = a_{99}$ so $a_{29} = -1$. By L.1 $a_{2.10} = 0$. Let $a_{9.10} = 1$ then by L.2 we have $a_{4.10} = -1 = a_{5.10}$ so $a_{7.10} = 1$. Thus we have

A	B	C	D	x	E	y	F	G	z
-1	0	0	0	0	0	-1	-1	-1	0
1	0	0	0	0	1	-1	0	-1	0
1	0	0	0	1	-1	0	-1	0	0
0	1	0	0	-1	0	1	0	0	-1
0	-1	0	0	-1	0	0	0	1	-1
0	0	1	0	1	1	1	0	0	0
0	0	-1	0	0	1	0	0	1	1
0	0	0	1	1	-1	0	1	0	0
0	0	0	-1	0	-1	0	1	0	1

Choose the coordinate system shown. From boundedness we have: from T.4 $b_3 > 0$; from T.5 $g_3 > 0$ from T.6 $c_3 e_3 < 0$; from T.7 at least one of $c_3 > 0$ and $e_3 < 0$ holds. Thus we must have both $c_3 > 0$ and $e_3 < 0$. From T.1 at least one of $a_3 < 0$ and $f_3 < 0$ holds; from T.3 at least one of $a_3 < 0$ and $f_3 > 0$ holds. Hence $a_3 < 0$. However T.2 is now unbounded so (B_3) cannot arise.

Thus we must have $a_{47} = 0 = a_{57}$ so $a_{77} = 1$. Let $a_{78} = 1$ then $a_{79} = 0 = a_{7.10}$. By L.2 $a_{48} = -1 = a_{58}$. By L.6 at least one of a_{25} and a_{28} is a $(+1)$ so we must have $a_{29} = a_{2.10}$. Let $a_{49} = 1$ then by L.3 and L.4 $a_{59} = 0$ so we may suppose $a_{5.10} = 1$. By L.1 $a_{4.10} = 0$.

Now if $a_{85} = 1$, by L.3 $a_{88} = 0$, so by symmetry we may suppose $a_{89} = 1$ ($a_{89} \neq -1$ by L.3). Hence by L.2 on R.8 $a_{19} = -1 = a_{39}$ and this is clearly the case (B_3) in an equivalent form.

Hence $a_{85} = 0$ so as one of a_{25} and a_{35} is a zero by (B_2), we must have $a_{15} = 1$. By L.3 $a_{18} = 0$ so one of a_{19} and $a_{1.10}$ must be a unit; by symmetry we may suppose it is a_{19}. By L.3 $a_{19} \neq -1$ so $a_{19} = 1$, then by L.2 $a_{89} = -1 = a_{99}$. Thus by L.3 $a_{88} = 0 = a_{98}$. By L.2 on R.5 $a_{8.10} = -1 = a_{9.10}$ which is impossible by L.4.

Thus (B) cannot occur.

Hence by symmetry we may suppose $a_{65} = -1$. Then by L.3 $a_{55} = 0 = a_{75}$. Further the units of C.6 must lie in R.l ($l = 2, 3,$ $5, 7, 8, 9$) so $a_{46} = 0 = a_{66}$. Clearly we may suppose $a_{96} = 1$, then by L.3 $a_{86} = 1$.

(C) Suppose a_{26} and a_{36} are of the same sign, then $a_{26} = a_{36} = -1$ otherwise we have four $(+1)$s in C.6. By symmetry we may clearly suppose $a_{56} = -1$, $a_{76} = 1$. By L.4 $a_{25} = 1 = a_{35}$ is impossible so we may suppose $a_{35} = 0$. Thus at least one of a_{85} and a_{95} is a $(+1)$ so we may suppose $a_{85} = 1$. Let $a_{87} = 1$ then by L.2 $a_{17} = -1 = a_{77}$. By L.3 $a_{j7} = 0$ ($j = 2, 3, 5, 6$) and by L.1 $a_{8l} = 0$ ($l = 8, 9, 10$). Let $a_{78} = 1$ then by L.2 $a_{18} = -1$ so by L.3 $a_{28} = 0 = a_{38}$. By L.1 $a_{79} = 0 = a_{7.10}$ and by L.2 we may suppose $a_{29} = 1 = -a_{39}$. By L.3 $a_{19} = 0 = a_{99}$. Now $a_{3.10}$ is a unit so suppose $a_{3.10} = 1$. By L.3 and L.4 $a_{2.10} = 0$ so we must have $a_{25} = 1$. By L.2 on R.2 $a_{59} = -1$ so by L.2 on R.3 $a_{5.10} = -1$. Thus $a_{58} = 0$. By L.2 on R.5 $a_{1.10} = 1 = a_{6.9}$. Hence $a_{15} = 0$ so $a_{95} = 1$. By L.3 and L.4 $a_{97} = 0$ so by L.2 on R.7 $a_{98} = -1$. However R.1 and R.9 now contradict L.2.

Hence (C) cannot occur and by symmetry we may suppose $a_{26} = 1 = -a_{36}$ so that $a_{56} = -1 = a_{76}$. By $L.2$ we may suppose $a_{57} = 1 = -a_{77}$, then by $L.3$ $a_{j7} = 0$ ($j = 2, 8, 9$). Now a_{47} and a_{67} cannot both be zeros for if they were we would have $a_{17} = -a_{37} \neq 0$ which is impossible by $L.3$. Thus one of a_{47} and a_{67} is a unit and by symmetry we may suppose it is a_{47}. By $L.3$ $a_{47} \neq -1$ so $a_{47} = 1$. Thus let $a_{78} = 1$, then by $L.2$ $a_{18} = -1 = a_{38}$ and by $L.3$ $a_{j8} = 0$ ($j = 2, 8, 9$). Now we cannot have either $a_{48} = 1$ or $a_{68} = 1$ for if we did, by $L.3$ $a_{15} = 0 = a_{35}$ so that $a_{j5} = 1$ ($j = 2, 8, 9$) which is impossible by $L.5$ on $C.5$ and $C.6$. Thus $a_{48} = 0 = a_{68}$ so $a_{58} = 1$. Hence by $L.3$ $a_{17} = 0 = a_{37}$ so $a_{67} = -1$. By $L.1$ $a_{5j} = 0 = a_{7j}$ ($j = 9, 10$). Now if the a_{ij} ($i = 8, 9$; $j = 9, 10$) are all units then by $L.3$ $a_{89} = a_{99}$, $a_{8.10} = a_{9.10}$ which is impossible by $L.4$. Thus we may suppose $a_{8.10} = 0$ so that $a_{85} = 1$. Now we may clearly suppose $a_{89} = 1$ so by $L.2$ we have $a_{19} = -1 = a_{29}$. By $L.3$ $a_{39} = 0$.

Two cases now arise: (I) $a_{99} = 1$ and (II) $a_{99} \neq 1$.

(I) Suppose $a_{99} = 1$, then by $L.4$ $a_{95} = 0$ so we may suppose $a_{9.10} = 1$. Clearly since $C.9$ represents a dodo $a_{49} = 0 = a_{69}$. Thus by $L.2$ on $R.9$ $a_{4.10} = -1 = a_{6.10}$ and we have

A	B	C	D	x	y	E	F	z	G
-1	0	0	0		0	0	-1	-1	
1	0	0	0		1	0	0	-1	
1	0	0	0		-1	0	-1	0	
0	1	0	0	-1	0	1	0	0	-1
0	-1	0	0	0	-1	1	1	0	0
0	0	1	0	-1	0	-1	0	0	-1
0	0	-1	0	0	-1	-1	1	0	0
0	0	0	1	1	1	0	0	1	0
0	0	0	-1	0	1	0	0	1	1

Choose the coordinate system shown. From boundedness we have: from $T.8$ $d_2 < 0$, $d_3 < 0$; from $T.9$ $g_2 < 0$, $g_3 < 0$. Now by $L.2$ either $a_{25} = 1$ or $a_{2.10} = 1$ but in either case we have from $T.2$ $a_3 > 0$. Similarly by $L.2$ either a_{15} or $a_{1.10} = 1$ but in either case from $T.1$ $f_3 < 0$. Hence if $a_{35} = 1$ $T.3$ is unbounded in the z-direction. Thus by $L.2$ $a_{3.10} = 1$ so $a_{1.10} = 0 = a_{2.10}$. Thus $a_{15} = a_{25} = 1$.

Hence from $T.2$ $a_2 < 0$; from $T.1$ $f_2 > 0$. However $T.3$ is now unbounded in the y-direction. Thus (I) cannot occur.

(II) We now have $a_{99} \neq 1$; by $L.3$ $a_{99} \neq -1$ so $a_{99} = 0$. Thus $a_{95} = 1$ and we may suppose $a_{9.10} = 1$. By $L.5$ on $C.5$ and $C.6$ $a_{25} = 0$. By $L.2$ on $R.9$ $a_{1.10} = -1 = a_{2.10}$ so $a_{15} = 0$. Hence $a_{35} = 1$ and $a_{3.10} = 0$. Thus

A	B	C	D	x	y	E	F	z	G
-1	0	0	0	0	0	0	-1	-1	-1
1	0	0	0	0	1	0	0	-1	-1
1	0	0	0	1	-1	0	-1	0	0
0	1	0	0	-1	0	1	0		
0	-1	0	0	0	-1	1	1	0	0
0	0	1	0	-1	0	-1	0		
0	0	-1	0	0	-1	-1	1	0	0
0	0	0	1	1	1	0	0	1	0
0	0	0	-1	1	1	0	0	0	1

Choose the coordinate system shown. From boundedness we have: from T.8 $d_2 < 0$; from T.9 $g_2 < 0$; from T.2 $a_2 < 0$; from T.1 $f_2 > 0$.

However T.3 is now unbounded and so (II) cannot arise.

Thus S_c cannot lead to a 9-con and so (iii) cannot arise.

Hence a 9-con containing a tetre cannot contain exactly ten D_m-planes. Thus from Theorem 6 we have:

THEOREM 7. If a 9-con exists then it cannot contain a tetre.

CHAPTER EIGHT

ON THE EXISTENCE OF A 9-CON

By USING the concept of a surplus, we analyse the possibilities of a 9-con containing more than ten or less than nine D_m-planes. By this means we show that if a 9-con exists, then it must contain exactly nine or exactly ten D_m-planes. With the aid of Chapter Four we can deduce from this result that a 9-con can contain at most two naiks. Finally, we show that a 9-con cannot contain nine chardhos.

If $R.l$ and $R.m$ $(m \neq l)$ represent chardhos then clearly we must have $T.l/T.m$ in a dodo. Thus we have the following lemma:

LEMMA 41. If the D_m-planes of a 9-con contain only one dodo then the 9-con contains at most two chardhos.

Proof. Suppose the 9-con contains three or more chardhos; then in the matrix representation of the 9-con we may clearly suppose that $R.1$, $R.2$ and $R.3$ all represent chardhos and that $C.1$ represents the dodo. As $T.1/T.2$ in the dodo and further $T.1/T.3$ in the dodo we may suppose $a_{11} = 1$, $a_{21} = -1 = a_{31}$. However, we must now have that $T.2/T.3$ in a D_m-plane other than the dodo which is impossible. The lemma now follows.

If a 9-con exists, from Theorem 7 none of its D_m-planes can be a tetre. Hence, each of its D_m-planes has a non-negative surplus, so letting l be the number of D_m-planes in the 9-con we have, as before, that $36 - 3l =$ sum of the surpluses of the D_m-planes $\geqslant 0$. Thus $l \leqslant 12$. Further, as a D_m-plane can now contain at most five faces of the 9-con, we must have $l \geqslant 36/5$; i.e. $l \geqslant 8$.

(I) Suppose twelve D_m-planes do occur, then the sum of the surpluses of the D_m-planes is zero, so each of them has a surplus of zero, i.e. each must be either a dotre or a uno. Since the D_m-planes must contain 36 faces, we must therefore have six dotres and six unos. By $L.18$ the six unos imply that six naiks occur in the 9-con. Consider the matrix representation of this set of

12*

planes. Because there are six dotres and no treuns, there are
twelve tripts in the matrix. As six rows represent naiks, six of
the rows must each contain two tripts so there must be three
rows which do not contain any tripts. Thus these rows must
represent chardhos. Since no dodos occur amongst the D_m-planes,
this is impossible for if $R.l$ and $R.m$ $(l \neq m)$ represent chardhos
then $T.l/T.m$ in a dodo. Thus (I) cannot arise.

(II) Suppose eleven D_m-planes are contained in a 9-con,
then the total surplus of the D_m-planes is 3, so at least eight of
them have a surplus of zero. As they contain 40 faces, eight
dotres clearly cannot occur. Also seven dotres cannot occur for
as they contain 35 faces, only one more D_m-plane $(m \geqslant 1)$
would exist. Further if only three dotres occur we must have
at least five unos, so that the three undetermined D_m-planes
would contain 16 faces so that a tetre would occur which is impossible. Hence only three cases arise for the cases when two
dotres, one dotre and no dotres occur obviously lead to the
existence of a tetre since the number of faces contained in the
eight planes with a surplus of zero must in each case be less than
the corresponding number in the case when three dotres occur.
Thus either (i) six dotres occur or (ii) four dotres occur, or (iii)
five dotres occur.

(i) Suppose six dotres occur, then the five undetermined
D_m-planes contain only 6 faces so four of them are unos, and
the other is a D_2-plane. As the D_2-plane must have a surplus
of 3, it must be a nodo. Thus we have the set S_1 of D_m-planes
consisting of six dotres, four unos and one nodo. However, S_1
cannot have a matrix representation for, if it did, clearly six
dotres and six unos would also have one and from the above
we know that it has not. Hence (i) does not lead to a permatrix.

(ii) Suppose four and only four dotres occur in the 9-con, then
from the above we have at least four unos. Hence the three
undetermined D_m-planes contain 12 faces so each of them is
a D_4-plane. As a treun has a surplus of 3 by itself, we must
have three dodos. Thus we have the set S_2 of D_m-planes consisting of four dotres, four unos and three dodos. By $L.18$ the
four unos imply that four naiks occur in the 9-con. Consider
the matrix representation of the 9-con. As S_2 contains four
dotres and no treuns, there are eight tripts in the matrix. As
there are four naiks in the 9-con four of the rows must each

contain two tripts so that the other five rows cannot contain any tripts and so must represent chardhos. Hence the 9-con consists of four naiks and five chardhos. We may clearly suppose that the first five rows represent the chardhos and the first three columns the dodos. Thus for l, $m = 1, \ldots 5$, $l \neq m$ we have $\mathrm{T}.l/\mathrm{T}.m$ in $C.k$ where $k = k(l,m)$ is one of 1, 2, 3. Considering $\mathrm{T}.1$, clearly for at least one value of k, say k_1, we must have $\mathrm{T}.1/\mathrm{T}.p$ in $C.k_1$, and $\mathrm{T}.1/\mathrm{T}.q$ in $C.k_1$ where $p \neq q$. We may clearly suppose $k_1 = 1$, $p = 2$ and $q = 3$ so that $a_{21} = a_{31} = -a_{11} = -1$ say. Thus we may suppose $a_{22} = 1 = -a_{32}$ so by $L.3$ $a_{12} = 0$. Hence we must have $a_{43} = a_{53} = -a_{13} = -1$ say. Now a_{41} and a_{51} cannot both be units and neither can both a_{23} and a_{33} so we may suppose $a_{51} = 0 = a_{33}$. Hence we must have $a_{52} = 1$ and thus $a_{42} = -1$ so that by $L.3$ $a_{41} = 0$. However we now have $\mathrm{T}.3/\mathrm{T}.4$ in a D_m-plane other than a dodo which is impossible. Thus (ii) does not lead to a permatrix.

(iii) Suppose five dotres occur in the 9-con. Then from the above at least three unos occur. Hence the three undetermined D_m-planes contain 8 faces and have a surplus of 3. Now either (A) a D_3-plane occurs or (B) no D_3-plane occurs.

(A) Suppose a D_3-plane occurs in the 9-con. As a notre has a surplus of 6, it must be a doun so that the two undetermined planes have a total surplus of 1. Thus one of them is a uno so that the other must be a D_4-plane with a surplus of 1, i.e. a dodo. Thus we have the set S_3 of D_m-planes consisting of five dotres, four unos, a doun and a dodo. Since there are four unos, four naiks must occur in the 9-con. Consider the matrix representation of the 9-con. As S_3 contains five dotres and no treuns there are ten tripts in the matrix. As there are four naiks, four rows must each contain two tripts so there are at least three rows which do not contain any tripts and so they represent chardhos. However since S_3 contains only one dodo, this is impossible by $L.41$. Thus (A) does not lead to a 9-con.

(B) We may now suppose that no D_3-plane occurs. Hence a D_4-plane must occur so that the other two D_m-planes must contain 4 faces and must therefore be two D_2-planes. As the total surplus of the three D_m-planes is only 3, we therefore can only have a dodo and two ununs. Thus we have the set S_4 of D_m-planes consisting of five dotres, three unos, two ununs and one dodo. As there are three unos, three naiks occur in the 9-con.

Also as S_4 contains only one dodo, by $L.41$, the 9-con contains at most two chardhos. Consider the matrix representation of the 9-con, then as S_4 contains five dotres and no treuns ten tripts appear in the matrix. As there are three naiks, three of the rows each contain two tripts so at least two of the rows contain no tripts and so represent chardhos. From the above there can be only two such rows, so that four of the rows must contain one and only one tript and hence they must represent thaiks. Hence the 9-con consists of three naiks, four thaiks and two chardhos. Now the two rows representing chardhos must have units of the opposite sign in the column representing the dodo, so at least one of the rows representing a naik must have a zero in this column and therefore three of the faces of this naik must be contained in dotres. Let $R.1$ represent this naik and $C.1$, $C.2$ and $C.3$ the dotres that contain three of its faces. Clearly we may suppose $a_{11} = 1$, $a_{1j} = -1 = a_{j1}$ $(j = 2, 3)$, $a_{l2} = 1 = a_{m3}$ $(l = 4, 5, 6; m = 7, 8, 9)$. By symmetry we may further suppose $a_{41} = 1$, then by $L.3$ $a_{22} = 0 = a_{32}$. Thus we may assume $a_{72} = -1$, $a_{82} = 0 = a_{92}$. By $L.3$ $a_{l3} = 0$ $(l = 4, 5, 6)$ so we may further suppose $a_{23} = -1$, $a_{33} = 0$. By $L.3$ $a_{m1} = 0$ $(m = 7, 8, 9)$ so we may assume $a_{51} = 1$, $a_{61} = 0$. Now $R.2$ contains two tripts so it must represent a naik. Thus we may suppose $a_{24} = 1$ so by $L.2$ $a_{34} = -1 = a_{64}$. By $L.3$ $a_{j4} = 0$ $(j = 1, 4, 5, 7)$. As $C.4$ cannot represent a doun, we may clearly suppose $a_{84} = 1$.

Now if $a_{94} = 1$, $R.3$ also contains two tripts so it must represent the third naik. Thus letting $a_{35} = 1$ we may suppose by $L.2$ $a_{64} = -1 = a_{74}$. But then by $L.3$ the remaining spaces of $C.5$ are zeros so that $C.5$ represents a doun which is impossible.

Thus $a_{94} = 0$ for by $L.3$ $a_{94} \neq -1$. Hence $C.4$ represents the dodo and so the chardhos must have units of opposite sign in $C.4$. Since $R.2$ and $R.3$ both contain tripts, the chardhos must clearly be represented by $R.6$ and $R.8$. Now let $C.5$ and $C.6$ represent the two remaining dotres, $C.7$ and $C.8$ the two ununs and $C.9$, $C.10$ and $C.11$ the three unos. By $L.17$ $a_{6j} = 0 = a_{8j}$ for $j = 7, \ldots 11$. Hence both a_{65} and a_{66} are units and so are both a_{85} and a_{86}. By $L.3$ $a_{65} = a_{85}$ and $a_{66} = a_{86}$ so we may suppose $a_{j5} = 1 = a_{j6}$ $(j = 6, 8)$. By $L.3$ on $R.8$ $a_{35} \neq -1$, $a_{36} \neq -1$ so that $R.6$ and $R.3$ contradict $L.2$. Thus (B) and *a fortiori* (iii) do not lead to a permatrix.

Hence eleven planes do not lead to a permatrix.

III. Suppose only eight D_m-planes occur in a 9-con then the total surplus of the D_m-planes is $36 - 24 = 12$. As the D_m-planes contain 36 faces, there must be at least four dotres among them. Since they contain 40 faces, eight dotres clearly cannot occur. Further, seven dotres also cannot occur because, as they contain 35 faces, the remaining D_m-plane must be a uno and then the total surplus of the eight D_m-planes would be zero. Thus only three cases arise: (i) six dotres occur, (ii) four dotres occur, and (iii) five dotres occur.

(i) Suppose six dotres occur, then the two undetermined D_m-planes must have a total surplus of 12, so that the only possibility is two notres. However six dotres and two notres cannot lead to a permatrix, for, if they did, so would six dotres and six unos and from the above we know that they do not. Thus (i) does not lead to a permatrix.

(ii) Suppose four and only four dotres occur, then the four undetermined D_m-planes contain 16 faces and have a total surplus of 12. Hence they are all D_4-planes and since a dodo only has a surplus of 1, they must all be treuns. Thus we have the set S_1 of D_m-planes consisting of four dotres and four treuns. Thus if a 9-con exists it does not contain any naiks. Further as S_1 does not contain a dodo at most one chardho can occur. Now in the matrix representation of the 9-con, there are twelve tripts so there are at least three rows containing two tripts and so they must represent dhoats. As at most one chardho can occur, there is at most one row that does not contain any tripts. Hence either six rows contain one and only one tript, so that they represent thaiks, or one row contains no tripts, four rows contain one and only one tript and the other rows contain two tripts. Thus for the tetrahedra of the 9-con we have either (α) six thaiks and three dhoats or (β) four thaiks, four dhoats and a chardho.

(α) Let the first six rows represent the thaiks and the first four columns the dotres, where we suppose each column only contains two (-1)s. Since $R.7$, $R.8$ and $R.9$ represent dhoats they clearly cannot contain any $(+1)$s in the first four columns so twelve $(+1)$s occur in the matrix $A = (a_{ij})$ $(i = 1, \ldots 6;$ $j = 1, \ldots 4)$. Now as S_1 does not contain a tetre or a unun, we must have $\mathbf{T}.l/\mathbf{T}.m$ in a treun where $l \neq m$ $(l, m = 7, 8, 9)$. Clearly for fixed l all three of T.7/T.8 in $C.l$, T.7/T.9 in $C.l$ and T.8/T.9 in $C.l$ cannot hold simultaneously so at least two of the six tripts contained in rows 7, 8 and 9 occur in columns representing treuns. Thus at least four (-1)s occur in A. As T.l $(l = 1, \ldots 6)$ represent thaiks we must therefore have two and only two $(+1)$s in each row of A and at most one (-1) in each row of A.

If two (-1)s in A lie in the same column we may clearly arrange that $a_{11} = -1 = a_{21}$. Thus we must have two of the a_{1j} $(j = 2, 3, 4)$ to be $(+1)$s and the other zero and two of the a_{2j} $(j = 2, 3, 4)$ to be $(+1)$s and the other zero. Hence T.1/T.2 in a treun so that one of $R.1$ and $R.2$ contains two tripts which is impossible.

As A contains at least four (-1)s we may therefore arrange that $a_{jj} = -1$ $(j = 1, 2, 3, 4)$. By symmetry we may clearly suppose $a_{12} = 1 = a_{13}$, $a_{14} = 0$. By $L.3$ $a_{21} = 0 = a_{31}$ so we must have $a_{23} = 1 = a_{24}$. By $L.3$ $a_{32} = 0$ so that at most one $(+1)$ occurs in the third row of A which contradicts the above.

Thus (α) does not have a permatrix.

(β) Let $R.1$ represent the chardho, $R.2$, $R.3$, $R.4$ and $R.5$ the dhoats and the first four columns the dotres where we suppose each column contains only two (-1)s. As the units representative of a chardho must be dopts we can only have $a_{1j} = 1$ $(j = 1, \ldots 4)$. As $R.l$ $(l \geqslant 6)$ represent dhoats no dopts can occur in the last three rows so the matrix $B = (a_{ij})$ $(i = 2, \ldots 5)$ $(j = 1, \ldots 4)$ must contain eight dopts. As T.l $(l = 2, \ldots 5)$ are thaiks we must have two and only two $(+1)$s in each row of B. Thus we may suppose $a_{22} = 1 = a_{23}$; by $L.2$ we may also assume $a_{21} = -1$ so by $L.3$ $a_{24} = 0$. Now two of the a_{j1} $(j = 3, 4, 5)$ must be $(+1)$s so we may suppose $a_{31} = 1 = a_{41}$. By $L.3$ $a_{j2} \neq -1$, $a_{j3} \neq -1$ $(j = 3, 4)$ so we must have by $L.2$ on $R.1$ $a_{34} = -1 = a_{44}$. However, $C.4$ contains two more $(+1)$s so at least one of them must be contained in rows 6, 7, 8 and 9 which is impossible, since they represent thaiks.

Thus (β) does not have a permatrix and hence (ii) does not lead to a permatrix.

(iii) Suppose five dotres occur, then the three undetermined D_m-planes contain 11 faces and have a total surplus of 12. Hence we must have two D_4-planes and one D_3-plane. Clearly one of the D_m-planes must have a surplus $\geqslant 4$ so the D_3-plane must be a notre. Thus, as a dodo only has a surplus of 1 the two

D_4-planes must be treuns. Thus we have the set S_2 of D_m-planes consisting of five dotres, two treuns and one notre. By $L.18$ the notre implies that the 9-con, if it exists, contains three naiks. Further as S_2 does not contain a dodo at most one chardho can occur. Since there are twelve tripts in the matrix representation of the 9-con and since at most one chardho occurs at least eight of the rows must contain at least one tript. Hence either three rows each contain two tripts, and six contain one and only one tript, or four rows each contain two tripts, four rows contain one and only one tript and one row contains no tripts. As three and only three naiks occur in the 9-con we have either (A) three naiks and six thaiks or (B) three naiks, four thaiks, one dhoat and one chardho.

In both cases let the first five columns represent the dotres, $C.6$ and $C.7$ the treuns, and $C.8$ the notre where the tripts of the first seven columns are all denoted by (-1). Now $C.6$, $C.7$ and $C.8$ only contain two tripts and no dopts, so at least one naik has three of its faces contained in dotres. Let this naik be represented by $R.1$ then we may clearly suppose $a_{11} = 1$, $a_{1j} = -1 = a_{j1}$ $(j = 2, 3)$, $a_{l2} = 1 = a_{m3}$ $(l = 4, 5, 6; m = 7, 8, 9)$. By symmetry we may suppose $a_{41} = 1$ so by $L.3$ $a_{22} = 0 = a_{32}$ so that we may suppose $a_{72} = -1$, $a_{82} = 0 = a_{92}$. By $L.3$ $a_{l3} = 0$ $(l = 4, 5, 6)$ so we may assume $a_{23} = -1$, $a_{33} = 0$. By $L.3$ $a_{m1} = 0$ $(m = 7, 8, 9)$ so we may suppose $a_{51} = 1$, $a_{61} = 0$. Thus we have

$$
\begin{array}{rrr}
1 & -1 & -1 \\
-1 & 0 & -1 \\
-1 & 0 & 0 \\
1 & 1 & 0 \\
1 & 1 & 0 \\
0 & 1 & 0 \\
0 & -1 & 1 \\
0 & 0 & 1 \\
0 & 0 & 1
\end{array}
$$

Consider (A); $R.2$ contains two tripts, so it must represent one of the naiks. Hence $R.2$ contains a dopt, so one of a_{24} and a_{25} must be a $(+1)$. We may clearly suppose $a_{24} = 1$, then by $L.2$ $a_{34} = -1 = a_{64}$ and by $L.3$ $a_{j4} = 0$ $(j = 1, 4, 5, 7)$ so we must have $a_{84} = 1 = a_{94}$. However $R.3$ now contains two tripts, so it must represent the third naik. Thus $R.3$ contains a dopt, so we must have $a_{35} = 1$. Hence by $L.2$ $a_{65} = -1 = a_{75}$ and by $L.3$ the remaining spaces of $C.5$ are zeros which is impossible, since $C.5$ represents a dotre.

Thus (A) does not have a permatrix.

Consider (B); the row representing the chardho must contain four dopts, so it must have four $(+1)$s in the first five columns. Hence it is clear from the above matrix that the only rows that can possibly represent the chardho are $R.4$ and $R.5$ and by symmetry we may clearly suppose that $R.4$ represents the chardho. Thus we must have $a_{44} = 1 = a_{45}$. By $L.2$ we may suppose $a_{54} = -1$ so that by $L.3$ $a_{j4} = 0$ $(j = 1, 2, 3, 7)$ so a_{64}, a_{84} and a_{94} are all units. However, $a_{64} \neq -1$, for if $a_{64} = -1$ then $a_{84} = a_{94} = 1$ and by $L.2$ on $R.4$ $a_{85} = -1 = a_{95}$ which is impossible by $L.4$. Thus $a_{64} = 1$ and we may suppose $a_{84} = 1 = -a_{94}$. By $L.2$ on $R.4$ $a_{65} = -1 = a_{85}$ so that by $L.3$ $a_{j5} = 0$ $(j = 1, 2, 5, 7, 9)$ so that $C.5$ can represent at most a D_4-plane which is a contradiction.

Hence (B) does not have a permatrix and hence (iii) does not lead to a permatrix.

Thus eight D_m-planes do not lead to a permatrix.

We have therefore proved the following theorem:

THEOREM 8. If a 9-con exists, it must contain either exactly nine or exactly ten D_m-planes.

From the above we can also deduce:

THEOREM 9. If a 9-con exists, it can contain at most two naiks.

Proof. We firstly remark that a 9-con cannot exist if it contains: either (i) ten D_m-planes one of which is a nodo or notre or (ii) nine D_m-planes one of which is a notre, or (iii) nine D_m-planes two of which are nodos.

For if a 9-con satisfying at least one of (i), (ii) and (iii) exists, consider one of its matrix representations. By $L.34$ or its Corollary it then follows that there exists a set of eleven D_m-planes which leads to a permatrix, and from the above we know that this is impossible.

Secondly a 9-con cannot exist if it contains: either (I) ten D_m-planes three of which are unos or (II) nine D_m-planes two of which are unos or (III) nine D_m-planes two of which are a uno and a nodo.

For if a 9-con satisfying at least one of (I), (II) and (III) exists, consider one of its matrix representations. By $L.33$ or its Corollary, it then follows that there exists a set of eight D_m-planes which leads to a permatrix and from the above we know that this is impossible.

Hence if a 9-con containing ten D_m-planes exists, it can contain at most two unos, no nodos and no notres whilst if a 9-con containing nine D_m-planes exists, it can contain either one nodo, no unos and no notres or at most one uno, no nodos and no notres.

The theorem now follows.

We now consider the possibility of nine chardhos occurring in a 9-con. If such a 9-con exists, then by $L.17$ its matrix representation can contain only dopts and so each column would represent a dodo. As the D_m-planes contain 36 faces, it follows that the 9-con must contain nine dodos. Thus the faces of the 9-con all lie in dodos, so by $L.39$ the matrix representation must contain a minor equivalent to one of G_1, G_2 and G_3.

Firstly, suppose a minor equivalent to G_1 occurs, we may clearly assume that G_1 is the matrix (a_{ij}) $(i = 1, \ldots 9; j = 1, \ldots 4)$ so that we have

$$
\begin{array}{rrrr}
1 & 1 & 1 & 1 \\
1 & -1 & 0 & 1 \\
-1 & 0 & 1 & 0 \\
-1 & 0 & 0 & 0 \\
0 & -1 & 0 & 0 \\
0 & 1 & -1 & 0 \\
0 & 0 & -1 & 0 \\
0 & 0 & 0 & -1 \\
0 & 0 & 0 & -1 \\
\end{array}
$$

By elementary transformations we may suppose $a_{25} = 1$, then by $L.2$ $a_{55} = -1 = a_{75}$ so by $L.3$ $a_{35} = 0 = a_{65}$. Two cases now arise: (A) $a_{45} = 1$ and (B) $a_{45} = 0$.

(A) Suppose $a_{45} = 1$ then $a_{85} = 0 = a_{95}$. Thus both $R.8$ and $R.9$ contain three units in the last four columns so at least two columns, which we may suppose are $C.6$ and $C.7$, contain units in both $R.8$ and $R.9$. By $L.2$ we may assume $a_{87} = 1 = -a_{97}$ then by $L.3$ $a_{86} = a_{96} = 1$ say. Clearly we may further suppose

$a_{88} = 1$, $a_{89} = 0$ then by $L.3$ and $L.4$ $a_{98} = 0$ so we may assume $a_{99} = 1$. As $a_{1j} = 0 = a_{2j}$ $(j > 5)$, two of the a_{j6} $(j = 3, .. 7)$ must be (-1)s so one of the a_{j6} $(j = 3, ... 6)$ is a (-1). Since the $C.l$ $(l = 1, 2, 4, 5)$ contain a minor equivalent to G_1 we see that the case $a_{36} = -1$ is equivalent to the case $a_{46} = -1$ and also that the case $a_{56} = -1$ is equivalent to the case $a_{66} = -1$ so only two effective cases arise: (A_1) $a_{36} = -1$ and (A_2) $a_{36} = 0 = a_{46}$, $a_{56} = -1$.

(A_1) Suppose $a_{36} = -1$ then we have

$$
\begin{array}{ccccccccc}
1 & 1 & 1 & 1 & 0 & 0 & 0 & 0 & 0 \\
1 & -1 & 0 & 1 & 1 & 0 & 0 & 0 & 0 \\
-1 & 0 & 1 & 0 & 0 & -1 & & & \\
-1 & 0 & 0 & 0 & 1 & & & & \\
0 & -1 & 0 & 0 & -1 & & & & \\
0 & 1 & -1 & 0 & 0 & & & & \\
0 & 0 & -1 & 0 & -1 & & & & \\
0 & 0 & 0 & -1 & 0 & 1 & 1 & 1 & 0 \\
0 & 0 & 0 & -1 & 0 & 1 & -1 & 0 & 1 \\
\end{array}
$$

By $L.3$ $a_{37} = 0$ so by $L.1$ one of a_{38} and a_{39} is a unit and by symmetry we may suppose it is a_{38}. By $L.3$ $a_{38} \neq -1$ so $a_{38} = 1$. Thus by $L.2$ on $R.3$ $a_{48} = -1 = a_{58}$ so $a_{68} = 0 = a_{78}$. By $L.3$ $a_{46} = 0 = a_{56}$. Two possibilities occur: (A_1^1) $a_{66} = -1$, $a_{76} = 0$ and (A_1^{11}) $a_{66} = 0$, $a_{76} = -1$.

(A_1^1) By $L.2$ on $R.8$ $a_{77} = -1$ then by $L.2$ on $R.9$ $a_{79} = -1$. By $L.3$ $a_{67} = 0$ so by $L.2$ on $R.7$ a_{69} and $a_{57} = 1$. Thus $a_{47} = 0$ and so $a_{49} = -1$. Thus we have

$$
\begin{array}{ccccccccc}
x & A & y & z & B & C & D & E & F \\
1 & 1 & 1 & 1 & 0 & 0 & 0 & 0 & 0 \\
1 & -1 & 0 & 1 & 1 & 0 & 0 & 0 & 0 \\
-1 & 0 & 1 & 0 & 0 & -1 & 0 & 1 & 0 \\
-1 & 0 & 0 & 0 & 1 & 0 & 0 & -1 & -1 \\
0 & -1 & 0 & 0 & -1 & 0 & 1 & -1 & 0 \\
0 & 1 & -1 & 0 & 0 & -1 & 0 & 0 & 1 \\
0 & 0 & -1 & 0 & -1 & 0 & -1 & 0 & -1 \\
0 & 0 & 0 & -1 & 0 & 1 & 1 & 1 & 0 \\
0 & 0 & 0 & -1 & 0 & 1 & -1 & 0 & 1 \\
\end{array}
$$

Choose the coordinate system shown. From boundedness we have: From $T.1$ $a_3 < 0$; from $T.2$ $b_3 < 0$; from $T.3$ $c_3 e_3 > 0$.

Now if $e_3 \geqslant 0$ then $c_3 > 0$ so from T.6 $f_3 > 0$. However T.4 is now unbounded.

Thus $e_3 < 0$ and thus $c_3 < 0$. From T.5 $d_3 < 0$. However T.8 is now unbounded.

Hence (A_1^1) cannot occur.

(A_1^{11}) We have $a_{66} = 0$, $a_{76} = -1$. By $L.2$ on $R.8$ $a_{67} = -1$ and then on $R.9$ $a_{69} = -1$. By $L.3$ $a_{77} = 0$, $a_{79} \neq -1$ so $a_{79} = 1$. By $L.3$ $a_{49} \neq -1$ so $a_{59} = -1$, $a_{47} = 1$. However columns 4, 6, 7, 8 and 9 contain a minor equivalent to G_1 and by transforming these columns into the first four columns and rearranging the rows we have a case equivalent to (A_1^1).

Thus (A_1^{11}) cannot occur and so neither can (A_1).

(A_2) Suppose $a_{36} = 0 = a_{46}$, $a_{56} = -1$. By $L.3$ $a_{57} = 0$ so one of a_{58} and a_{59} is a unit and by symmetry we may suppose it is a_{58}. By $L.3$ $a_{58} \neq -1$ so $a_{58} = 1$. By $L.2$ on $R.5$ $a_{38} = -1 = a_{78}$ so $a_{48} = 0 = a_{68}$. By $L.3$ $a_{76} \neq -1$ so $a_{66} = -1$, $a_{76} = 0$. By $L.3$ $a_{67} = 0$, $a_{69} \neq -1$ so $a_{69} = 1$. By $L.3$ $a_{39} \neq -1$ so $a_{49} = -1 = a_{79}$. By $L.2$ on $R.9$ $a_{37} = 1$ and then on $R.3$ $a_{47} = -1$. Thus we have

x	A	y	B	C	D	z	E	F
1	1	1	1	0	0	0	0	0
1	-1	0	1	1	0	0	0	0
-1	0	1	0	0	0	1	-1	0
-1	0	0	0	1	0	-1	0	-1
0	-1	0	0	-1	-1	0	1	0
0	1	-1	0	0	-1	0	0	1
0	0	-1	0	-1	0	0	-1	-1
0	0	0	-1	0	1	1	1	0
0	0	0	-1	0	1	-1	0	1

Choose the coordinate system shown. From boundedness we have: from T.3 $e_2 > 0$; from T.4 $c_2 f_2 > 0$; from T.7 at least one of $c_2 < 0$ and $f_2 < 0$ holds. Hence both $c_2 < 0$ and $f_2 < 0$ hold.

Now if $a_2 \geqslant 0$ from T.1 $b_2 < 0$ and T.2 is then unbounded.

Thus $a_2 < 0$. From T.6 $d_2 < 0$ and T.5 is now unbounded.

Hence (A_2) cannot occur and so neither can (A).

(B) We have $a_{45} = 0$ so by symmetry we may suppose $a_{85} = 1$, $a_{95} = 0$. Thus we have

1	1	1	1	0	0	0	0	0
1	-1	0	1	1	0	0	0	0
-1	0	1	0	0				
-1	0	0	0	0				
0	-1	0	0	-1				
0	1	-1	0	0				
0	0	-1	0	-1				
0	0	0	-1	1				
0	0	0	-1	0				

By $L.1$ we may assume $a_{4j} = 1$ $(j = 6, 7, 8)$, $a_{49} = 0$. By $L.2$ we may suppose $a_{97} = -1$. By $L.1$ at least one of a_{96} and a_{98} is a unit and by symmetry we may assume a_{96} is a unit; by $L.3$ $a_{96} \neq -1$ so $a_{96} = 1$. Now $a_{98} \neq 1$ for if $a_{98} = 1$ let the remaining (-1) of $C.7$ be $a_{17} = -1$; by $L.3$ $a_{16} \neq -1$, $a_{18} \neq -1$ so $R.l$ and $R.9$ contradict $L.2$. By $L.3$ $a_{98} \neq -1$ so $a_{98} = 0$. Thus we may assume $a_{99} = 1$. Now columns 1, 2, 4 and 5 contain a minor equivalent to (G_1) so it is easily seen that the case when $a_{36} = -1$ is equivalent to that when $a_{86} = -1$ and that the case when $a_{56} = -1$ is equivalent to that when $a_{66} = -1$. As two (-1)s must occur amongst the a_{j6} $(j = 3, 5, 6, 7, 8)$, a (-1) must occur among the a_{16} $(l = 3, 5, 6, 8)$ so we need only consider the following two cases: (B_1) $a_{36} = -1$ and (B_2) $a_{36} = 0 = a_{86}$, $a_{56} = -1$.

(B_1) Suppose $a_{36} = -1$. By $L.3$ $a_{37} = 0$ so by $L.1$ either (B_{11}) $a_{39} = 0$ or (B_{12}) $a_{38} = 0$.

(B_{11}) Suppose $a_{39} = 0$, then by $L.3$ $a_{38} \neq -1$ so $a_{38} = 1$. By $L.2$ $a_{58} = -1 = a_{88}$ so $a_{68} = 0 = a_{78}$. By $L.3$ $a_{56} = 0 = a_{86}$ and we have

x	A	y	z	B	C	D	E	F
l	1	1	1	0	0	0	0	0
1	-1	0	1	1	0	0	0	0
-1	0	1	0	0	-1	0	1	0
1	0	0	0	0	1	1	1	0
0	-1	0	0	-1	0		-1	
0	1	-1	0	0			0	
	0	-1	0	-1			0	
0	0	0	-1	1	0		-1	
0	0	0	-1	0	1	-1	0	1

Choose the coordinate system shown. From boundedness we have: from T.1 $a_3 < 0$; from T.2 $b_3 < 0$; from T.3 $c_3 e_3 > 0$; hence from T.4 $c_3 d_3 < 0$.

Now if $c_3 \leqslant 0$ then $e_3 < 0$, $d_3 > 0$ and from T.9 $f_3 > 0$. If $a_{57} = 1$, T.5 is unbounded so by $L.2$ on $R.9$ $a_{59} = -1$. Thus by $L.2$ on $R.5$ $a_{79} = 1$. Now $a_{76} \neq -1$, $a_{77} \neq 1$ otherwise T.7 would be unbounded. However, $R.7$ and $R.9$ now contradict $L.2$.

Thus $c_3 > 0$ so $e_3 > 0$, $d_3 < 0$. Now $a_{87} \neq 1$ otherwise T.8 is unbounded, so by $L.2$ $a_{89} = -1$. From T.8 $f_3 < 0$. Further, by $L.2$ $a_{69} = 1$. Now $a_{66} \neq -1$, $a_{67} \neq 1$ otherwise T.6 is unbounded. Thus $R.6$ and $R.9$ contradict $L.2$. Hence (B_{11}) does not arise.

(B_{12}) Suppose $a_{38} = 0$, then by $L.3$ $a_{39} \neq -1$ so $a_{39} = 1$. By $L.2$ $a_{59} = -1 = a_{89}$ so $a_{69} = 0 = a_{79}$ and then by $L.3$ $a_{56} = 0 = a_{86}$. Thus either (B_{12}^1) $a_{66} = -1$ or (B_{12}^{11}) $a_{76} = -1$.

(B_{12}^1) Suppose $a_{66} = -1$ then by $L.3$ $a_{67} = 0$, $a_{68} \neq -1$ so $a_{68} = 1$. By $L.2$ on $R.6$ $a_{78} = -1 = a_{88}$ and by $L.2$ again $a_{57} = -1$, $a_{77} = 1$. Thus we have

x	A	y	z	B	C	D	E	F
1	1	1	1	0	0	0	0	0
1	−1	0	1	1	0	0	0	0
−1	0	1	0	0	−1	0	0	1
−1	0	0	0	0	1	1	1	0
0	−1	0	0	−1	0	−1	0	−1
0	1	−1	0	0	−1	0	1	0
0	0	−1	0	−1	0	1	−1	0
0	0	0	−1	1	0	0	−1	−1
0	0	0	−1	0	1	−1	0	1

Choose the coordinate system shown. From boundedness we have: from T.1 $a_3 < 0$; from T.2 $b_3 < 0$; from T.3 $c_3 f_3 > 0$.

Now if $f_3 \leqslant 0$ then $c_3 < 0$ so from T.9 $d_3 < 0$. However, T.5 is now unbounded.

Thus $f_3 > 0$ so $c_3 > 0$ and from T.8 $e_3 < 0$. However, T.6 is now unbounded. Hence (B_{12}^1) cannot arise.

(B_{12}^{11}) Suppose $a_{76} = -1$ then by $L.3$ $a_{77} = 0$, $a_{78} \neq -1$ so $a_{78} = 1$. By $L.2$ on $R.7$ $a_{68} = -1 = a_{58}$ so $a_{88} = 0$. Thus by

$L.2$ $a_{87} = -1$, $a_{67} = 1$. However columns 4, 5, 6, 7 and 9 contain a minor equivalent to (G_1) and by transforming these columns into the first four columns and rearranging the rows, we have a case equivalent to (B_{11}).

Thus (B_{12}) cannot occur and so neither can (B_1).

(B_2) Suppose $a_{36} = 0 = a_{86}$, $a_{56} = -1$ then by $L.3$ $a_{57} = 0$. Thus two cases arise, either (B_{21}) $a_{59} = 0$ or (B_{22}) $a_{58} = 0$.

(B_{21}) Suppose $a_{59} = 0$ then by $L.3$ $a_{58} \neq -1$ so $a_{58} = 1$. By $L.2$ on $R.5$ $a_{38} = -1 = a_{78}$ so $a_{68} = 0 = a_{88}$ and then by $L.3$ $a_{76} = 0$ so $a_{66} = -1$. By $L.3$ $a_{67} = 0$, $a_{69} \neq -1$ so $a_{69} = 1$. Thus by $L.3$ $a_{39} \neq -1$ so by $L.2$ on $R.9$ $a_{37} = 1$. Now by $L.1$ $a_{39} = 0$ so $a_{79} = -1 = a_{89}$ and then by $L.1$ again $a_{77} = 0$ so $a_{87} = -1$.

Thus we have

x	y	A	z	B	C	D	E	F
1	1	1	1	0	0	0	0	0
1	-1	0	1	1	0	0	0	0
-1	0	1	0	0	0	1	-1	0
-1	0	0	0	0	1	1	1	0
0	-1	0	0	-1	-1	0	1	0
0	1	-1	0	0	-1	0	0	1
0	0	-1	0	-1	0	0	-1	-1
0	0	0	-1	1	0	-1	0	-1
0	0	0	-1	0	1	-1	0	1

Choose the coordinate system shown. From boundedness we have: from T.1 $a_2 < 0$; from T.2 $b_2 > 0$.

Now if $d_2 \leqslant 0$, from T.8 $f_2 > 0$ and from T.9 $c_2 < 0$. However T.6 is now unbounded. Thus $d_2 > 0$. From T.9 at least one of $c_2 > 0$ and $f_2 > 0$ holds; from T.6 at least one of $c_2 > 0$ and $f_2 < 0$ holds. Hence $c_2 > 0$. From T.4 $e_2 < 0$. However, T.5 is now unbounded.

Thus (B_{21}) cannot occur.

(B_{22}) We have $a_{58} = 0$; by $L.3$ $a_{59} \neq -1$ so $a_{59} = 1$. By $L.2$ on $R.5$ $a_{39} = -1 = a_{79}$ so $a_{69} = 0 = a_{89}$. By $L.3$ $a_{76} = 0$ so $a_{66} = -1$ and then by $L.3$ $a_{67} = 0$, $a_{68} \neq -1$ so $a_{68} = 1$. By $L.2$ on $R.6$ $a_{78} = -1 = a_{88}$ so $a_{38} = 0 = a_{77}$. Thus by $L.3$ $a_{37} = -1$, $a_{87} = 1$ and we have

x	y	A	z	B	C	D	E	F
1	1	1	1	0	0	0	0	0
1	-1	0	1	1	0	0	0	0
-1	0	1	0	0	0	-1	0	-1
-1	0	0	0	0	1	1	1	0
0	-1	0	0	-1	-1	0	0	1
0	1	-1	0	0	-1	0	1	0
0	0	-1	0	-1	0	0	-1	-1
0	0	0	-1	1	0	1	-1	0
0	0	0	-1	0	1	-1	0	1

Choose the coordinate system shown. From boundedness we have: from T.1 $a_2 < 0$; from T.2 $b_2 > 0$; if $d_2 \geqslant 0$, from T.8 $e_2 > 0$; from T.4 $c_2 < 0$ and from T.9 $f_2 > 0$. However, T.3 is now unbounded.

Thus $d_2 < 0$. From T.6 at least one of $c_2 > 0$ and $e_2 < 0$ holds; from T.4 at least one of $c_2 > 0$ and $e_2 > 0$ holds. Hence $c_2 > 0$. From T.9 $f_2 < 0$. However T.5 is now unbounded. Thus (B_2) cannot occur and so neither can (B).

Hence G_1 does not lead to a 9-con containing nine chardhos.

Remark 1. In considering G_2 and G_3 we may ignore cases that contain a minor equivalent to $\begin{pmatrix} 1 & 1 \\ 1 & 1 \end{pmatrix}$ for the columns containing units in these two rows must contain a minor equivalent to G_1 since neither G_2 nor G_3 contains a minor equivalent to $\begin{pmatrix} 1 & 1 \\ 1 & 1 \end{pmatrix}$.

Consider G_2; we have

$$
\begin{array}{rrrr}
1 & 1 & 1 & 1 \\
1 & -1 & 0 & 0 \\
-1 & 0 & 1 & 0 \\
-1 & 0 & 0 & 1 \\
0 & -1 & 0 & 0 \\
0 & 1 & -1 & 0 \\
0 & 0 & -1 & 0 \\
0 & 0 & 0 & -1 \\
0 & 0 & 0 & -1 \\
\end{array}
$$

Clearly we may assume $a_{25} = 1 = a_{26}$, $a_{2j} = 0$ ($j = 7, 8, 9$). By L.2 we may further suppose $a_{55} = -1$. Now $a_{75} \neq -1$ for if $a_{75} = -1$ then by L.2 $a_{86} = -1 = a_{96}$ and the case may be ignored by Remark 1. Hence by $L.2$ $a_{76} = -1$ and by symmetry $a_{85} = -1 = a_{96}$. By $L.3$ $a_{45} = 0 = a_{65} = a_{36} = a_{46}$. By Remark 1, $a_{56} \neq 1$ so $a_{56} = 0$. We may nows uppose $a_{47} = 1 = a_{48}$, $a_{49} = 0$ then by $L.2$ we may assume $a_{37} = -1$. By $L.3$ $a_{38} \neq -1$ and by Remark 1 $a_{38} \neq 1$ so $a_{38} = 0$. Now $a_{57} \neq -1$ for if $a_{57} = -1$, then by $L.2$ on $R.4$ $a_{68} = -1 = a_{78}$ and by Remark 1 the case may be ignored. Thus by $L.2$ on $R.4$ $a_{58} = -1$. Further $a_{57} \neq 1$ for if $a_{57} = 1$ let a_{3l} be the remaining unit of $R.3$. Then by $L.2$ $a_{8l} = a_{9l} = -a_{3l}$ and, since $l \neq 4$, the case may be ignored by Remark 1. By $L.3$ $a_{57} \neq -1$ so $a_{57} = 0$. Thus we may suppose $a_{59} = 1$. Two cases now arise, either (A) $a_{86} = 1$ or (B) $a_{66} = 1$.

(A) Suppose $a_{86} = 1$ then $a_{66} = 0$ and by $L.3$ $a_{75} = 0 = a_{95}$, so $a_{35} = 1$. By $L.1$ $a_{39} = 0$ and by $L.2$ on $R.3$ $a_{97} = 1$. By Remark 1 $a_{98} \neq 1$ so by $L.2$ on $R.5$ $a_{99} = -1$ and so by $L.1$ $a_{98} = 0$. By Remark 1 $a_{89} \neq -1$ so by $L.2$ on $R.5$ $a_{88} = 1$. By $L.2$ on $R.8$ $a_{68} = -1$ and then by $L.3$ $a_{87} = 0 = a_{89} = a_{67}$, $a_{69} \neq -1$ so $a_{69} = 1$. However by Remark 1 the case may now be ignored. Thus (A) cannot arise.

(B) Suppose $a_{66} = 1$ then $a_{86} = 0$. Thus two of the a_{8j} $(j = 7,$ $8, 9)$ are units. By $L.3$ $a_{87} \neq -1$, $a_{88} \neq -1$ and by Remark 1 $a_{87} = a_{97} = 1$ is also impossible, so a_{89} must be a unit; by Remark 1 $a_{89} \neq 1$ so $a_{89} = -1$. By $L.3$ $a_{88} = 0$ so $a_{87} = 1$ and then by $L.3$ again $a_{35} = 0$, $a_{39} \neq 1$ so $a_{39} = -1$. By $L.2$ on $R.3$ $a_{99} = 1$ so $a_{69} = 0 = a_{79}$ and then by $L.3$ $a_{97} = 0 = a_{95}$, $a_{98} \neq -1$ so $a_{98} = 1$. Also $a_{75} = 1$ so $a_{77} = 0$. Hence $a_{78} = -1$ so $a_{68} = 0$, $a_{67} = -1$ and we have

x	y	z	A	B	C	D	E	F
1	1	1	1	0	0	0	0	0
1	−1	0	0	1	1	0	0	0
−1	0	1	0	0	0	−1	0	−1
−1	0	0	1	0	0	1	1	0
0	−1	0	0	−1	0	0	−1	1
0	1	−1	0	0	1	−1	0	0
0	0	−1	0	1	−1	0	−1	0
0	0	0	−1	−1	0	1	0	−1
0	0	0	−1	0	−1	0	1	1

Choose the coordinate system shown. From boundedness we have: from T.1 $a_3 < 0$.

Now if $b_3 \leqslant 0$, from T.2 $c_3 > 0$; from T.7 $e_3 < 0$; from T.4 $d_3 > 0$; from T.8 $f_3 > 0$. However T.5 is now unbounded.

Thus $b_3 > 0$. From T.2 $c_3 < 0$; from T.6 $d_3 < 0$; from T.4 $e_3 > 0$; from T.9 $f_3 < 0$. However T.3 is now unbounded.

Hence (B) cannot occur and so G_2 cannot lead to a 9-con containing nine chardhos.

Remark 2. We may now ignore cases that contain a minor equivalent to

$$
\begin{array}{rrrr}
1 & 1 & 1 & 1 \\
0 & 0 & 0 & -1 \\
0 & 0 & 0 & -1
\end{array}
$$

for the columns represented in the minor clearly cannot contain a minor equivalent to G_3 and therefore the columns must contain a minor equivalent to either G_1 or G_2.

Consider G_3; we have

$$
\begin{array}{rrrr}
1 & 1 & 1 & 1 \\
1 & -1 & 0 & 0 \\
-1 & 0 & 0 & 1 \\
-1 & 0 & 0 & 0 \\
0 & -1 & 0 & 0 \\
0 & 1 & -1 & 0 \\
0 & 0 & -1 & 0 \\
0 & 0 & 1 & -1 \\
0 & 0 & 0 & -1
\end{array}
$$

Clearly we may suppose $a_{25} = 1 = a_{26}$, $a_{2j} = 0$ ($j = 7, 8, 9$) and by $L.2$ we may further assume $a_{55} = -1$. Now $a_{75} \neq -1$ for if $a_{75} = -1$ then by $L.2$ $a_{86} = -1 = a_{96}$ and the case may be ignored by Remark 1. Thus by $L.2$ $a_{76} = -1$. Two cases now arise: (A) $a_{85} = -1$ and (B) $a_{85} \neq -1$.

(A) Suppose $a_{85} = -1$, then by $L.3$ $a_{86} = 0 = a_{j5}$ ($j = 3, 6, 7$). By $L.2$ on $R.2$ $a_{96} = -1$, then by $L.3$ $a_{36} = 0$. By Remark 2 we may ignore the case when $a_{95} = 0$ so we have $a_{95} = 1$, $a_{45} = 0$, and then by $L.3$ $a_{56} = 0$. Further, by Remark 2 $a_{46} \neq 0$ so we have $a_{46} = 1$, $a_{66} = 0$. Let $a_{97} = 1$ then by $L.2$ $a_{67} = -1 = a_{77}$ and the case may be ignored by Remark 1.

Thus (A) cannot arise.

(B) Suppose $a_{85} \neq -1$, then by $L.2$ $a_{86} = -1$ and $a_{95} = -1$.

By $L.3$ $a_{35} = 0 = a_{36} = a_{65}$ and by Remark 1 $a_{56} = 0$. By Remark 2 one of a_{75} and a_{85} is a unit so $a_{45} = 0$. Also by Remark 2 $a_{46} \neq 0$ so $a_{46} = 1$, $a_{66} = 0 = a_{96}$. Let a_{8l} be the remaining unit of $R.8$, then by $L.2$ $a_{5l} = a_{9l} = -a_{8l}$. The case when $l \neq 5$ may be ignored by Remark 1 so $a_{85} = 1$, $a_{75} = 0 = a_{8j}$ $(j = 7, 8, 9)$. Clearly we may assume $a_{37} = 1 = a_{38}$, $a_{39} = 0$. Then by $L.2$ we may also suppose $a_{67} = -1$. By Remark 1 $a_{77} \neq -1$ so by $L.2$ on $R.3$ $a_{78} = -1$.

Now if $a_{58} = -1$, then by $L.2$ $a_{47} = -1$ so by $L.3$ $a_{57} = 0 = a_{77}$ and the case may be ignored by Remark 2 on columns 1, 4, 7 and 8.

Thus $a_{58} \neq -1$ so by $L.2$ $a_{57} = -1 = a_{48}$. By Remark 2 on columns 1, 4, 7 and 8 the remaining $(+1)$ of $C.8$ must be either a_{58} or a_{68} so by $L.3$ $a_{47} = 0 = a_{77}$. By $L.1$ both a_{49} and a_{79} are units. However by $L.3$ $a_{49} = a_{79}$ and the case may be ignored by Remark 1. Thus (B) cannot arise.

Hence G_3 does not lead to a 9-con containing nine chardhos and the following theorem has been proved.

THEOREM 10. If a 9-con exists, it cannot contain nine chardhos.

CHAPTER NINE

ON THE NON-EXISTENCE OF A 10-CON

WE BEGIN the chapter by defining an operation on the tetrahedra of a 10-con. From this operation we obtain a function defined over the D_m-planes of a 10-con that is analogous to the surplus of a D_m-plane of a 9-con. We then obtain an equality concerning these functions and use it to enumerate the sets of D_m-planes which may possibly be contained in a 10-con. Hence we show that a 10-con cannot exist and so we have:

THEOREM 12. An n-con can exist only if $n < 9$.

We firstly remark that if a 10-con exists none of its D_m-planes can be tetres. For, if one or more are, take any one of them, D say, remove from the 10-con one of the tetrahedra that does not have any of its faces contained in D and we immediately have a contradiction to Theorem 7.

As before, we use A, B, C ... to represent distinct tetrahedra, no pair of which are overlapping; a_i, b_i, c_i, ... $(i = 1, ... 4)$ to represent the faces of A, B, C ...; and x_1, x_2, x_3 and x_4 to represent the planes that contain a_1, a_2, a_3 and a_4 respectively. As A/BCDE in a plane is impossible by $L.16$, there are effectively only three distinct types of tetrahedra in the 10-con, for:

Either A/BCD in x_1, A/EFG in x_2 and A/HIJ in x_3, in which case A is called a treno,

Or A/BCD in x_1, A/EFG in x_2, A/HI in x_3 and A/J in x_4, in which case A is called a daik,

Or A/BCD in x_1, A/EF in x_2, A/GH in x_3 and A/IJ in x_4, in which case A is called a tredho.

Suppose a 10-con exists; if more than one does, choose any one. Take the general tetrahedron A of the 10-con. Its face a_1 is a triangle, so join the mid-points of the sides of this triangle so that a_1 is divided up into four triangles which we shall call trianglets. Repeat this process for each face of A. Having done this for each face of the 10-con we may therefore associate with

a_1 of the general tetrahedron **A** the trianglets of those faces in which the tetrahedra meet **A** in x_1. Clearly we may do the same for a_2, a_3 and a_4 so that we have associated with each face of the 10-con a number of trianglets. For example, associated with the faces a_i $(i = 1, \ldots 4)$ of a daik we have twelve, twelve, eight and four trianglets respectively. Further, we may associate with each D_m-plane the trianglets that are contained in the D_m-plane so that $4m$ trianglets are associated with each D_m-plane.

Using the above definitions we now define an operation **O** on a tetrahedron of a 10-con as follows:

If **A** is a treno, we take three of the trianglets associated with a_1, three associated with a_2 and three associated with a_3 and we associate them with a_4 instead.

If **A** is a daik we take three of the trianglets associated with a_1, three associated with a_2 and we associate five of them with a_4 and one of them with a_3.

If **A** is a tredho we take three of the trianglets associated with a_1 and we associate one of them with a_2, one with a_3 and one with a_4.

Thus with each face of the tetrahedron **A** the operation **O** has associated exactly nine trianglets.

If a 10-con exists, take any one of its tetrahedra, **A** say, and perform the operation **O**. Then take another tetrahedron, **B** say, and perform the operation **O** on **B**, neglecting the effect of the operation **O** on **A**. Take a third tetrahedron and perform the operation **O** on it, neglecting the effect of the operation **O** on **A** and **B**. Proceed in this manner until the operation **O** has been performed on all the tetrahedra of the 10-con. Clearly the order in which the tetrahedra are operated on is immaterial.

The effect of this operation on the D_m-planes is tabulated below in the second column. The first term of this column represents the number of trianglets originally associated with the D_m-plane, the second term the number of trianglets added to the D_m-plane by the operation and the third term the number of trianglets subtracted from the D_m-plane by the operation. For the third column we have the second column's total -13 and we define this number to be the surplust of the D_m-plane.

Now the total number of trianglets in the 10-con is 160 so the D_m-planes contained in the 10-con must contain 160 trian-

D_m-plane	Effect of 0 on D_m-plane	Surplust
Dotre	$20 + 3 - 6 = 17$	4
Dodo	$16 + 4 - 0 = 20$	7
Treun	$16 + 15 - 3 = 28$	15
Notre	$12 + 27 - 0 = 39$	26
Doun	$12 + 11 - 0 = 23$	10
Nodo	$8 + 18 - 0 = 26$	13
Unun	$8 + 10 - 0 = 18$	5
Uno	$4 + 9 - 0 = 13$	0

glets. As the operation only transfers a trianglet from one D_m-plane of the 10-con to another, we must therefore have:

$160 = 13l +$ the sum of the surplusts of the D_m-planes, where l is the number of D_m-planes contained in the 10-con.

We now use this formula to enumerate the sets of D_m-planes which may possibly be contained in a 10-con.

From the above all the possible D_m-planes have a surplust $\geqslant 0$ so $160 - 13 l \geqslant 0$, i.e. $l \leqslant 12$. Further the D_m-planes must contain 40 faces of the 10-con so, as a D_m-plane can contain at most five faces of the 10-con, we must have $l \geqslant 8$. However we cannot have $l = 8$ for, if we did, by removing one of the tetrahedra from the 10-con, we would have a 9-con containing at most eight D_m-planes which is impossible by Theorem 8. Hence $12 \geqslant l \geqslant 9$.

(I) Suppose a 10-con contains twelve D_m-planes, then the D_m-planes have a total surplust of $160 - 156 = 4$, so that from the table we must have eleven unos and one dotre. However, the D_m-planes then contain only sixteen of the forty faces of the 10-con so the case clearly cannot arise.

(II) Suppose a 10-con contains eleven D_m-planes, then the D_m-planes have a total surplust of $160 - 143 = 17$. As the lowest positive surplust is 4 we must therefore have at least seven D_m-planes with a surplust of zero, i.e. at least seven D_m-planes are unos. However the four undetermined D_m-planes must then contain 33 faces of the 10-con and this is clearly impossible so the case cannot arise.

(III) Suppose a 10-con contains ten D_m-planes, then the D_m-planes have a total surplust of $160 - 130 = 30$. As the lowest positive surplust is 4 at least three of the D_m-planes must be unos. However the seven undetermined D_m-planes must then contain 37 faces of the 10-con which is impossible, so this case cannot arise either.

Hence if a 10-con exists it must contain exactly nine D_m-planes. Further, a uno cannot occur in the D_m-planes for, if it did, we remove from the 10-con the tetrahedron that contained a face in the uno and we are then left with a 9-con containing at most eight D_m-planes, and this is impossible by Theorem 8.

(IV) Now suppose a 10-con contains nine D_m-planes, then the D_m-planes have a total surplust of $160 - 117 = 43$. Nine dotres cannot occur, since they contain forty-five faces. Further eight dotres cannot occur for as they contain forty faces, another D_m-plane could not exist. However, since the D_m-planes contain forty faces at least four of them must be dotres.

If only four dotres occur, the five undetermined D_m-planes contain 20 faces and have a total surplust of $160 - 117 - 16 = 27$. From the former we can only have five D_4-planes. But this is impossible by the latter, since the surplust of a D_4-plane is at least 7.

If only five dotres occur the four undetermined D_m-planes contain 15 faces and have a total surplust of $43 - 20 = 23$. From the former we must have three D_4-planes and one D_3-plane. But this is impossible by the latter, since the surplust of a D_4-plane is at least 7 and the surplust of a D_3-plane at least 10.

Hence only two possibilities now arise: (A) six dotres occur, and (B) seven dotres occur.

(A) Suppose only six dotres occur, then the three undetermined D_m-planes contain 10 faces and have a total surplust of $43 - 24 = 19$. From the former we must have either one D_4-plane and two D_3-planes or two D_4-planes and one D_2-plane. However the first alternative cannot occur as a D_3-plane has a surplust of at least 10. Thus we have two D_4-planes and one D_2-plane with a total surplust of 19. As a D_4-plane has a surplust of at least 7 the D_2-plane cannot be a nodo so it must be a unun. Hence the two D_4-planes have a total surplust of 14, and so they must both be dodos. Thus we have the set S_1 of D_m-planes consisting of six dotres, two dodos and a unun. Clearly as S_1 contains no unos, nodos or notres, no trenos can occur in the 10-con and as it only contains one unun, no douns and no treuns, two and only two daiks occur. Thus the 10-con must contain eight tredhos.

(i) Suppose at least one of the tredhos, A say, has its faces contained in four dotres. Let $C.1$ represent the unun with $a_{81} = 1 = -a_{91}$, $C.l$ ($l = 2, \ldots 7$) which we suppose contain only two (-1)s each the dotres, and $C.8$ and $C.9$ the dodos. Since $R.8$ and $R.9$ contain sipts they must clearly represent the daiks. Let $R.10$ represent A, then we may clearly suppose $a_{10\cdot2} = -1$ $a_{10\cdot j} = 1$ ($j = 3, 4, 5$), $a_{10\cdot l} = 0$ ($l > 5$), since $R.10$ contains one and only one tript. Now the row that contains the other (-1) of $C.2$ must, by $L.2$ on $R.10$, have a (-1) in one of columns 3, 4 and 5. Hence this row contains two tripts and so must represent one of the daiks. By symmetry we may therefore suppose $a_{92} = -1 = a_{93}$. By $L.3$ $a_{82} = 0$ so we may suppose $a_{j2} = 1$ ($j = 5, 6, 7$), $a_{12} = 0$ ($l = 1, 2, 3, 4$). By $L.3$ $a_{j3} = 0$ ($j = 5, 6, 7$), $a_{83} \neq 1$ so we may suppose $a_{33} = 1 = a_{43}$. As T.5, T.6 and T.7 are tredhos, their rows must contain one and only one tript. Hence since $a_{jl} \neq -1$ ($j = 5, 6, 7$; $l = 3, 4, 5$) by $L.3$, we may assume by symmetry that $a_{56} = -1 = a_{66} = a_{77}$. As T.8 is a daik, $R.8$ must contain two tripts and so as only one of a_{8j} ($j = 3, 4, 5$) can be a (-1) by $L.3$, we must have $a_{87} = -1$. By $L.3$ $a_{96} = 0 = a_{97}$.

(a) Suppose one of a_{94} and a_{95} is a $(+1)$. We may clearly assume $a_{94} = 1$ then $a_{9l} = 0$ ($l > 4$). By $L.2$ we have $a_{14} = -1 = a_{24}$ then by $L.3$ $a_{13} = 0 = a_{23}$ so $a_{83} = -1$. Hence by $L.2$ on $R.10$ $a_{35} = -1 = a_{45}$ so by $L.3$ $a_{85} = 0 = a_{37} = a_{47}$. Thus at least one of a_{17} and a_{27} is a $(+1)$ and at least one of a_{57} and a_{67} is a $(+1)$. Hence by $L.3$ $a_{j4} = 0 = a_{j6}$ ($j = 7, 8$). Thus at least one of a_{16} and a_{26} is a $(+1)$ and at least one of a_{36} and a_{46} is a $(+1)$. Hence by $L.3$ $a_{j4} = 0 = a_{j5}$ ($j = 5, 6$). Thus at least one of a_{15} and a_{25} is a $(+1)$ so that $a_{34} = 0 = a_{44}$. Thus $C.4$ represents a dodo which is impossible.

Hence (a) cannot arise and we may assume $a_{94} = 0 = a_{95}$ since $a_{94} \neq -1$, $a_{95} \neq -1$ by $L.3$. Thus one of a_{98} and a_{99} is a unit and we may clearly suppose $a_{98} = 1$. By $L.2$ $a_{18} = -1 = a_{28}$. Now by $L.3$ $a_{jl} \neq -1$ ($j = 5, 6$; $l = 4, 5$) so as the (-1)s of $C.7$ and $C.8$ are already determined we can only have T.5/T.6 in $C.9$ and so we may suppose $a_{59} = 1 = -a_{69}$.

(b) Suppose $a_{57} = 0 = a_{67}$ then at least one of a_{17} and a_{27} is a $(+1)$ so by $L.3$ $a_{78} = 0 = a_{88}$. Also at least one of a_{37} and a_{47} is a $(+1)$ so by $L.3$ $a_{83} = 0$ and we may suppose $a_{13} = -1$, $a_{23} = 0$. By $L.3$ $a_{38} = 0 = a_{48}$ so one of a_{58} and a_{68} is a $(+1)$;

by symmetry we may suppose $a_{58} = 1$, $a_{68} = 0$. Thus by $L.3$ $a_{16} = 0 = a_{26}$ and by $L.1$ $a_{54} = 0 = a_{55}$. Now one of a_{64} and a_{65} is a unit and by $L.3$ the unit is a $(+1)$; clearly we may suppose $a_{64} = 1$, $a_{65} = 0$. As $C.9$ contains only two $(+1)$s we cannot have both a_{19} and a_{29} $(+1)$s. Hence by $L.2$ on $R.6$ at least one of a_{14} and a_{24} is a (-1). By $L.3$ on $R.10$ $a_{14} \neq -1$ so $a_{24} = -1$. Since $a_{14} \neq -1$, by $L.2$ $a_{19} = 1$, and so by $L.3$ $a_{j9} = 0$ $(j = 2, 3, 4)$. Thus one of a_{79} and a_{89} is a (-1) so $a_{17} = 0$ and $a_{j7} = 1$ $(j = 2, 3, 4)$. Thus a_{25} is a unit and by $L.3$ $a_{25} \neq -1$ so $a_{25} = 1$. By $L.3$ $a_{15} \neq -1$ so by $L.2$ on $R.2$ $a_{14} = 1$. By $L.3$ $a_{34} \neq -1$, $a_{44} \neq -1$ so by $L.2$ on $R.10$ $a_{35} = -1 = a_{45}$ which is impossible by $L.4$.

Hence (b) cannot arise and we have that one of a_{57} and a_{67} is a $(+1)$; by symmetry we may clearly suppose $a_{57} = 1$, then by $L.4$ $a_{67} \neq 1$ and by $L.3$ $a_{67} \neq -1$ so $a_{67} = 0$. By $L.3$ $a_{76} = 0 = a_{86}$. Thus at least one of a_{16} and a_{26} is a $(+1)$ so by $L.3$ $a_{58} = 0 = a_{68}$. Further at least one of a_{64} and a_{65} is a unit and by $L.3$ it must be a $(+1)$; by symmetry we may suppose $a_{64} = 1$, $a_{65} = 0$. By $L.1$ $a_{54} = 0 = a_{55}$. By $L.3$ $a_{74} \neq -1$ so by $L.2$ on $R.6$ $a_{79} = 1$. As $C.9$ contains only two $(+1)$s $a_{89} \neq 1$ so by $L.2$ on $R.6$ $a_{84} = -1$. By $L.3$ $a_{83} = 0$ so we may suppose $a_{13} = -1$, $a_{23} = 0$. By $L.3$ $a_{38} = 0 = a_{48}$ so one of a_{78} and a_{88} is a $(+1)$. Hence by $L.3$ $a_{17} = 0 = a_{27}$ and so $a_{37} = 1 = a_{47}$. Thus since both $a_{34} = -1 = a_{44}$ and $a_{35} = -1 = a_{45}$ are impossible by $L.4$ we may suppose by $L.2$ on $R.10$ that $a_{34} = -1 = a_{45}$. Hence by $L.3$ $a_{74} = 0 = a_{75} = a_{85}$. Thus since $C.8$ represents a dodo one of $R.7$ and $R.8$ can contain only three units since $a_{89} = 0$ by $L.3$.

Hence (i) cannot occur.

Thus each tredho of the 10-con can have at most three of its faces contained in dotres and so as the daiks can obviously have at most three, every tetrahedron of the 10-con has at most three of its faces contained in dotres. However, since the six dotres contain thirty faces of the 10-con each tetrahedron of the 10-con must have exactly three of its faces contained in dotres. Hence if we let $C.1$ and $C.2$ represent the dodos and $C.3$ the unun, each row contains one and only one unit in the first three columns. We may therefore suppose that $a_{11} = a_{21} = 1$, $a_{31} = a_{41} = -1$, $a_{52} = a_{62} = 1$, $a_{72} = -1 = a_{82}$, $a_{93} = 1 = -a_{10.3}$. Now $C.l$ $(l = 4, \ldots 9)$ represent dotres so we shall assume $C.l$ $(l = 4, \ldots 9)$ contain only two (-1)s each. As $R.9$ and $R.10$ contain the sipts they must clearly represent the daiks so we

may suppose $a_{10.4} = -1 = a_{10.5}$, $a_{10.6} = 1$, $a_{10.j} = 0$ $(j = 7, 8, 9)$.
As $R.l$ $(l = 1, \ldots 8)$ represents a tredho one and only one tript
occurs in $R.l$ $(l = 1, \ldots 8)$. Let $a_{j6} = -1 = a_{m6}$ $(m \neq j)$ then
by $L.3$ on $R.10$ $m \neq 9$, $j \neq 9$ so $m \leqslant 8$, $j \leqslant 8$. Now if $T.j/T.m$ in
$C.l$ where $l > 3$ then one of $R.j$ and $R.m$ must contain two tripts
and this is impossible from the above. Thus $T.j/T.m$ in $C.1$ or
$C.2$ and so by symmetry we may suppose $j = 1$, $m = 3$. By $L.3$
$a_{j4} \neq 1$, $a_{j5} \neq 1$ $(j = 1, 3)$ so $a_{j4} = 0 = a_{j5}$ $(j = 1, 3)$. Further
by $L.3$ $a_{26} = 0 = a_{46}$. Since $R.1$ already contains a tript, by $L.2$
we may suppose $a_{17} = 1 = -a_{27}$, then by $L.3$ $a_{37} = 0 = a_{47}$.
Hence since $R.3$ already contains a tript by $L.2$ we may suppose
$a_{38} = 1 = -a_{48}$, then by $L.3$ $a_{18} = 0 = a_{28}$. Hence we must have
$a_{19} = a_{39} = 1$. Let $a_{k7} = -1$ then by $L.3$ $a_{k6} \neq 1$ and $a_{k9} \neq -1$
so by $L.2$ on $R.3$ we have $a_{k8} = -1$. Thus $R.k$ contains two tripts
so we must have $k = 9$; by $L.3$ $a_{96} = 0$. The remaining unit of
$R.9$ must clearly be a dopt so, as $a_{94} \neq 1$, $a_{95} \neq 1$ by $L.3$, we must
have $a_{99} = 1$. By $L.1$ $a_{94} = 0 = a_{95}$ and by $L.3$ $a_{29} \neq -1$. However $R.2$ and $R.9$ now contradict $L.2$.

Thus S_1 does not lead to a 10-con and so neither does (A).

(B) Suppose seven dotres occur, then the two undetermined
D_m-planes contain five faces and have a total surplust of
$43 - 28 = 15$. Since a uno cannot occur, from the former we
must have one D_3-plane and one D_2-plane. As a notre has a surplust of 26 the D_3-plane must be a doun so that the D_2-plane
can only be a unun. We therefore have the set S_2 of D_m-planes
consisting of seven dotres, a doun and a unun. As S_2 contains
no unos, nodos or notres, no trenos can occur in the 10-con and
as it contains only one doun, one unun and no treuns, only four
daiks occur. Thus the 10-con contains six tredhos and four daiks.
Let $C.1$ represent the unun with $a_{11} = 1 = -a_{21}$, $C.2$ the doun
which we suppose contains only one (-1) and $C.l$ $(l = 3, \ldots 9)$
the dotres which we suppose contain only two (-1)s. We may
suppose that the first four rows represent the daiks so that we
must have $a_{32} = 1 = a_{42}$.

Now if the 10-con has a matrix representation with $a_{12} = -1$,
by omitting the first row we have a matrix representation of
a 9-con which contains three nopts; by $L.18$ three naiks must
occur in the 9-con and this is impossible by Theorem 9.

Hence we may suppose $a_{12} = 0$ and by symmetry $a_{22} = 0$.
Hence we may put $a_{52} = -1$. As $T.5$ is a tredho $R.5$ contains

only one tript so we may suppose $a_{53} = 1 = a_{54}$, $a_{55} = -1$. By
$L.3$ $a_{jl} \neq -1$ $(j = 3, 4; l = 3, 4)$ and at most two of the a_{jl} $(j = 1, 2; l = 3, 4)$ are (-1)s. Hence at least two of the tripts of $C.3$
and $C.4$ lie in rows 6 to 10 inclusive. By $L.3$ $a_{l3} = -1 = a_{l4}$ is
impossible so we may suppose one of the (-1)s lies in $R.6$ and
another in $R.7$. Now the situations $a_{6j} = -1 = a_{7j}$ $(j = 3, 4)$
and $a_{63} = -1 = a_{74}$, $a_{64} = 0 = a_{73}$ are both impossible for in
either case $T.6/T.7$ in $C.l$ where $l > 4$ and so in a dotre; hence
one of $R.6$ and $R.7$ would contain two tripts which is impossible.
It follows immediately that we must therefore have $a_{63} = -1 = a_{74}$ and one of a_{64} and a_{73} equal to $(+1)$. Clearly we may suppose
$a_{64} = 1$, then by $L.3$ $a_{73} = 0$. Clearly by exactly the same argu-
ment none of a_{j3} and a_{j4} $(j = 8, 9, 10)$ can be (-1)s. Thus by
$L.2$ on $R.5$ $a_{j5} = 1$ $(j = 8, 9, 10)$. By $L.2$ on $R.5$ again we may
suppose $a_{13} = -1 = a_{24}$ then by $L.3$ $a_{14} = 0 = a_{23}$. Since both
$R.6$ and $R.7$ already contain a tript $a_{65} = 0 = a_{75}$. Let $a_{66} = 1$
then by $L.2$ we may suppose $a_{16} = -1$. By $L.3$ $a_{26} = 0 = a_{56}$.
Now if $a_{76} \neq 1$, by $L.3$ $a_{76} = 0$ so we may put $a_{77} = 1$ and then
by $L.2$ we could suppose $a_{17} = -1$; however this is clearly impossible since $R.1$ then contains three tripts and a sipt. Hence
$a_{76} = 1$. For the same reason $a_{15} = 0$. Let $a_{77} = 1$ then by $L.2$
we may suppose $a_{27} = -1$. By $L.3$ $a_{j7} = 0$ $(j = 1, 5, 6)$. As $R.2$
contains only two tripts $a_{25} = 0$. Now none of the a_{j6} $(j = 8, 9, 10)$
are (-1)s since if $a_{86} = -1$ say, by $L.3$ $a_{83} \neq 1$ so, letting $a_{18} = 1$
we must have by $L.2$ $a_{88} = -1$ and so $R.8$ would contain two
tripts which is impossible. Further none of the a_{j7} $(j = 8, 9, 10)$
are (-1)s since if $a_{87} = -1$ say, by $L.3$ $a_{84} \neq 1$, so letting $a_{28} = 1$
we must have by $L.2$ $a_{88} = -1$ and $R.8$ again contains two tripts.
By $L.3$ $a_{16} = -1 = a_{17}$ is impossible so we may suppose $a_{36} = -1 = a_{47}$. By $L.3$ $a_{34} = 0 = a_{44}$ so we may suppose $a_{84} = 1$,
$a_{94} = 0 = a_{10.4}$. Let $a_{78} = 1$ then by $L.2$ $a_{9.8} = -1 = a_{10.8}$.
However as $T.9/T.10$ in a dotre this is impossible since one of
$R.9$ and $R.10$ would contain two tripts.

Thus S_2 does not lead to a 10-con and so neither does (B).

Hence a 10-con cannot contain nine D_m-planes and we have
proved the following theorem:

THEOREM 11. A 10-con does not exist.

An immediate consequence of Theorem 11 is:

THEOREM 12. An n-con can exist only if $n \leqslant 9$.

CHAPTER TEN

ON THE EXISTENCE OF AN 8-CON

IN THIS chapter we show by giving an example that an 8-con does in fact exist.

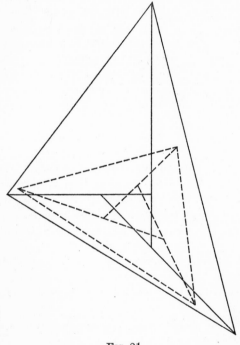

FIG. 21

Consider the diagram. If we suppose the plane of the paper to be $x = 0$, then by joining the four triangles defined by dotted lines to a point in $x > 0$ and the other four triangles to a point in $x < 0$ it is easily seen that we obtain a set of eight tetrahedra possessing Crum's Property. Hence we have:

THEOREM 13. An 8-con exists.

CHAPTER ELEVEN

CONCLUSIONS

THEOREMS 12 and 13 show that the answer to the problem: "What is the maximum number of non-overlapping tetrahedra such that any pair of them have an intersection of positive area?" is either 8 or 9. The problem is therefore reduced to "Does a 9-con exist?" Although we have not found the answer to this problem we have obtained various conditions which a 9-con must satisfy if it is to exist. Theorem 7 tells us that a plane cannot contain six or more faces of a 9-con, whilst Theorem 8 says that a 9-con can only contain either nine or ten D_m-planes. We have also obtained two conditions concerning the types of tetrahedra that can occur in a 9-con, namely Theorem 9 which states that at most two naiks can occur in a 9-con, and Theorem 10 which says that nine chardhos cannot occur in a 9-con. The main interest in the latter result is that it excludes the case which one may regard as the most symmetrical, for nine chardhos is the case when each tetrahedron of the 9-con is such that each of its faces has a positive area in common with two of the tetrahedra of the 9-con. These results therefore encourage us to conjecture that a 9-con does not exist or, what from the above is equivalent to it, that the maximum number of non-overlapping tetrahedra such that any pair of them have an intersection of positive area is 8.

Concerning the existence of a 9-con we can also deduce the following rather minor results:

(I) A 9-con contains at most five dotres.

Proof. Suppose a 9-con contains at least six dotres, then the D_m-planes apart from six of the dotres must contain 6 faces.

If the 9-con contains ten D_m-planes at least two of the planes must be unos. However, only two unos can occur for, if three do, by $L.18$ three naiks occur and this is impossible by Theorem 9. Hence the two undetermined planes must both be D_2-planes.

However since they must have a total surplus of 6 we can only have two nodos and so by $L.18$ six naiks occur in the 9-con which is impossible by Theorem 9.

Thus the 9-con must contain nine D_m-planes. By $L.18$ a notre would imply that the 9-con contains three naiks, so by Theorem 9 a notre cannot occur. Hence the three remaining D_m-planes must each have a surplus of 3. Three nodos cannot occur for, if they did, by $L.18$ the 9-con would contain six naiks. Thus a treun must occur and so the two remaining D_m-planes must contain only two faces, i.e. they must both be unos. As unos have a surplus of zero this is impossible and the proof is complete.

(II) A 9-con must contain at least one dotre.

Proof. Suppose a 9-con does not contain a dotre, then each of its D_m-planes contains at most 4 faces.

Thus if the 9-con contains nine D_m-planes each of them must be a D_4-plane; however as their total surplus is 9 they must all be dodos and hence the 9-con would contain nine chardhos which is impossible by Theorem 10.

Thus the 9-con must contain ten D_m-planes and so at least six of the D_m-planes must be D_4-planes; as the ten planes have a total surplus of 6 there can only be six D_4-planes and they must all be dodos. Hence the remaining four planes have a total surplus of zero, so all four are unos. However, the planes now only contain 28 faces and the proof is complete.

By using the concept of a surplus we can of course enumerate the possible sets of D_m-planes which may be contained in a 9-con. However no general method has been obtained to deal with the cases so enumerated, with the result that a large number of individual cases would have to be analysed. In fact in order to analyse the case when only one dotre occurs we would have to consider quite a large number of permatrices (some of which would of course be equivalent) for, consider a permatrix of nine dodos that contains a minor equivalent to $\begin{pmatrix} 1 & 1 \\ 1 & 1 \end{pmatrix}$; thus in the permatrix we may clearly suppose $a_{ij} = 1$ $(i = 1, 2; j = 1, 2)$, $a_{l1} = -1 = a_{m2}$, $a_{l2} = 0 = a_{m1}$ $(l = 3, 4; m = 5, 6)$. Now for $l = 3$ or 4 by replacing $a_{l1} = -1$ by $a_{l1} = 0$ and $a_{l2} = 0$ by $a_{l2} = -1$ we have a permatrix of one dotre, one doun and seven dodos. A similar result holds when for $m = 5$ or 6 we replace in the original permatrix $a_{m2} = -1$ by $a_{m2} = 0$ and $a_{m1} = 0$ by $a_{m1} = -1$. With a few alterations in the proof of Theorem 10, it is seen that there are in fact seven non-equivalent permatrices of nine dodos which contain a minor equivalent to $\begin{pmatrix} 1 & 1 \\ 1 & 1 \end{pmatrix}$ and that five of these contain at least two such minors. Thus even though the number of non-equivalent permatrices of one dotre, one doun and seven dodos may be small the number of permatrices to be considered would nevertheless be quite large. It therefore appears that some new idea is required to prove the conjecture that a 9-con does not exist, for to employ the methods used so far would be a long and tedious operation.

INDEX

Algebraic total   60

Chardho   58
Δ-contact   59
∇-contact   59
Crum's Property   1

Daik   197
Dhoat   58
D_m-plane   1
Dodo   58
Dopt   57
Dotre   58
Doun   58

Face of an n-con   1

Matrix representation of an
   n-con   2

Naik   58
n-con   1

Nodo   58
Nopt   57
Notre   58

Permatrix   94

Sipt   57
Surplus   60
Surplust   198

Tem-column   11
Tem-column w. r. t. sub-
   matrix   18
Tem-plane   11
Tetre   58
Thaik   58
Tredho   197
Treno   197
Treun   58
Trianglets   197
Tript   57

Uno   58
Unun   58

OTHER TITLES IN THE SERIES IN
PURE AND APPLIED MATHEMATICS

Vol. 1. WALLACE—*An Introduction to Algebraic Topology*

Vol. 2. PEDOE—*Circles*

Vol. 3. SPAIN—*Analytical Conics*

Vol. 4. MIKHLIN—*Integral Equations*

Vol. 5. EGGLESTON—*Problems in Euclidean Space: Application of Convexity*

Vol. 6. WALLACE—*Homology Theory on Algebraic Varieties*

Vol. 7. NOBLE—*Methods Based on the Wiener-Hopf Technique for the Solution of Partial Differential Equations*

Vol. 8. MIKUSINSKI—*Operational Calculus*

Vol. 9. HEINE—*Group Theory in Quantum Mechanics*

Vol. 10. BLAND—*The Theory of Linear Viscoelasticity*

Vol. 11. KURTH—*Axiomatics of Classical Statistical Mechanics*

Vol. 12. FUCHS—*Abelian Groups*

Vol. 13. KURATOWSKI—*Introduction to Set Theory and Topology*

Vol. 14. SPAIN—*Analytical Quadrics*

Vol. 15. HARTMAN and MIKUSINSKI—*The Theory of Lebesgue Measure and Integration*

Vol. 16. KULCZYCKI—*Non-Euclidean Geometry*

Vol. 17. KURATOWSKI—*Introduction to Calculus*

Vol. 18. GERONIMUS—*Polynomials Orthogonal on a Circle and Interval*

Vol. 19. ELSGOLC—*Calculus of Variations*

Vol. 20. ALEXITS—*Convergence Problems of Orthogonal Series*

Vol. 21. FUCHS and LEVIN—*Functions of a Complex Variable and Some of their Applications, Volume II*

Vol. 22. GOODSTEIN—*Fundamental Concepts of Mathematics*

Vol. 23. KEENE—*Abstract Sets and Finite Ordinals*

Vol. 24. DITKIN and PRUDNIKOV—*Operational Calculus in Two Variables and its Applications*

Vol. 25. VEKUA—*Generalized Analytic Functions*

Vol. 26. AMIR-MOÉZ and FASS—*Elements of Linear Spaces*

Vol. 27. GRADSHTEIN—*Direct and Converse Theorems*

Vol. 28. FUCHS—*Partially Ordered Algebraic Systems*

Vol. 29. POSTNIKOV—*Foundations of Galois Theory*

Vol. 30. BERMANT—*A Course of Mathematical Analysis, Part II*

Vol. 31. LUKASIEWICZ—*Elements of Mathematical Logic*

Vol. 32. VULIKH—*Introduction to Functional Analysis for Scientists and Technologists*

Vol. 33. PEDOE—*An Introduction to Projective Geometry*

Vol. 34. TIMAN—*Theory of Approximation of Functions of a Real Variable*

Vol. 35. CSÁSZÁR—*Foundations of General Topology*

Vol. 36. BRONSHTEIN and SEMENDYAYEV—*A Guide-Book to Mathematics for Technologists and Engineers*

Vol. 37. MOSTOWSKI and STARK—*Introduction to Higher Algebra*

Vol. 38. GODDARD—*Mathematical Techniques of Operational Research*

Vol. 39. TIKHONOV and SAMARSKII—*The Equations of Mathematical Physics*

Vol. 40. McLEOD—*Introduction to Fluid Dynamics*

Vol. 41. MOISIL—*The Algebraic Theory of Switching Circuits*

Vol. 42. OTTO—*Nomography*

Vol. 43. RANKIN—*An Introduction to Mathematical Analysis*

Vol. 44. BERMANT—*A Course of Mathematical Analysis, Part I*

Vol. 45. KRASNOSEL'SKII—*Topological Methods in the Theory of Nonlinear Integral Equations*

Vol. 46. KANTOROVICH and AKILOV—*Functional Analysis in Normed Spaces*

Vol. 47. JONES—*The Theory of Electromagnetism*

Vol. 48. FEJES TÓTH—*Regular Figures*

Vol. 49. YANO—*Differential Geometry on Complex and Almost Complex Spaces*

Vol. 50. MIKHLIN—*Variational Methods in Mathematical Physics*

Vol. 51. FUCHS and SHABAT—*Functions of a Complex Variable and Some of their Applications, Volume 1*

Vol. 52. BUDAK, SAMARSKII and TIKHONOV—*A Collection of Problems on Mathematical Physics*

Vol. 53. GILES—*Mathematical Foundations of Thermodynamics*

Vol. 54. SAUL'YEV—*Integration of Equations of Parabolic Type by the Method of Nets*

Vol. 55. PONTRYAGIN et al.—*The Mathematical Theory of Optimal Processes*

Vol. 56. SOBOLEV—*Partial Differential Equations of Mathematical Physics*

Vol. 57. SMIRNOV—*A Course of Higher Mathematics, Volume I*

Vol. 58. SMIRNOV—*A Course of Higher Mathematics, Volume II*

Vol. 59. SMIRNOV—*A Course of Higher Mathematics, Volume III, Part 1*

Vol. 60. SMIRNOV—*A Course of Higher Mathematics, Volume III, Part 2*

Vol. 61. SMIRNOV—*A Course of Higher Mathematics, Volume IV*

Vol. 62. SMIRNOV—*A Course of Higher Mathematics, Volume V*

Vol. 63. NAIMARK—*Linear Representations of the Lorentz Group*

Vol. 64. BERMAN—*A Collection of Problems on a Course of Mathematical Analysis*

Vol. 65. MESHCHERSKII—*A Collection of Problems of Mechanics*

Vol. 66. ARSCOTT—*Periodic Differential Equations*

Vol. 67. SANSONE and CONTI—*Non-linear Differential Equations*

Vol. 68. VOLKOVYSKII, LUNTS and ARAMANOVICH—*A Collection of Problems on Complex Analysis*

Vol. 69. LYUSTERNIK and YANPOL'SKII—*Mathematical Analysis, Functions, Limits, Series, Continued Fractions*

Vol. 70. KUROSH—*Lektures in General Algebra*

Made in Great Britain